NATURAL
LOGIC

Edinburgh

*

NATURAL LOGIC

NEIL TENNANT

Edinburgh University Press

*

Edinburgh University Press
22 George Square, Edinburgh

Set in Times Roman by
Speedspools, Edinburgh
and printed in Great Britain by
Redwood Press Limited
Trowbridge, Wilts

First edition 1978
Reprinted in paperback with corrections 1990

British Library Cataloguing
in Publication Data
Tennant, Neil, *1950–*
Natural logic. – Rev. ed
1. Mathematical logic
I. Title
511.3

ISBN 0 85224 579 3

PREFACE

My debts to the literature will be acknowledged at the appropriate places. I have a particular debt to Timothy Smiley, from whom I first learned logic. I should also thank the many students in Edinburgh who have helped me improve my understanding of the subject.

The book is dedicated to Winifred Rushforth OBE for dreams made true.

N.W.T. Edinburgh 1978

ACKNOWLEDGEMENTS FOR THE REPRINTING

I am especially indebted to Göran Sundholm, Wilfried Sieg and Tatsuo Fujimara for drawing my attention to mistakes and misprints in the first printing.

N.W.T. Ann Arbor 1986

CONTENTS

Introduction p.ix

1

Preliminaries *p.1*

2

Form and structure of sentences *p.9*

3

Classical truth conditions *p.21*

4

Form and structure of proofs *p.39*

5

Propositional metalogic *p.87*

6

First order metalogic *p.115*

7

First order theories *p.135*

Notes p.178

References p.181

Exercises p.185

Glossary p.191

Index p.193

*

INTRODUCTION

This is a logic text that attempts to reach major results with a minimum of fuss. It has grown out of lectures in the University of Edinburgh on introductory and mathematical logic. In writing it I have had in mind two kinds of reader. The first is the student of philosophy who is studying logic and who wishes to acquaint himself with results of a mathematical nature. The second is the student of mathematics who finds mathematical logic sufficiently different from the staples of algebra and analysis to need a gentler introduction to the ideas behind logical systems.

Chapters 1–4 provide material for an introductory course in logic. How much of the technical material in Chapter 4 is used will depend on the ability of the class. Easy exercises on translation and proof can no doubt be supplied by the tutor. More interesting exercises on the introductory material are supplied at the end of the text. These have been drawn from past examination papers in the University of Edinburgh.

Chapters 4–7 provide material for a course in mathematical logic. Again, how much material from earlier chapters is used will depend on the class. The main feature of our treatment is that the elegant systems of natural deduction due to Gentzen and Prawitz are made the object of both syntactic and semantic investigation. We prove all the main completeness and incompleteness results. In doing so we illustrate the three main methods of proof employed by the mathematical logician. These are (i) induction on complexity of syntactic objects (sentences, proofs, etc.), (ii) consistent maximalization of sets of sentences and the construction of natural models (Henkin's method), and (iii) diagonalization. Incompleteness of arithmetic is established twice over, by diagonalization within and diagonalization without.

We assume familiarity with the rudiments of set theory. The growing interest in intuitionism among philosophers of language is served by an account of the relationship between classical and intuitionistic logic, and of Kripke semantics for the latter. Also of interest to the philosopher will be the account of universally free logic for descriptions in Chapter 7.

CHAPTER 1

Preliminaries

1.1
Arguments *p.2*
1.2
Validity of arguments; sentences and situations *p.2*
1.3
First order language *p.4*
1.4
Proofs and systems of proof *p.5*
1.5
The place of logic in mathematics and philosophy *p.7*

1.1 Arguments. Logic is the study of arguments. An argument is understood here to consist of a set of premisses, an inference marker and a conclusion. For brevity we shall let Δ stand for a set of premisses. A slash will represent the inferential move, and φ will stand for the conclusion. The schematic form of an argument is therefore Δ/φ, or $\frac{\Delta}{\varphi}$. In summary settlement of Cartesian controversy we offer as an example {Cogito}/Sum.

By talking of Δ as a set of premisses we are ruling that the order in which the premisses are given is irrelevant. No premiss should depend, for its meaning or argumentative force, on the order in which the premisses are given.

No premiss should be ambiguous. In particular the context of the argument should be determinate enough to fix the reference of words like 'I', 'you', 'here' and 'now', so as to fix the force of premisses containing them.

These observations apply to the conclusion of an argument as well.

An argument may have infinitely many premisses. That one would not be able to finish stating them one by one we shall regard as a strictly non-logical difficulty.

Arguments can be trivial, simple, obvious; tortuous, ingenious, profound. The main properties of logical interest, however, are validity and provability.

1.2 Validity of arguments; sentences and situations. We take validity first. Perhaps the best explanation of this notion is by way of the following informal definition:

> Δ/φ is *valid* if and only if whenever all the premisses in Δ are true, the conclusion φ is true also.

A valid argument is a truth-preserving one. By our definition an argument Δ/φ is *in*valid if and only if there could be some situation in which all the premisses in Δ were true, but the conclusion φ was false. Such a situation would be called a *counterexample* to the argument.

When Δ/φ is valid, we also say that Δ logically implies φ, or that φ is a logical consequence of Δ. We write $\Delta \models \varphi$.

So far we have used 'premiss' and 'conclusion' neutrally, without saying exactly what kind of entity premisses and conclusions are. Are they utterances? inscriptions? statements? sentences? propositions? Are they physical, mental or otherwise abstract entities? Finally – a question raised by our definition of validity – in what does their being true or false consist?

At this point we are obliged to take an expository leap. Premisses and conclusions will be understood to be sentences of some given language. A sentence is an abstract and internally structured entity of a kind that makes it comprehensible to say that a sentence has been written twice but never uttered, or that there is a sentence that is so long that no person could ever utter it or write it down. Following a more mathematical approach, one might construe a sentence as a finite sequence of symbols. Sequences are abstract, set-theoretic entities. Moreover the symbols involved are themselves abstract entities not identifiable with any of their concrete or physical realizations as utterances or inscriptions.

Relying on these brief remarks to clarify the status of sentences, we observe that there now remains the task of explicating the notion

sentence φ is true in situation $\mathfrak{A}$

(Capital Germanic letters are used in speaking about situations; or, more precisely, as variables ranging over situations.)

Thereafter we can define $\Delta \vDash \varphi$ to mean

for every situation $\mathfrak{A}$, if every member of Δ is true in $\mathfrak{A}$
then φ is true in $\mathfrak{A}$ also

thereby making precise the phrase 'whenever' in the informal definition of validity above.

The situations under consideration may be abstract or concrete. An abstract example would be that consisting of the counting numbers $0, 1, 2, \ldots$ with their usual additive and multiplicative structure. A concrete example would be a party of people in various spatial, emotional and legal relationships. Hybrid examples, like Pascal sitting alone and thinking of numbers, are somewhat recalcitrant and best left to philosophers.

Built into the notion of a situation is the correlation of words with things – of names with the individuals named, and of predicates ('... is bald', '... loves ___') with the individuals of which they hold. Only the so-called logical words such as 'not', 'and', 'all' have interpretations that are held constant for all situations. Thus we construe the term 'situation' broadly enough to prise non-logical words loose from their usual meanings. Logically, we might have a situation in which the predicate '... is a dog' applied to cats, or to members of any arbitrary collection of things.

This explanation of 'situation' raises the question how one distinguishes between logical and non-logical words. There is as yet no universally accepted formulation of a criterion or principle for drawing the distinction, but we are usually left in no doubt as to particular cases. At worst, we can simply write down a definitive list of those words we intend to treat as logical.

The need to specify the situation in which a sentence is true should be apparent. For example, even with the usual interpretations of 'greater than' and 'less than', the sentence 'No number is greater than 0 but less than 1' is true of the counting numbers 0, 1, 2,... but is not true of the rational numbers, since $\frac{1}{2}$ is greater than 0 but less than 1. Here, of course, the problem is what are to count as numbers in the situation concerned.

A full specification of any particular situation would in principle settle all problems such as this. In general a situation consists of a domain of individuals, often called the universe of discourse, along with a correlation of non-logical words with those individuals. The individuals in the domain are all and only those deemed to exist in the situation concerned. A predicate such as '... is bald' would be correlated with just those individuals of which it is deemed to hold; and so on. Considerable simplification and idealization is involved here. We are assuming that the domain of individuals can be clearly circumscribed. We are assuming also that there is a determinate answer to the question whether a given individual possesses a certain 'property' (as expressed by some predicate), or enters into a certain 'relation' with other individuals. More fundamentally we are assuming that, in order to account for how sentences are true or false, we should regard their subject matter – the reality to which they are addressed – as composed of discrete individuals standing in determinate relations to one another. We shall not attempt a detailed philosophical justification of this atomistic ontology, but simply draw the reader's attention to its central importance for logical semantics. We shall content ourselves with showing that if it is adopted then a most satisfactory account can be given of the truth conditions of sentences of a certain language.

1.3 First order language. The language in question is simple but of considerable expressive power. It is adequate for the expression of almost all mathematics. Moreover, within limits to be expected of any idealization, its sentences can be regarded as representing the underlying logical forms of sentences of English. It therefore lends itself to two uses: the development of mathematics, and the provision of workable 'translations' for English sentences. We are thus able to assess the validity of each of a wide class of English arguments by translating its premisses and conclusion into sentences of this special language and then assessing the validity of the translated version of the argument. Because sentences of our special language are unambiguous and because we shall have a very precise understanding of the conditions under which they are true or false, we shall be well placed to assess the validity of the translated argument.

The special language in question, which has come to be known as the language of first order logic, is due essentially to Frege. The language is of first order because it permits generalizations about individuals but not about their properties and relations. For example, in a first order language one can express

John loves everyone but Mary

but not

John is everything but a lover to Mary.

Sentences of a first order language can be used to describe the elementary situations discussed above. How precisely a given situation can be described in this way is a deep and interesting question. In the mathematical literature situations are called *models*. Model theory is that branch of mathematical logic that addresses itself to questions such as the last one. In model theory we investigate the algebraic properties of models, on the one hand, and their connection with the structural (or syntactical) properties of sets of sentences used to describe those models, on the other. Certain model-theoretic results obtained in later chapters will give the reader some idea of the expressive limitations of first order languages.

1.4 Proofs and systems of proof. An argument may be valid without its validity being at all obvious. Remember that we are using 'argument' in such a way that any set of premisses, followed by a conclusion, counts as an argument. Thus Hilbert's axioms for Euclidean geometry, followed by Pythagoras's Theorem about squares on sides of right triangles, form an argument. It happens to be valid. If, however, I were to state Hilbert's axioms, pause, say 'therefore' and then state Pythagoras's Theorem, you may remain quite unpersuaded that Pythagoras's Theorem *is* a logical consequence of Hilbert's axioms. To take another example, no-one yet knows whether every even number greater than two is the sum of two prime numbers. That this is so might, however, at some future date be discovered to follow logically from arithmetical axioms that we presently hold true of the counting numbers.

In order to demonstrate the validity of an argument one needs a *proof*. A proof of an argument is a detailed representation of valid transition from its premisses, taken as starting points, to its conclusion as terminus. Within a proof this transition is effected by a series of steps, or 'inferences', each one of which is obviously valid.

A system of proof is a codification of these obviously valid kinds of inference, which we call rules of inference. An example of a rule of inference is 'From φ, ψ infer $\varphi \& \psi$'. A proof in accordance with these rules must, in order to meet the demands of certainty, satisfy the following conditions.

(i) It must be of finite size.

(ii) Every one of its steps must be effectively checkable: that is, a machine or some other kind of comprehensively briefed moron must be able to determine of each step, in a finite time, whether it is in accordance with one of the basic rules of inference of the system.

(iii) We must be able effectively to read off the premisses and con-conclusion from the proof – otherwise we shall not know what argument's validity the proof establishes.

Depending on the strength of the proof system, a valid argument whose validity is not obvious may be turned into a proof by expanding the inferential move in the statement of the argument into a series of inferences, each in accordance with one of the rules of inference of the system. Converting a valid argument into a proof in this way is the penultimate step in perfecting the argument. Once we have *a* proof we may try to improve matters further by

(i) eliminating dead ends (sub-proofs whose conclusions are not used as intermediate premisses on the way to the main conclusion);

(ii) eliminating detours (sub-proofs which amount to a proof of something from itself); and

(iii) seeking a new proof from fewer of the premisses, or from weaker premisses.

A proof system on whose proofs the first two of these operations can always be carried out fully is said to have the *normalization* property. Success in the last operation depends not on the system but on the user.

Obviously there must be no invalid proofs in our system. The system, that is, must be *sound* for the language concerned. Moreover we wish to be able to prove any valid argument expressible in the language. The system, that is, must be *complete* for the language. Note that since proofs employ only finitely many premisses the proof system will be complete for the language only if the relation of logical consequence in that language is *compact* – which means that any logical consequence of given premisses is a logical consequence of only finitely many of those premisses.

Logical consequence in our first order language is compact; and we shall develop a proof system that is sound and complete for the language, and that has the normalization property. This proof system, due to Gentzen and Prawitz, is the system of so-called *natural deduction*. Proofs in this system reflect underlying patterns of ordinary reasoning as closely as sentences of our formal language reflect the underlying forms of sentences of ordinary language. Proof theory, that branch of mathematical logic complementary to model theory, is best approached via natural deduction and kindred systems of proof. In proof theory we study ways of manipulating, transforming and simplifying proofs so as to learn more about the properties of the whole proof system.

1.5 The place of logic in mathematics and philosophy. Formal languages and proof systems have been developed first and foremost for the rigorous expression and exposition of mathematical theories. These involve modest resources of expression (by comparison with ordinary language) but long and complicated chains of reasoning (by comparison with ordinary argumentation) and are therefore eminently suitable for logical treatment.

It is also possible, as observed above, to use the formal language to formalize English arguments and to use the proof system to construct rigorous proofs of them. Honesty, though, compels one to admit that ordinary arguments for which this is not overly complicated tend to be of a rather humdrum variety. This has lead, among other things, to the immortalization of Socrates by simple arguments purporting to establish his mortality. Nevertheless, translating back and forth between English sentences and sentences in the formal language, and constructing proofs of valid arguments and counterexamples to invalid ones are the main skills to be acquired at an introductory level. At an intermediate level one is introduced to relatively easy results about the internal workings of the proof system.

The 'logical treatment' of mathematical theories alluded to above is really of a different nature. It is actually very difficult to give strict logical proofs of even simple mathematical theorems from the axioms of the mathematical theory concerned. Mathematicians use many definitional abbreviations and long jumps in reasoning, and a clear, convincing mathematical argument is usually no more than a very sketchy recipe for finding the corresponding strict, logical argument in the formal system of proof. The importance of logic for mathematics does not lie in doggedly translating axioms and theorems into formal notation and then supplying the missing minutiae of reasoning. It lies, rather, in answering certain general foundational questions about any mathematical theory. What is the structure of the language in which the theory is expressed? What are the primitive notions and principles on which the theory is based? What are the methods of definition and proof by which the theory is developed? Answers to these questions yield a language and a proof system in which the theory is expressed and developed. One can then ask: Does the proof system provide proofs for all and only the valid arguments expressible in the language? Is the theory consistent? To what extent does it say all that can be said about its subject matter? To what extent does it characterize exactly the structure of its subject matter? Is there a mechanical method for deciding of any given sentence whether it is a theorem of the theory?

Questions such as these are the concern of so-called metalogic and metamathematics. Foundational research has provided a body of results which, within reasonable margins of interpretation, provide determinate answers to these questions. Languages and deductive systems have been formalized, axiom systems have been investigated. Limits of expressive and deductive power have been charted. A family of metalogical and metamathematical notions has grown up, and their interrelationships have been clearly worked out. The resulting clarification of the concepts of number and set, finitude and infinity, construction and proof, mechanical and non-mechanical procedure, is one which no philosophy of mathematics can ignore.

Modern logic has encountered and generated many problems of continuing philosophical interest. These are not of a parochial and technical kind, but lie at the heart of modern metaphysics. Questions about reference, identity and existence, and about truth and meaning cannot now be discussed without knowledge of the standard analyses provided by logic. Philosophers have also extended their logical investigations to other central areas of metaphysics. The notions of time and causality, necessity and possibility, belief and knowledge, obligation, permission, power and prohibition, to name a few, have been studied from a logical point of view. Formal languages have been developed with new vocabulary for the new notions. Guidelines have been provided for translation between the formal languages and fragments of English involving terms for these notions. Accounts have been given of how the formal languages are to be interpreted, and of how the truth or falsity of their sentences depends on these interpretations. In some cases proof systems have been provided to generate the new arguments formulable in the extended formal language. In trying thus to systematize and clarify these important notions philosophical logicians have made a substantial impact on the form of modern metaphysical discussion.

CHAPTER 2

Form and structure of sentences

2.1
Logical form and surface form *p.10*
2.2
Categories and categorial analysis *p.12*
2.3
Logical vocabulary *p.15*
2.4
Quantifiers and bound variables *p.16*
2.5
Formulae *p.18*

2.1 Logical form and surface form. Aristotle was perhaps the first logician to see that an argument is valid by virtue of its *form.* The notion of logical form is a difficult one to analyse, and is best understood by way of examples.

Aristotelian syllogisms are basic forms of valid argument. A syllogism such as

All *A*'s are *B*'s
All *B*'s are *C*'s
―――――――
All *A*'s are *C*'s

represents the form of particular valid arguments which may be called *instances* of that form. Examples of particular arguments with the form above are

All Armenians are Bolsheviks
All Bolsheviks are Communists
―――――――
All Armenians are Communists

and

All tigers are humans
All humans have tails
―――――――
All tigers have tails

The latter example makes the well-known point that one may reason validly from false premisses to a true conclusion.

Aristotle perfected arguments by interpolating steps of basic syllogistic form between premisses and conclusion. His method works, however, only for a limited class of arguments, since he allows as premisses and conclusions of syllogisms only sentences of the forms All *A*'s are *B*'s, Some *A*'s are *B*'s, All *A*'s are not *B*'s, and Some *A*'s are not *B*'s. Consequently Aristotelian syllogistic is unable to classify as valid or invalid arguments such as

All horses are animals
―――――――
All horses' tails are animals' tails

or

Someone is loved by everyone
―――――――
Everyone loves someone

The limitations of Aristotle's method are nowhere more apparent than in mathematics, where arguments usually involve sentences with multiple occurrences of phrases involving the words 'some' and 'every', such as

For every number *a* and for every number *b* if *a* is not zero then there is some number *q* and some number *r* such that $b=(a.q)+r$.

It was in order to deal with such cases of so-called ***multiple quantification*** that Frege invented the formal language to be developed in this chapter.

A well-known form of valid argument is

$P(a)$	*a* has property *P*
$a=b$	*a* is identical to *b*
$P(b)$	*b* has property *P*

known as the law of substitutivity of identicals, or Leibniz's Law. Now it would appear that the following invalid argument is of this form:

The colour of the sky is changing
The colour of the sky is blue
―――――――――――
Blue is changing

In this case, however, appearances are deceptive. ***On the surface***, one might say, the argument appears to have the form of a substitution of identicals. A deeper analysis, however, reveals a complexity in the phrase 'is changing' whose concealment is responsible for the argument's apparent conformity to Leibniz's Law. This analysis results in a reformulation of the two premisses, which, upon substitution of identicals, validly yield a revised conclusion:

The colour which happens to be the colour of the sky now is different from the colour which will happen to be the colour of the sky a little later than now
The colour which happens to be the colour of the sky now is the colour blue
―――――――――――
The colour blue is different from the colour which will happen to be the colour of the sky a little later than now.

This new argument genuinely conforms to Leibniz's Law. The lesson is that we must distinguish the surface forms of sentences from their logical forms when appraising arguments involving them.

On the other hand, some arguments can be seen to be valid without having to reveal every detail of the logical form of the sentences involved. For example, the argument

Either someone is rich or everyone is bald
Not everyone is bald
____
Someone is rich

is valid because it is an instance of the form

Either φ or ψ
Not-ψ
____
φ

In order to show this argument to be valid it is not necessary to uncover the details of the logical form of the sub-sentences 'Someone is rich' and 'Everyone is bald'. Quine has formulated what he calls the maxim of shallow analysis: do not uncover any more logical form than is necessary in order to show an argument to be valid. For another illustration of this maxim see 4.14.

2.2 Categories and categorial analysis. What forms of sentences are to be provided for in our formal language? The answer to this question is the precise definition below of *well-formed formula*. In order to understand how we arrive at this definition we must first examine the method of categorizing expressions and analysing their categorial structure. We begin by considering sentences of the simplest kind, whose surface and logical form are more or less indistinguishable.

For present purposes we need only two *basic* categories of expression – *Sentence* and *Name*, abbreviated as *S* and *N* respectively. Each has a peculiar importance, which may be offered as good reason for taking it to be basic. First, sentences are our truthbearers. They are the minimal linguistic units by which we can make a statement or assertion, or express a proposition. Secondly, names effect the most primitive connection between language and its subject matter. In our conception of the truth or falsity of a sentence arising in a determinate way from its structure and from correlations between certain of its expressions and the world, no such correlation can be simpler than the naming relation, the relation between a name and the single object for which it stands.

Obviously not all expressions are of category *S* or *N*, so non-basic categories will have to be invented. This cannot be done in an arbitrary or random way, since the guiding principle behind correct categorization of expressions is that we should be able to explain the powers of combination of various expressions to form new ones.

Let us illustrate this with an example. There is no doubt that the expression 'John is fat' is a sentence and that the contained expression 'John' is a name. What about the remainder? If we remove the name from the sentence there remains the non-basic expression '___ is fat'. This expression deserves definite categorization because of its power of combination with names to produce sentences: John is fat, Mary is fat, Bill is fat, etc. Each of these sentences is produced by completing the non-basic expression '___ is fat' with a name. For this reason '___ is fat' is also called an *incomplete* expression. We assign it to that category of expressions that, upon completion by a name, yield a sentence. We label this category $1SN$ because completion of any expression in it by *one* expression of category N yields an expression of category S.

Now consider the sentence 'John loves Mary'. Upon removal of both names we are left with the incomplete expression '___ loves ...'. This expression, upon completion by *two* names, yields a sentence. Thus its category is $2SNN$. But had we removed only the name 'John' we would have obtained '___ loves Mary', which, like '___ is fat' may be completed by one name to yield a sentence. Thus '___ loves Mary' is of category $1SN$. Obviously this is not all that can be said; for we see that '___ loves Mary' results from completion of the second blank of '___ loves ...' by the name 'Mary'. Thus '___ loves Mary' is an expression of category $1SN$ built up by combining expressions of category $2SNN$ and N:

$$\text{\_\_\_ loves } \overbrace{\ldots \text{ Ma}}\text{ry} = \text{\_\_\_ loves Mary}$$

$$2SN\overbrace{N \quad N} = 1SN.$$

Thus we have not only *categorized* '___ loves Mary' as $1SN$; we have also given it the *categorial analysis* $1SN = 2SN\overbrace{N \quad N}$.

In general, given any expression we may try both to categorize it and to give it a categorial analysis. As can be seen from our example, a successful categorial analysis will tell us what the overall category is. The best way to categorize an expression is to regard it as the result of removing expressions of known categories from an expression of known category. We have to ensure that our earliest categorizations are correct for this method to work. So we work with very simple expressions in order to reduce the possibility of error.

One mistake we must not make is to assign to category N any expression that has not first been seen to satisfy certain minimal requirements. Let us therefore formulate some *necessary* conditions for n to be a name – conditions that must be satisfied by any name, even though their satisfaction by an expression is no *guarantee* that it is a name.

First, the inferences

$$\begin{array}{l} \text{John is fat} \\ \text{John is bald} \\ \hline \text{John is fat and bald} \end{array} \qquad \begin{array}{l} \text{John is fat or bald} \\ \hline \text{John is fat or John is bald} \end{array}$$

are obviously valid. We make it a requirement that, for *n* to be a name, the English forms of inference

$$\begin{array}{l} n \text{ is } P \\ n \text{ is } Q \\ \hline n \text{ is } (P \text{ and } Q) \end{array} \qquad \begin{array}{l} n \text{ is } (P \text{ or } Q) \\ \hline n \text{ is } P \text{ or } n \text{ is } Q \end{array}$$

be valid. Secondly, the inference

$$\begin{array}{l} \text{John loves Mary} \\ \hline \text{Mary is loved by John} \end{array}$$

is obviously valid. We make it a requirement that, for *m* and *n* to be names, the English form of inference

$$\begin{array}{l} m\ R\text{'s } n \\ \hline n \text{ is } R\text{'d by } m \end{array}$$

be valid.

Now let us attempt a categorial analysis of the sentences 'Someone is fat' and 'Everyone is fat'. If 'Someone' and 'Everyone' are names, then the analysis in each case will be $S = 1S\overline{NN}$. But are they names? Definitely not, as we see from the invalidity of the following three infererences:

$$\begin{array}{l} \text{Someone is fat} \\ \text{Someone is bald} \\ \hline \text{Someone is fat and bald} \end{array} \qquad \begin{array}{l} \text{Everyone loves someone} \\ \hline \text{Someone is loved by everyone} \end{array}$$

$$\begin{array}{l} \text{Everyone is fat or bald} \\ \hline \text{Everyone is fat or everyone is bald} \end{array}$$

There is a simple counterexample to all three inferences. Suppose John and Mary are the only individuals, John is bald but not fat and does not love himself, Mary is fat but not bald but does not love herself, and they love one another. In this situation the premisses of each inference are true but its conclusion is false.

The question now arises, if 'Someone' and 'Everyone' are not names, what *is* their category? Following the simple method suggested above, consider the sentence 'Someone is fat'. We already know that the category of '____ is fat' is $1SN$. Upon removing it from the sentence we obtain 'Someone ____' which we thus assign to the category $1S1SN$ – since upon completion by one expression of category $1SN$ it yields a sentence. By the same procedure, 'Everyone ___' is of category $1S1SN$ also. What now of the categorial analysis of the sentence 'Someone is fat'?

We have

Someone ___ is fat = Someone is fat

where the blank in 'Someone ___' is filled by '___ is fat' *without any blanks remaining.* This elision of blanks is represented in the categorial notation thus:

$$S = 1S1SN \quad 1SN$$

The mode of combination represented here is called *quantification.* It is in cases of multiple quantification that our categorial analysis is conspicuously successful. We are able to distinguish between the modes of combination in 'Everyone loves someone' and 'Someone is loved by everyone' as follows:

Everyone ___ ___ loves... Someone ___

$1S1SN \quad 2SNN \quad 1S1SN$ Everyone loves someone

$1S1SN \quad 2SNN \quad 1S1SN$ Someone is loved by everyone

Obviously very complicated categories and modes of combination can be generated by the method followed so far. We shall be interested only in those involved in the formal language to be developed below. The general and precise definition of category, and statement of rules of combination, is beyond the scope of this book. Suffice it to say that categorial analysis along these lines helps to clarify the logical form of sentences as it arises out of their order of construction from simpler expressions of known categories. It was this analysis, due to Frege, which gave rise to modern logic. Sentences are regarded as internally structured in an hierarchical fashion; and this internal structure is an important determinant of both their truth conditions and their logical interrelationships.

2.3 Logical vocabulary. The internal structure of a sentence should be clear from any representation of its logical form. The same structure may be represented in different ways; we are interested in structure which is represented by, and invariant with respect to changes of, formal logical notation.

The following is a list of the categories of expression with which we shall be concerned. In the case of each category we give the standard terminology for it, along with a simple English expression of the category concerned, and the corresponding notation of our formal language. No formal expression belongs to more than one category.

S	Sentence	John is fat	$F(j)$
N	Name	John	j
$1SN$	One-place predicate	___ is fat	$F(\ )$
$2SNN$	Two-place predicate	___ loves ...	$L(\ ,\ )$
$3SNNN$	Three-place predicate	___ is between ... and ___	$B(\ ,\ ,\ )$
	etc.		
$1NN$	One-place function	___'s father	$f(\ )$
$2NNN$	Two-place function	___ plus ...	$g(\ ,\ )$
	etc.		
$1SS$	One-place connective	it is not the case that ___	$\sim(\ )$
$2SSS$	Two-place connective	___ and ...	$(\ )\&(\ )$
		___ or ...	$(\ )\vee(\ )$
		___ only if ...	$(\ )\supset(\ )$
$1S1SN$	Quantifier	something ___	$\exists(\ )$
		everything ___	$\forall(\ )$

In our formal language expressions of any category other than S which are as simple as possible are called *primitive*. Expressions of category N are in general called *terms* rather than names. Sentences formed by filling blanks of primitive predicates with terms are called *atomic* sentences. Connectives and quantifiers are called *logical operators*.

Expressions of our formal language can be combined to form new expressions in systematic ways which are implicit in their categorizations. For example, the formal sentence $\sim(L(f(j), m))$ could be taken as representing the English sentence 'It is not the case that John's father loves Mary'. The only method of combination which is not straightforward is that of quantification. The other methods displayed in the last example – functional application, predication and connection – should need no further explanation.

2.4 Quantifiers and bound variables. With quantification we have the problem of needing in our formal notation a method to parallel that of eliding the blanks:

Someone is fat = Someone ___ is fat

to which corresponds the method of categorial interlocking:

$S = 1S1SN \quad 1SN$

So far our formal notation suggests only the following:

$\exists(F(\ ))$

in which a gap for a term is still conspicuously, and quite illegitimately, available for completion. We must somehow indicate that completing the quantifier by the predicate seals off the gap which the predicate brings with it against further possible completion by terms (and against further possible sealings by quantifiers). This we do by inserting a link between the quantifier and the predicate gap concerned:

$\exists(F(\ ))$

This, however, has the consequence that the sentence is not a linear sequence of signs. In order to restore linearity of notation we use a *bound variable*, whose sole purpose is to indicate the linkage depicted above by occurring at the ends of the link:

$\exists xF(x)$

(where we have now omitted the outer brackets).

Of course, more than one link may emanate from a quantifier:

$\exists L(\ ,\ )$	$\exists xL(x,x)$	Someone loves himself

Here the occurrences of the bound variable show which gaps are sealed off by the quantifier. Moreover, in cases of multiple quantification the occurrences of the bound variables show *which* gaps are sealed off by *which* quantifier occurrence:

$\forall\exists L(\ ,\ )$	$\forall x\exists yL(x,y)$	Everyone loves someone
$\exists\forall L(\ ,\ )$	$\exists x\forall yL(y,x)$	Someone is loved by everyone
$\forall\exists L(\ ,\ )$	$\forall x\exists yL(y,x)$	Everyone is loved by someone
$\exists\forall L(\ ,\ )$	$\exists x\forall yL(x,y)$	Someone loves everyone

Note that the alphabetical choice of bound variable is unimportant, so long as the intended pattern of links is established. In some cases it is possible to use the same variable for two quantifications:

$\forall(F(\ )\,\&\,\exists B(\ ))$ $\quad\quad$ $\forall x(F(x)\,\&\,\exists xB(x))$

In other cases, however, different variables must be used. For example, different variables must be used in

 $\forall x(F(x) \,\&\, \exists y L(y,x))$

since if the same variable were used for both quantifications a quite different pattern of links would be established:

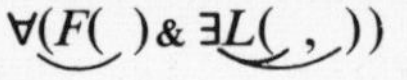 $\forall x(F(x) \,\&\, \exists x L(x,x))$

In a sentence of the form

 $\exists x \psi(\text{-}x\text{-}x\text{-}x\text{-})$

the initial quantifier occurrence is said to *bind* the occurrences of the variable x. Moreover by placing the *quantifier prefix* $\exists x$ in front of the *formula* $\psi(\text{-}x\text{-}x\text{-}x\text{-})$ we bind every available occurrence of x therein. Those occurrences of x in ψ that are available for binding (i.e. which have not already been bound) are called *free*.

Which occurrences of variables in ψ are free and which are bound can be determined from the way in which ψ was constructed from simpler expressions. This is why we can always determine what pattern of links the bound variables establish. Our two earlier examples illustrate this. The sentence $\forall x(F(x) \,\&\, \exists y L(y,x))$ was constructed as follows:

$L(y,x)$	each occurrence of y, x free
$F(x) \quad \exists y L(y,x)$	each occurrence of x free
$F(x) \,\&\, \exists y L(y,x)$	each occurrence of x free
$\forall x(F(x) \,\&\, \exists y L(y,x))$	no occurrences of variables free

while the sentence $\forall x(F(x) \,\&\, \exists x L(x,x))$ was constructed as follows:

$L(x,x)$	each occurrence of x free
$\exists x L(x,x)$	*no* occurrence of x free
$F(x)$	that occurrence of x free
$F(x) \,\&\, \exists x L(x,x)$	leftmost occurrence of x free
$\forall x(F(x) \,\&\, \exists x L(x,x))$	no occurrences of x free

2.5 Formulae. The internal structure of a sentence of our formal language is a by-product of its order of construction. In general each stage of construction yields a *formula* with certain occurrences of variables free. The *sentences* of the formal language are those formulae that have no occurrences of variables free.

Each stage of construction involves concatenating expressions according to fixed rules formulable from categorial considerations.

These rules constitute an inductive definition of *formula with such-and-such occurrences of variables free*. They may be regarded as the grammar of our formal language:

(i) Any name is a term with no free occurrences of variables.

(ii) Any variable is a term, with that occurrence of itself free.

(iii) Any n-place function sign followed by n occurrences of terms is a term whose free occurrences of variables are just those which are free in one of those occurrences of terms.

(iv) Any n-place predicate followed by n occurrences of terms is a formula whose free occurrences of variables are just those which are free in one of those occurrences of terms.

(v) If ψ is a formula then so is $(\sim\psi)$, whose free occurrences of variables are just those which are free in ψ.

(vi) If φ and ψ are formulae then so are $(\varphi \& \psi)$, $(\varphi \vee \psi)$ and $(\varphi \supset \psi)$, whose free occurrences of variables are just those which are free in φ or free in ψ.

(vii) If ψ is a formula with x free, then $(\exists x\psi)$ and $(\forall x\psi)$ are formulae whose free occurrences of variables are just those, save of x, which are free in ψ.

(viii) Nothing is a term or formula unless its being so follows from rules (i)–(vii).

Note that by this definition terms may contain variables. Terms that do not are called *closed* terms. The reason for allowing terms to contain variables is to make every 'place for a name' accessible to quantification. Unless we did so we would not have the sentence $\forall xL(f(x), m)$ (Everyone's father loves Mary), to give but one example.

One must not lose sight of the fact that variables are a notational device used solely in order to indicate linkages established by quantification. Even though our definition of formula allows one to introduce a free occurrence of a variable at one stage of construction and then bind it only at a later stage, this is necessary only because we have opted for a linear notation. Quantification is still a unitary operation from the categorial point of view.

Formulae as defined above contain brackets. The order of bracketing reflects the order of construction and is important for distinguishing between formulae which involve the same logical operators but which have been constructed, using those operators, in different ways. Thus we may distinguish $(\varphi \& (\psi \vee \theta))$ from $((\varphi \& \psi) \vee \theta)$, and we may distinguish $(\exists x(\varphi \& \psi))$ from $((\exists x\varphi) \& \psi)$. It is customary to omit brackets in writing down a formula when there is no danger of confusion about how the formula was constructed.

The notation used here is sometimes called the 'bracket plus infix' notation since two-place operators are infixed between formulae to obtain a new one. In so-called *Polish notation* dominant operators are written first. Thus the Polish version of $(\varphi \,\&\, \psi)$ is $\&\varphi\psi$. In Polish notation no brackets are needed to indicate the order of construction of a formula. The examples in the last paragraph would be written respectively as $\&\varphi\vee\psi\theta$, $\vee\&\varphi\psi\theta$, $\exists x\&\varphi\psi$ and $\&\exists x\varphi\psi$. As mentioned above, all that is important is the invariant structure represented by the two notations. We know what that structure is from either the bracket plus infix notation or the Polish notation because we understand the rules for constructing formulae in each of those notations.

We may even find it useful to use a picturesque two-dimensional notation which makes the tree-like order of construction of a formula even more obvious:

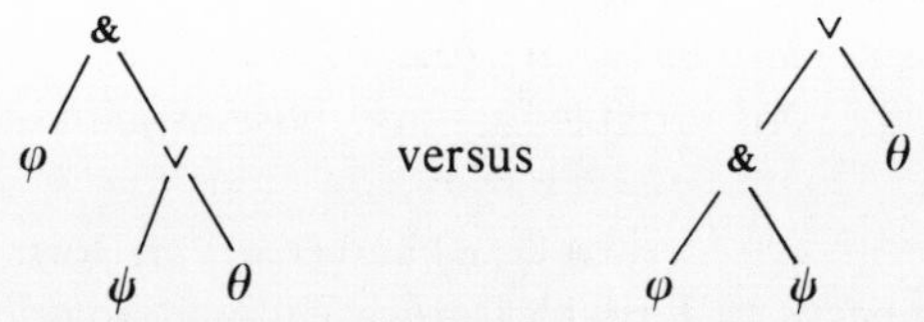

Certainly these tree diagrams give a vivid sense to an operator's being *dominant* in a formula: & is dominant in the one on the left, while $\vee$ is dominant in the one on the right. In general the displayed occurrence of a logical operator is dominant in formulae of the forms $\sim\psi$, $\varphi\&\psi$, $\varphi\vee\psi$, $\varphi\supset\psi$, $\exists x\psi$ and $\forall x\psi$. The displayed subformulae in each case are said to be within the *scope* of the occurrence of the operator concerned.

CHAPTER 3

Classical truth conditions

3.1
Atomic sentences *p.22*
3.2
Connected sentences *p.22*
3.3
Quantified sentences *p.24*
3.4
Satisfaction and truth; Tarski's adequacy condition *p.25*
3.5
Models *p.29*
3.6
Finite and infinite models *p.30*
3.7
Categoricity *p.32*
3.8
Counterexamples to invalid arguments *p.33*
3.9
Game theoretic semantics *p.35*

3.1 Atomic sentences. Now that we have an account of the structure of the sentences of our formal language we may show how the structure of a sentence contributes to its truth conditions. How does the 'form' of a sentence, once revealed, enable us to understand the conditions under which it would be true?

First we must understand the conditions under which atomic sentences are true. In general an atomic sentence has the form $P(t_1, \ldots, t_n)$ where an *n*-place primitive predicate *P* has been completed by *n* occurrences of closed terms. The simplest and most obvious account is then the following. Each closed term stands for an individual, and the predicate represents a relation between individuals. If this relation holds between the individuals in question, the atomic sentence is true. If not, it is false.

Three philosophical problems are being skirted here. The first, Ramsey's, is that of explaining why the atomic sentence 'Socrates is mortal' should be regarded as having the form $M(s)$ and being true just in case the individual Socrates (for which the name 'Socrates' stands) possesses the property of mortality (which the predicate '___ is mortal' represents). Why not rather assign the sentence some logical form which shows that the property of mortality (for which the phrase 'is mortal' stands) possesses the property of Socratising (which the word 'Socrates' represents)?

The second problem is the problem of universals. We have spoken of names *standing for* individuals but of predicates *representing* properties and relations. Does the latter form of words embody a conception of properties and relations somehow existing along with individuals and inhering in them? Or can we employ this form of words while maintaining that the only existents are *individuals*, and that they can have properties and enter into relations with one another without there being such 'things' as properties and relations that are enjoyed or entered into?

The third problem is the problem of non-denoting terms. If our language allows the formation of terms such as 'the square root of Jupiter' or 'the empty set's wife', are we to regard these as denoting any objects? Our present answer is simple and evasive. We design our language so that this problem never arises. We secure every name a denotation, and we ensure that every function is 'everywhere defined'. Thus every term denotes, and the term 'the problem of non-denoting terms' does not. In section 7.10, however, we consider a less evasive solution to the problem.

3.2 Connected sentences. Suppose we settle for this simple account of the truth conditions of atomic sentences. The truth conditions of complex sentences with *connectives* dominant are as follows:

$\sim\psi$ is true	if and only if	ψ is not true
$(\varphi \& \psi)$ is true	if and only if	φ is true and ψ is true
$(\varphi \vee \psi)$ is true	if and only if	φ is true or ψ is true
$(\varphi \supset \psi)$ is true	if and only if	φ is true only if ψ is true

Here it is assumed, of course, that one has a clear understanding of what is meant by 'not', 'and', 'or' and 'only if'. In the absence of such a clear understanding the truth conditions specified on the right are not clear. It is customary, in the assumed absence of a clear and common understanding of the quoted English connectives, to resort to *truth tables* in order to show exactly how the truth value of a sentence with a connective dominant depends on the truth values of the connected sentences:

ψ	$\sim\psi$
T	F
F	T

φ	ψ	$\varphi \& \psi$
T	T	T
T	F	F
F	T	F
F	F	F

φ	ψ	$\varphi \vee \psi$
T	T	T
T	F	T
F	T	T
F	F	F

The truth table shows that we are imposing on $\varphi \vee \psi$ the meaning conveyed by the English form of words 'φ or ψ (or perhaps both)' rather than 'φ or ψ (but not both)'.

The truth table for $\supset$ has to be constructed with some explanation. Consider the sentence

(1) Every *F* is a *G*.

This is equivalent to

(2) Everything is such that if it is an *F* then it is a *G*,

which can be represented in our logical notation as

(3) $\forall x(F(x) \supset G(x))$

Now it is the meaning of 'if ... then ...' *according to which* (1) *may be paraphrased as* (2) that the truth table for $\supset$ is to confer on $\supset$. In order that (2) be true, the predicate 'if ___ is an *F* then ___ is a *G*' must be true of every individual. Thus it must be true of non-*F*'s (if there are any) since the *G*-ness of non-*F*'s is irrelevant to the truth of (2). The existence of even one *F* that is not a *G* would falsify (2), and an *F* that is a *G* cannot count against the truth of (2). Thus the truth table for $\supset$ is

φ	ψ	$\varphi\supset\psi$
T	T	T
T	F	F
F	T	T
F	F	T

Note that our explanation of the truth table for $\supset$ does *not* constitute a justification for translating 'If ... then ...' into logical notation as $\supset$ in all contexts. Indeed, such translation is inadequate in many kinds of context: as, for example, in a counterfactual construction such as

If the butler didn't do it then the gardener did.

Here the falsity of the antecedent would in no way render the claim true.

3.3 Quantified sentences. Finally we have to consider quantification. How do we explain the truth conditions of a sentence with a quantifier dominant, in terms of the truth conditions of the part within the scope of the quantifier?

Consider a simple example: $\exists xF(x)$, or its ur-version $\exists F(\ )$, with F primitive. $\exists F(\ )$ is true if and only if there is at least one individual of which the predicate $F(\ )$ is true.

We have introduced the relational notion of a predicate's being *true of* an individual. Let us speak conversely of an individual's *satisfying* a predicate. In our example $\exists F(\ )$ we might think of the link, with the quantifier $\exists$ excised, as latching onto some individual α that satisfies the predicate:

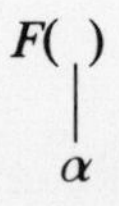

In a slightly more complicated case, such as $\exists L(\ ,\ )$, when we excise the quantifier we produce the picture,

of the links latching onto some individual α from two different gaps in the predicate. For α to satisfy $L(\ ,\ )$ at those two gaps it would have to bear to itself the relation that the predicate represents.

The same explanation of the truth conditions of sentences of the form $\exists\psi(\ \ ,\ \ )$ is available when ψ is complex. For example, with

$\exists(F(\ )\&G(\ ))$ excision of $\exists$ results in the picture

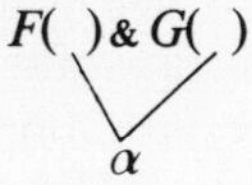

The truth condition for $\exists(F(\ )\&G(\ ))$ is that there be at least one individual α onto which the links could latch so that the depicted assignment of α to the gaps in the complex predicate $F(\ )\&G(\ )$ satisfies it. This in turn is the condition that there be at least one individual α such that the assignment of α to the gap in $F(\ )$ satisfies $F(\ )$ *and* the assignment of α to the gap in $G(\ )$ satisfies $G(\ )$.

Notice that we have advanced from saying

> α satisfies ψ when assigned to its gaps

to saying

> the assignment of α to the gaps in ψ satisfies it

Now there is a natural way of locating the new gaps in a predicate upon excision of a dominant quantifier. They are the gaps that, in our linear notation, are occupied by occurrences of the variable that are *freed* by the removal of the quantifier prefix. The formula $\exists x\psi(\text{-}x\text{-}x\text{-}x\text{-})$ with the indicated occurrences of x bound by the dominant occurrence of $\exists x$ becomes, upon removal of $\exists x$, the formula $\psi(\text{-}x\text{-}x\text{-}x\text{-})$ in which the indicated occurrences of x are now free. We may now advance to saying

> the assignment of α to the variable x satisfies $\psi(\text{-}x\text{-}x\text{-}x\text{-})$

or, briefly,

> (x/α) satisfies $\psi(\text{-}x\text{-}x\text{-}x\text{-})$

Our account is still not quite general enough. For a predicate might have been exposed by removing more than one occurrence of quantifiers. Consider a simple multiple quantification: $\exists x\forall yL(x,y)$. This is true just in case there is an individual α such that (x/α) satisfies $\forall yL(x,y)$. But what is it for (x/α) to satisfy $\forall yL(x,y)$? Simply that α should bear to every individual the relation represented by L: i.e., that for every individual $\beta,(x/\alpha)(y/\beta)$ satisfies $L(x,y)$. So $\exists x\forall yL(x,y)$ is true just in case there is an individual α such that for every individual β, α bears to β the relation represented by L.

3.4 Satisfaction and truth: Tarski's adequacy condition. An assignment of individuals to variables may be thought of as temporarily making the variables concerned behave like names of the respective individuals assigned to them. We shall call the denotation of any name a (the individual for which a stands) simply $\underline{a}$. Thus a denotes $\underline{a}$ irrespective of any assignment of individuals to variables which may be under consideration. We shall call the operation on individuals represented by any function sign f simply $\underline{f}$. The denotation of a variable x relative to any assignment s which deals with x is obviously $s(x)$. We may complete an inductive definition of $s[t]$ – the denotation of a term t relative to any assignment s which deals with all the variables in t – as follows:

$$s[a] = \underline{a}; \text{ and } s[f(t_1, \ldots, t_n)] = \underline{f}(s[t_1], \ldots, s[t_n])$$

The device of underlining symbols of our formal language is generally useful as a succinct indication of translation into the *metalanguage*, the language in which we are stating satisfaction and truth conditions. Our metalanguage is presently a mélange of English and informal mathematical jargon. We shall now agree to make it a little more austere. Instead of writing the English phrases

it is not the case that ..., and, or, only if, there is at least one individual α such that ..., for every individual α

we shall write respectively

$\underline{\sim}$, $\underline{\&}$, $\underline{\vee}$, $\underline{\supset}$, $\underline{\exists}\alpha$, $\underline{\forall}\alpha$

Likewise instead of writing atomic sentences like

α stands to β in the relation represented by L

we shall write

$\underline{L}(\alpha,\beta)$

In our discussion above we moved from talk of truth conditions of sentences, which have no free variables, to talk of satisfaction conditions of formulae. For uniformity we should re-state the truth conditions for sentences with connectives dominant as satisfaction conditions for formulae with connectives dominant. As a limiting case we may regard the truth of a sentence (with no free variables) as consisting in its satisfaction by the *null assignment* $\emptyset$.

An assignment may be extended or modified to deal with a variable newly freed by the removal of a quantifier prefix. If s is an assignment then $s(x/\alpha)$ will be the assignment which results from extending or modifying s so that it assigns α to x. Note that $s(x/\alpha)[x]$ is obviously α, while $s(x/\alpha)(x/\beta)[x]$ is β. In general we look to the last extension or modification with respect to x to find what the assignment assigns to x.

We may talk of an assignment satisfying a formula only when the assignment deals with all the free variables of the formula. Our analysis of satisfaction conditions proceeds by unravelling formulae according to their structure and then invoking the satisfaction conditions of atomic formulae. On the assumption that s deals with all the free variables of the formula concerned, the precise inductive definition of satisfaction is as follows.

(i)	s satisfies $P(t_1, \ldots, t_n)$	iff	$\underline{P}(s \lfloor t_1 \rfloor, \ldots, s \lfloor t_n \rfloor)$
(ii)	s satisfies $\sim\psi$	iff	$\underline{\sim}$ s satisfies ψ
(iii)	s satisfies $\varphi \& \psi$	iff	s satisfies $\varphi \ \underline{\&}\ s$ satisfies ψ
(iv)	s satisfies $\varphi \vee \psi$	iff	s satisfies $\varphi \ \underline{\vee}\ s$ satisfies ψ
(v)	s satisfies $\varphi \supset \psi$	iff	s satisfies $\varphi \ \underline{\supset}\ s$ satisfies ψ
(vi)	s satisfies $\exists x \psi$	iff	$\underline{\exists} \alpha\ s(x/\alpha)$ satisfies ψ
(vii)	s satisfies $\forall x \psi$	iff	$\underline{\forall} \alpha\ s(x/\alpha)$ satisfies ψ

Finally, a *sentence* φ is true iff $\emptyset$ satisfies φ.

Let us now consider some consequences of these definitions in the case of two of our examples above, $\exists x(F(x) \& G(x))$ and $\exists x \forall y L(x,y)$. Each link in the following chains of equivalences is justified by one of the clauses above, or by an obvious identity.

$\exists x(F(x) \& G(x))$ is true
iff $\emptyset$ satisfies $\exists x(F(x) \& G(x))$
iff $\underline{\exists} \alpha\ \emptyset(x/\alpha)$ satisfies $F(x) \& G(x)$ by (vi)
iff $\underline{\exists} \alpha(\emptyset(x/\alpha)$ satisfies $F(x)\ \underline{\&}\ \emptyset(x/\alpha)$ satisfies $G(x))$ by (iii)
iff $\underline{\exists} \alpha(\underline{F}(\emptyset(x/\alpha)\lfloor x \rfloor)\ \underline{\&}\ \underline{G}(\emptyset(x/\alpha)\lfloor x \rfloor))$ by (i)
iff $\underline{\exists} \alpha(\underline{F}(\alpha)\ \underline{\&}\ \underline{G}(\alpha)$.

Thus we have proved $\exists x(F(x) \& G(x))$ is true iff $\underline{\exists} \alpha(\underline{F}(\alpha)\ \underline{\&}\ \underline{G}(\alpha))$.

$\exists x \forall y L(x,y)$ is true
iff $\emptyset$ satisfies $\exists x \forall y L(x,y)$
iff $\underline{\exists} \alpha\ \emptyset(x/\alpha)$ satisfies $\forall y L(x,y)$ by (vi)
iff $\underline{\exists} \alpha\ \underline{\forall} \beta\ \emptyset(x/\alpha)(y/\beta)$ satisfies $L(x,y)$ by (vii)
iff $\underline{\exists} \alpha\ \underline{\forall} \beta\ \underline{L}(\emptyset(x/\alpha)(y/\beta)\lfloor x \rfloor, \emptyset(x/\alpha)(y/\beta)\lfloor y \rfloor)$ by (i)
iff $\underline{\exists} \alpha\ \underline{\forall} \beta\ \underline{L}(\alpha,\beta)$

Thus we have proved $\exists x \forall y L(x,y)$ is true iff $\underline{\exists} \alpha\ \underline{\forall} \beta\ \underline{L}(\alpha,\beta)$.

It is easily established by induction on the complexity of formulae that we can prove

$$s \text{ satisfies } \psi(x_1, \ldots, x_n) \quad \text{iff} \quad \underline{\psi}(s\lfloor x_1 \rfloor, \ldots, s\lfloor x_n \rfloor)$$

where $\underline{\psi}$ is a verbatim translation of the formula ψ into the metalanguage. In particular we can prove for any *sentence* φ that

φ is true iff $\underline{\varphi}$

as illustrated twice above. Our definition of truth – or, more precisely, the theory of truth to which it belongs – therefore satisfies what is known as Tarski's adequacy condition. This is the condition that every instance of the last schema should be provable in the truth theory.

We have given our account of the truth conditions of sentences of our formal language by using a metalanguage containing translations of these sentences. Only if we have a thorough understanding of the metalanguage can we claim to have characterized truth conditions of sentences of the formal language. The formal language is often called the *object language*, since it is presently the object of our study.

We have used expressions like

$\exists xF(x)$

as metalinguistic designations of formulae of the object language. $\exists xF(x)$ is the result of concatenating $\exists$, x, F, (, x, and) in that order. Precisely *what* entities these are does not matter: they might even turn out to be '$\exists$', 'x', 'F', '(', 'x' and ')' respectively. Metalinguistically we have used concatenation of designations to represent concatenation of things designated. These remarks prepare the stage for a precise statement of Tarski's adequacy condition on any theory of truth T:

> Every instance of the metalinguistic schema
>
> φ is true iff $\underline{\varphi}$
>
> should be provable in T, where an instance is obtained by replacing 'φ' by a metalinguistic designation of a sentence of the object language, and replacing '$\underline{\varphi}$' by a translation of that sentence into the metalanguage.

The theory of truth given here is sometimes called the *pure* theory because it makes no mention of the situations in which sentences are true or false. It is therefore not well tailored for the definition of logical consequence:

$\Delta \models \varphi$ iff for every situation $\mathfrak{A}$ if all the members of Δ are true-in-$\mathfrak{A}$ then φ is true-in-$\mathfrak{A}$ also

which involves the relativised notion of truth-in-a-situation.

As remarked in Chapter 1, in the mathematical literature situations are usually called *models*, and we shall henceforth adopt this terminology. We shall now characterize models and relativize the definitions of satisfaction and truth.

3.5 Models. A model $\mathfrak{A} = (A, \_)$ consists of a domain A of individuals and an assignment _ which assigns to each *distinguished* name a some member $\underline{a}$ of A; to each n-place function sign f an n-place operation $\underline{f}$ everywhere defined in A; and to each n-place predicate P a set $\underline{P}$ of n-tuples of members of A. The reason for *distinguishing* certain names is that subsequently, in the construction of proofs, we shall be employing undistinguished names as names for 'arbitrary' objects considered in the course of a proof (a method of reasoning common in mathematics). In subsequent discussion we shall implicitly assume that the formulae and sentences involved contain no undistinguished names when we consider conditions for their satisfaction and truth in a model.

Suppose s assigns members of A to certain variables. On the assumption that s deals with all the variables in a term t, we define $s_{\mathfrak{A}}[t]$, the denotation of t in $\mathfrak{A}$ relative to s, inductively as follows:

$$s_{\mathfrak{A}}[x] = s(x)$$
$$s_{\mathfrak{A}}[a] = \underline{a}$$
$$s_{\mathfrak{A}}[f(t_1, \ldots, t_n)] = \underline{f}(s_{\mathfrak{A}}[t_1], \ldots, s_{\mathfrak{A}}[t_n])$$

Instead of $\langle \alpha_1, \ldots, \alpha_n \rangle \in \underline{P}$ we shall write $\underline{P}(\alpha_1, \ldots, \alpha_n)$. Instead of

s satisfies ψ in $\mathfrak{A}$

we shall write $\mathfrak{A} \models \psi[s]$. (The use of $\models$ in this way must not be confused with its use to represent logical consequence.) Instead of

there is a member α of A such that

we shall write $\underline{\exists}\alpha \in A$, and likewise for the universal quantifier.

The model-relative definition of satisfaction is given by the following clauses.

(i)	$\mathfrak{A} \models P(t_1, \ldots, t_n)[s]$	iff	$\underline{P}(s_{\mathfrak{A}}[t_1], \ldots, s_{\mathfrak{A}}[t_n])$
(ii)	$\mathfrak{A} \models \sim\psi[s]$	iff	$\underline{\sim}\mathfrak{A} \models \psi[s]$
(iii)	$\mathfrak{A} \models \varphi \& \psi[s]$	iff	$\mathfrak{A} \models \varphi[s] \ \underline{\&}\ \mathfrak{A} \models \psi[s]$
(iv)	$\mathfrak{A} \models \varphi \vee \psi[s]$	iff	$\mathfrak{A} \models \varphi[s] \ \underline{\vee}\ \mathfrak{A} \models \psi[s]$
(v)	$\mathfrak{A} \models \varphi \supset \psi[s]$	iff	$\mathfrak{A} \models \varphi[s] \ \underline{\supset}\ \mathfrak{A} \models \psi[s]$
(vi)	$\mathfrak{A} \models \exists x\psi[s]$	iff	$\underline{\exists}\alpha \in A\ \mathfrak{A} \models \psi[s(x/\alpha)]$
(vii)	$\mathfrak{A} \models \forall x\psi[s]$	iff	$\underline{\forall}\alpha \in A\ \mathfrak{A} \models \psi[s(x/\alpha)]$

Finally a sentence φ is true in $\mathfrak{A}$ iff $\mathfrak{A} \models \varphi[\emptyset]$.

It is easily seen that this definition yields all instances of the adequacy schema where each instance now has on its right-hand side a model relative translation of the designated sentence. Thus our earlier examples would become

$\exists x(F(x) \mathbin{\&} G(x))$	is true in $\mathfrak{A}$	iff	$\underline{\exists}\alpha \in A(\underline{F}(\alpha) \underline{\&} \underline{G}(\alpha))$
$\exists x \forall y L(x,y)$	is true in $\mathfrak{A}$	iff	$\underline{\exists}\alpha \in A \underline{\forall}\beta \in A \underline{L}(\alpha,\beta)$

3.6 Finite and infinite models. If the domain A is infinite it is not in general possible to determine in a mechanical way whether a sentence is true in $\mathfrak{A}$. This is because clauses (vi) and (vii) for the quantifiers require possibly infinite searches through the domain. So although it might (in a classical sense) be mathematically well-determined whether a given sentence φ is true or false in $\mathfrak{A}$, it might nevertheless be impossible for us to discover by routine application of the definitional clauses above, whether φ was true or false. In such a case, where $\mathfrak{A}$ is an infinite model of some interest and φ a sentence whose truth or falsity in that model has to be determined, we might have to resort to *proving* φ from other sentences which are 'obviously' true in $\mathfrak{A}$. An example is the case where $\mathfrak{A}$ is the model consisting of the counting numbers (natural numbers) 0, 1, 2, ... with the usual additive and multiplicative operations. This model is usually called $\mathbb{N}$. As mentioned in 1.4, no-one has yet determined the truth or falsity in $\mathbb{N}$ of the sentence

> φ: Every even number greater than two is the sum of two prime numbers.

To do so 'by inspection' might require an infinite search through the even numbers. We might one day discover an even number greater than two which is *not* a sum of any two preceding primes, and this would enable us to say that φ was false in $\mathbb{N}$. We would still, of course, have had to 'verify' that only preceding primes need be inspected. No such counterexample, however, has yet been discovered. A mathematician who believes φ is true in $\mathbb{N}$, and who wishes to establish this conclusively, must resort to proving φ from axioms which are 'obviously' true in $\mathbb{N}$. No such proof has yet been discovered.

In contrast to the infinite case, the truth or falsity of φ in $\mathfrak{A}$ can always be determined when A is finite. Any sentence φ contains only finitely many extra-logical expressions. For each such expression E there is a finite specification of $\underline{E}$ in the model. So if the domain A is finite we need inspect only a finite amount of information in order to determine whether φ is true or false.

Consider, for example, the sentence $\forall x \exists y Lxy$ and the model $\mathfrak{A}$ whose domain A consists of just two individuals α and β and in which $\underline{L}$ is specified as $\{\langle\alpha,\beta\rangle,\langle\beta,\alpha\rangle\}$. The truth or falsity of $\forall x \exists y Lxy$ in $\mathfrak{A}$ is determined by a proof or refutation of the metastatement

$\forall x \exists y Lxy$ is true in $\mathfrak{A}$

within the truth theory. In fact, we can prove this statement (rather than refute it) from the basic information about $\mathfrak{A}$ (expressed in the metalanguage) as follows:

$$\dfrac{\dfrac{\dfrac{\dfrac{\underline{L}(\alpha,\beta)}{\mathfrak{A} \models Lxy[(x/\alpha)(y/\beta)]} \quad \beta \in A}{\underline{\exists} \gamma \in A \; \mathfrak{A} \models Lxy[(x/\alpha)(y/\gamma)]}}{\mathfrak{A} \models \exists y Lxy[(x/\alpha)]} \qquad \dfrac{\dfrac{\dfrac{\underline{L}(\beta,\alpha)}{\mathfrak{A} \models Lxy[(x/\beta)(y/\alpha)]} \quad \alpha \in A}{\underline{\exists} \gamma \in A \; \mathfrak{A} \models Lxy[(x/\beta)(y/\gamma)]}}{\mathfrak{A} \models \exists y Lxy[(x/\beta)]} \quad A = \{\alpha,\beta\}}{\dfrac{\underline{\forall} \gamma \in A \; \mathfrak{A} \models \exists y Lxy[(x/\gamma)]}{\mathfrak{A} \models \forall x \exists y Lxy}} (\times)$$

The step marked $(\times)$ in this proof highlights the difference between the finite and infinite case. For, consider once more the infinite model $\mathbb{N}$. In 'proving' within our truth theory a conclusion of the form

$$\underline{\forall} \alpha \in \mathbb{N} \; \mathbb{N} \models \varphi[s(x/\alpha)]$$

in a manner analogous to that above we would apply the infinitary inference

$$\dfrac{\begin{matrix}\vdots \\ \mathbb{N} \models \varphi[s(x/0)]\end{matrix} \quad \begin{matrix}\vdots \\ \mathbb{N} \models \varphi[s(x/1)]\end{matrix} \quad \begin{matrix}\vdots \\ \mathbb{N} \models \varphi[s(x/2)]\end{matrix} \quad \cdots \qquad N = \{0,1,2,\ldots\}}{\underline{\forall} \alpha \in \mathbb{N} \quad \mathbb{N} \models \varphi[s(x/\alpha)]} (\times)$$

which involves infinitely many subproofs and so would make the proof infinite.

As mentioned earlier, in order to establish universal statements about the counting numbers mathematicians must resort to certain axiomatic principles. Among these is the principle of mathematical induction. According to this principle, if you have proved $\varphi(0)$ and, on the inductive hypothesis $\varphi(n)$ (for 'arbitrary' n), you have proved $\varphi(n+1)$ then you may conclude $\forall x \varphi(x)$ independently of the inductive hypothesis. Schematically, we may write this as

$$\dfrac{\varphi(0) \qquad \begin{matrix}\overline{\varphi(n)} \\ \vdots \\ \varphi(n+1)\end{matrix}}{\forall x \varphi(x)}$$

The idea behind this principle is that the proof of $\varphi(n+1)$ from $\varphi(n)$ can be repeated ad infinitum to produce infinitely many subconclusions from which the universal statement follows:

$$
\begin{array}{cccc}
 & & \vdots & \\
 & & \varphi(0) & \\
 & \vdots & \vdots & \\
 & \varphi(0) & \varphi(1) & \\
\vdots & \vdots & \vdots & \\
\varphi(0) & \varphi(1) & \varphi(2) & \ldots \\
\hline
\multicolumn{4}{c}{\forall x \varphi(x)}
\end{array}
$$

The principle of mathematical induction can therefore be understood as an attempt to ensure that 0, 1, 2, ... *are the only individuals in* $\mathbb{N}$. (Compare the steps marked ($\times$) above.) The extent to which it succeeds will be examined in Chapter 7.

3.7 Categoricity. Two models $\mathfrak{A}=(A,\_)$ and $\mathfrak{A}=(B,\sim)$ are *isomorphic* if there is a one-one mapping h from A onto B such that for every name a, $h(\underline{a})=\underset{\sim}{a}$; for every n-place function sign f, $\underline{f}(\alpha_1, \ldots, \alpha_n) = \underset{\sim}{f}(h(\alpha_1), \ldots, h(\alpha_n))$; and for every n-place predicate P, $\underline{P}(\alpha_1, \ldots, \alpha_n)$ iff $\underset{\sim}{P}(h(\alpha_1), \ldots, h(\alpha_n))$. Isomorphic models have the same number of individuals and possess the same structure. They make exactly the same sentences of the formal language true.

If the formal language has the *identity predicate* =, which in any model $\mathfrak{A}$ represents the identity relation $\{\langle\alpha,\alpha\rangle | \alpha \in A\}$, then the condition for an *onto* map h to be an isomorphism is

for any *atomic* formula $\psi(x_1, \ldots, x_n)$, $\quad \mathfrak{A} \models \psi[(x_1/\alpha_1) \ldots (x_n/\alpha_n)]$
iff $\quad \mathfrak{A} \models \psi[(x_1/h(\alpha_1)), \ldots, (x_n/h(\alpha_n))]$.

A set of sentences is called *categorical* if any two of its models are isomorphic. A categorical set of sentences determines exactly one model 'up to isomorphism'. Such a model is said to be *categorically describable.*

Every model with a finite domain is categorically describable provided that the formal language has the identity predicate, and is categorically describable by a single sentence provided in addition that the formal language has only finitely many names, function signs and predicates. To illustrate this last claim consider the formal language with just one name a, one one-place function sign f, and one one-place predicate F. Consider a model $(\{\alpha,\beta\},\_)$ where $\underline{a}=\alpha$, $\underline{f}(\alpha)=\underline{f}(\beta)=\beta$, and $\underline{F}=\{\alpha\}$. Let us introduce the name b temporarily to stand for β. First we specify the *census*:

$$\sim a=b \quad ; \quad \forall x(x=a \vee x=b)$$

Next we specify all the functional identities:

$$f(a)=b \quad ; \quad f(b)=b$$

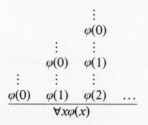

Then we specify all the atomic predications and their negations:

$$F(a) \quad ; \quad \sim F(b)$$

Finally we form the conjunction of all these sentences and quantify existentially with respect to b (since in the model to be described β is nameless):

$$\exists y(\sim a=y \,\&\, \forall x(x=a \vee x=y) \,\&\, f(a)=y \,\&\, f(y)=y \,\&\, F(a) \,\&\, \sim F(y))$$

This sentence obviously describes the model categorically. The general method for finding a sentence which categorically describes a finite model of finitely many extra-logical expressions is implicit in our example.

3.8 Counterexamples to invalid arguments. The reader will recall that an argument is invalid if and only if there is some model in which all the premisses are true but the conclusion is false. To invalidate an argument with finitely many premisses we need only find a model for the conjunction of all the premisses with the negation of the conclusion.

A well-known invalid argument is that of 'quantifier switch':

$$\frac{\forall x \exists y\ \psi xy}{\exists y \forall x\ \psi xy}$$

The following simple model, in which arrows represent the relation expressed by ψ, serves as a counterexample, making the premiss true but the conclusion false:

Another model which invalidates the quantifier switch argument is that consisting of the positive and negative integers, with ψ interpreted as 'is strictly less than'. Every integer is strictly less than some integer, but there is no integer such that every integer (including itself) is strictly less than it.

Consider the English sentences

(1) No-one has fooled everyone.
(2) No-one has been fooled by everyone.
(3) Someone has fooled someone.
(4) Everyone has either fooled someone or been fooled by someone.
(5) Everyone has fooled himself only if he has fooled someone else.
(6) Everyone has fooled himself only if he has been fooled by someone else.

(7) Everyone who has fooled someone has fooled himself.
(8) Everyone has fooled himself only if everyone has fooled someone else.
(9) Everyone has fooled himself only if everyone has been fooled by someone else.
(10) Everyone who has been fooled by someone has fooled himself.
(11) Everyone has both fooled someone and been fooled by him.

The translations of (1)-(11) into logical notation are as follows:

(1) $\sim\exists x\forall yFxy$
(2) $\sim\exists x\forall yFyx$
(3) $\exists x\exists yFxy$
(4) $\forall x(\exists yFxy \vee \exists yFyx)$
(5) $\forall x(Fxx \supset \exists y(\sim y = x \,\&\, Fxy))$
(6) $\forall x(Fxx \supset \exists y(\sim y = x \,\&\, Fyx))$
(7) $\forall x(\exists yFxy \supset Fxx)$
(8) $\forall xFxx \supset \forall x\exists y(\sim y = x \,\&\, Fxy)$
(9) $\forall xFxx \supset \forall x\exists y(\sim y = x \,\&\, Fyx)$
(10) $\forall x(\exists yFyx \supset Fxx)$
(11) $\forall x\exists y(Fxy \,\&\, Fyx)$

For each i between 1 and 9 the premisses (1)-(i) fail logically to imply conclusion (11). Counterexamples are as follows, with arrows representing F.

(1) and (2) true, but (11) false.

(1), (2) and (3) true, but (11) false.

(1)-(6) true, but (11) false.

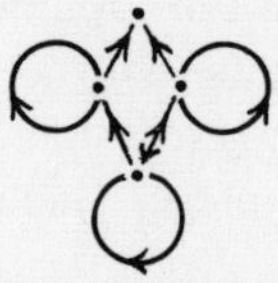
(1)-(9) true, but (11) false.

Strictly speaking only the last counterexample is needed, but we have given the other three as well because of their greater simplicity.

As soon as we add (10) to the premisses the argument becomes valid. In fact, premisses (4), (7) and (10) logically imply the conclusion (11). In the following chapter on proofs we shall return to this example, to show how to perfect the argument (4), (7), (10)/(11) by means of a proof. Having a proof of the argument is the only way to establish its validity, for it is impossible to survey all possible models of (4), (7), and (10) to check that in each of them (11) is true.

The last four counterexamples were finite. We saw also that the quantifier switch argument, although it possessed an infinite counterexample, had also a finite one. Not every invalid argument, however, has a finite counterexample. For, from the premisses

$$\exists x \exists y \sim x = y$$
$$\forall x \sim x < x$$
$$\forall x \forall y \forall z ((x < y \,\&\, y < z) \supset x < z)$$
$$\forall x \forall y \forall z (x < y \vee y < x \vee x = y)$$

which ensure that $<$ represents a non-trivial strict ordering, the conclusion

$$\sim \forall x \forall y (x < y \supset \exists z (x < z \,\&\, z < y))$$

which says that the ordering is not dense, does not follow. This is because *some* non-trivial strict orderings *are* dense (e.g. the ordering of the rational numbers). All such orderings, however, are infinite. Thus there is no finite counterexample to this invalid argument.

If, however, the formal language contained only names and one-place predicates and no function signs then any sentence that had a model would have a finite model. Thus any invalid argument from finitely many premisses would have a finite counterexample. This will be proved in Chapter 6.

Other model-theoretic results to be proved in Chapter 6 are the Löwenheim-Skolem theorem:

> If a countable set of sentences has an infinite model then it has a model of every infinite cardinality

and the Compactness theorem:

> If every finite subset of a set of sentences has a model, then it too has a model.

Both these theorems have interesting consequences for the foundations of mathematics.

3.9 Game theoretic semantics. Consider a formal language with $\sim$, &, $\vee$, $\exists$ and $\forall$ as its logical operators. Suppose I assert a sentence φ, understood as an assertion about a well-defined model $\mathfrak{A}$. Suppose you challenge my assertion. How might I convince you or you convince me?

(i) If φ is atomic then of course we look to the model to see who is correct. If φ is true, I win. If not, you win.

(ii) If φ is $\sim\psi$ then you would undertake to assert ψ and I would undertake to challenge ψ. Thus our roles would be exchanged.

(iii) If φ is $\psi \vee \theta$ then I would have to assert ψ or assert θ. Whichever I asserted you would have to challenge.

(iv) If φ is $\psi \& \theta$ then you would have to challenge ψ or challenge θ. Whichever you challenge I would have to assert.

(v) If φ is $\exists x\psi$ then I would have to choose a member α of the domain as a verifying instance. So I would be asserting $\psi(x)$ where x would now be understood as a name of α. You would have to challenge $\psi(x)$ on the same understanding.

(vi) If φ is $\forall x\psi$ then you would have to choose a member α of the domain as a falsifying instance. So you would be challenging $\psi(x)$ where x would now be understood as a name of α. I would have to assert $\psi(x)$ on the same understanding.

As we make our choices according to these rules, we successively reduce the complexity of the sentence whose truth value is contested. After finitely many moves an atomic sentence will be reached and one of us will win.

Now it is important to distinguish between happening to win a particular play of this 'game', and having a winning strategy. A winning strategy is a game plan that ensures a win regardless of the moves one's opponent might make. For example, suppose ψ is true but θ is false. Then I have a winning strategy on $\psi \vee \theta$ – namely to choose ψ and follow my winning strategy on *it*. But suppose I *mis-execute* my winning strategy by mistakenly choosing θ. Then *you* would possess a winning strategy. If you executed it properly, you would win. So you might, as a result of my mistake, win a particular play without having had a winning strategy at the outset. Thus the way to 'convince' one's opponent is to win in many plays of the game, and never to lose. This will provide him with inductive evidence that you possess a winning strategy.

At each state of play exactly one of us has a winning strategy. If the possessor of a winning strategy misexecutes it then he ceases to be, and his opponent becomes, the possessor of a winning strategy. To execute a winning strategy properly is to retain one's position as the possessor of a winning strategy. At the final state of play – where an atomic formula has been reached – the possessor of a winning strategy is, degenerately, he who wins.

At each state of play one of us is asserting the subformula remaining, the other challenging it. Let us say the former occupies role T and the latter role F. The assertion and denial must, of course, be made on the understanding that the free variables in the remaining subformula name the individuals that have been correlated with them in the course of play. In other words, the assertion is of a formula relative to an assignment of individuals to its free variables.

Thus each state of play is characterized by the following three components:

(i) a role assignment R, where $R(T)$ is the person who occupies role T at that state, and $R(F)$ is the person who occupies role F;
(ii) a formula φ with respect to which play is to continue; and
(iii) an assignment s of individuals from the domain of $\mathfrak{A}$ to the free variables in φ.

Play takes place against the background of the model $\mathfrak{A}$. At each state of play it is determined which of us has a winning strategy. Our discussion shows that $P(R,\varphi,s)$ – the possessor of a winning strategy at state of play (R,φ,s) – may be defined inductively as follows:

Let $\bar{R}$ be the reversal of R, so $\bar{R}(T)=R(F)$ and $\bar{R}(F)=R(T)$. Then

(i)	$P(R,\psi,s)=R(T)$	iff	$\mathfrak{A}\models\psi[s]$, for atomic ψ
(ii)	$P(R,\sim\psi,s)=R(T)$	iff	$P(\bar{R},\psi,s)=\bar{R}(F)$
(iii)	$P(R,\psi\vee\theta,s)=R(T)$	iff	either $P(R,\psi,s)=R(T)$ or $P(R,\theta,s)=R(T)$
(iv)	$P(R,\psi\,\&\,\theta,s)=R(F)$	iff	either $P(R,\psi,s)=R(F)$ or $P(R,\theta,s)=R(F)$
(v)	$P(R,\exists x\psi,s)=R(T)$	iff	$\exists\alpha\in A\ P(R,\psi,s(x/\alpha))=R(T)$
(vi)	$P(R,\forall x\psi,s)=R(F)$	iff	$\exists\alpha\in A\ P(R,\psi,s(x/\alpha))=R(F)$

It follows immediately by induction on the complexity of ψ that

$$P(R,\psi,s)=R(T) \quad \text{iff} \quad \mathfrak{A}\models\psi[s]$$

Thus a sentence φ is true in $\mathfrak{A}$ if and only if he who starts as player T in the 'language game' on φ has a winning strategy.

Just as in finite models the truth value of φ could be mechanically computed, so also against the background of a finite model a winning strategy in the game on φ can be mechanically devised and executed. In principle it would be a routine matter to choose subformulae and individuals correctly in the course of play. Against the background of an infinite model, however, such as the counting numbers, the sense in which one might 'have' a winning strategy might be somewhat tenuous. In an ideal mathematical sense the strategy might exist without its 'possessor' being in a position knowingly to execute it. This difference between the finite and the infinite case is a ground of disagreement between classical and intuitionistic mathematicians.

CHAPTER 4

Form and structure of proofs

4.1
Explanation and motivation of rules of inference *p.40*
4.2
Rules of inference as inductive clauses in a definition of proof *p.49*
4.3
The rules of section 1 construed in the manner of section 2 *p.52*
4.4
Remarks on discharging assumptions *p.56*
4.5
Intuitionistic and classical logic *p.57*
4.6
Some simple proofs – mimicking truth tables, and dualities *p.59*
4.7
Expressive completeness and interderivability of rules *p.61*
4.8
Reasons for restrictions on quantifier rules *p.64*
4.9
Substitutions in proofs *p.65*
4.10
Reduction procedures *p.69*
4.11
Soundness of classical logic *p.71*
4.12
Harmony and containment *p.74*
4.13
Identity and extensionality *p.77*
4.14
Some simple proofs *p.81*

4.1 Explanation and motivation of rules of inference. In this section we shall examine in detail some very simple arguments. We shall fill in all the steps which could possibly be required in order to convince one of their validity. We shall then show how to transcribe the perfected agruments into our logical notation for proofs. This process parallels that of transcribing disambiguated English sentences into formulae.

Some of the arguments may appear so obviously valid that no further perfection or formal representation by means of proofs is required. We shall nevertheless carry out these operations fully, in order comprehensively to illustrate every aspect of the proof system.

To begin we shall state and name certain rules of immediate inference which are so obviously valid and whose application is so straightforward that it is unnecessary to introduce the reader to them by means of their applications in particular examples.

Rule of Contradiction, or ~-Elimination

From φ and $\sim\varphi$ we may immediately infer 'Contradiction!' for which we use the symbol ※:

$$\frac{\varphi \quad \sim\varphi}{※}$$

Rule of &-Introduction

From φ and ψ we may immediately infer $\varphi \& \psi$:

$$\frac{\varphi \quad \psi}{\varphi \& \psi}$$

Rule of &-Elimination

From $\varphi \& \psi$ we may immediately infer φ, likewise ψ:

$$\frac{\varphi \& \psi}{\varphi} \qquad \frac{\varphi \& \psi}{\psi}$$

Rule of ∨-Introduction

From φ we may immediately infer $\varphi \vee \psi$; likewise from ψ:

$$\frac{\varphi}{\varphi \vee \psi} \qquad \frac{\psi}{\varphi \vee \psi}$$

Rule of ⊃-Elimination, or Modus Ponens

From φ and $\varphi \supset \psi$ we may immediately infer ψ:

$$\frac{\varphi \quad \varphi \supset \psi}{\psi}$$

Rule of $\exists$*-Introduction*

From φ(t) we may immediately infer $\exists x\varphi(x)$:

$$\frac{\varphi(t)}{\exists x\varphi(x)}$$

In applying this rule one need not replace *every* occurrence of the term t in the sentence $\varphi(t)$ by an occurrence of the variable x. Thus from $L(t,t)$ one may infer any one of $\exists xL(x,x)$, $\exists xL(t,x)$ or $\exists xL(x,t)$. One must also ensure that in $\varphi(t)$ no occurrence of t which is to be replaced by x occurs within the scope of any quantifier binding x. If necessary, choose a new variable. Thus from $\forall xL(t,x)$ one would not infer $\exists x\forall xL(x,x)$ but rather $\exists y\forall xL(y,x)$.

Rule of $\forall$*-Elimination*

From $\forall x\varphi(x)$ we may immediately infer $\varphi(t)$:

$$\frac{\forall x\varphi(x)}{\varphi(t)}$$

In applying this rule one replaces every free occurrence of x in $\varphi(x)$ by t.

In order to motivate the rules whose formal statement is less easy to understand let us consider some very simple arguments:

(1) All *F*'s are *G*'s
All *G*'s are *H*'s
———————
All *F*'s are *H*'s

Translated into logical notation this argument becomes

$$\frac{\begin{array}{l}\forall x(Fx\supset Gx)\\ \forall x(Gx\supset Hx)\end{array}}{\forall x(Fx\supset Hx)}$$

An informal proof would run as follows:

Let *a* be an arbitrary object.
Suppose *a* is an *F*.
Since all *F*'s are *G*'s, *a* is a *G*.
Since all *G*'s are *H*'s, *a* is an *H*.
So *if a* is an *F then a* is an *H*.
But *a* was arbitrary.
Thus all *F*'s are *H*'s.

In logical notation the pattern of argument, with extra details filled in, is

$$\dfrac{\dfrac{\dfrac{\overline{Fa}^{(1)} \quad \dfrac{\forall x\, Fx \supset Gx}{Fa \supset Ga}}{Ga} \quad \dfrac{\forall x\, Gx \supset Hx}{Ga \supset Ha}}{\dfrac{Ha}{Fa \supset Ha}(1)}}{\forall x\, Fx \supset Hx}$$

At the inference marked with the lower (1) we *discharged* the assumption *Fa*, as indicated by the corresponding upper (1). The assumption *Fa* had been assumed only 'for the sake of argument' to establish *Ha*. By making the dependence of *Ha* on *Fa* explicit in $Fa \supset Ha$ the latter no longer itself depends on *Fa*. The rule being applied here is the

Rule of ⊃-Introduction, or Conditional Proof

Given a proof of ψ from φ and certain other premisses, we may immediately infer $\varphi \supset \psi$. This conclusion does not depend on φ, but only on the other premisses:

$$\dfrac{\begin{array}{c}\overline{\varphi}^{(i)} \\ \vdots \\ \psi\end{array}}{\varphi \supset \psi}(i)$$

In applying this rule there does not *have* to be an assumption of the form φ on which ψ depends; *if* there is, however, it may be discharged.

The final step of the proof above was an application of the

Rule of ∀-Introduction

Given a proof of $\varphi(a)$ where the name *a* does not occur in any premiss on which $\varphi(a)$ depends, we may immediately infer $\forall x \varphi(x)$:

$$\dfrac{\begin{array}{c}\vdots \\ \varphi(a)\end{array}}{\forall x \varphi(x)}$$

In applying this rule we replace *every* occurrence of *a* in $\varphi(a)$ by *x*. The variable *x* must not be bound by any quantifier in $\varphi(a)$ that has *a* within its scope. Thus from $\exists x L(a,x)$ one would not infer $\forall x \exists x L(x,x)$ but rather $\forall y \exists x L(y,x)$.

The final step of the informal argument was justified by noting that *a* was 'arbitrary'. The proof-theoretic condition for *a*'s being 'arbitrary' is that *a* occurs in no premiss on which $\varphi(a)$ depends. *a* is 'arbitrary' in any argument by whose final step any assumption about *a* has been discharged. If *a* does not occur in any premiss on which $\varphi(a)$ depends then by appropriate substitutions of any given term *t* we can obtain a proof of $\varphi(t)$. It is for this reason that we are justified in concluding $\forall x\varphi(x)$. These observations will be justified in more detail below.

We can draw an instructive analogy between $\forall$ and $\&$. Suppose the domain consists of just two individuals named 0 and 1. Then $\forall x\varphi(x)$ is equivalent to $\varphi(0)\,\&\,\varphi(1)$. Now suppose we have a proof of $\varphi(a)$ for 'arbitrary' a. Substituting 0 for a in an appropriate way we shall obtain a proof of $\varphi(0)$. Likewise we may obtain a proof of $\varphi(1)$. We then have the analogy

$$\dfrac{\begin{matrix}\vdots\\ \varphi(a)\end{matrix}}{\forall x\varphi(x)} \qquad\leftrightarrow\qquad \dfrac{\begin{matrix}\vdots\ a/0\\ \varphi(0)\end{matrix}\qquad \begin{matrix}\vdots\ a/1\\ \varphi(1)\end{matrix}}{\varphi(0)\,\&\,\varphi(1)}$$

The analogy obviously extends, by multiple $\&$-introductions, to the case where the domain consists of any *finite* number of named individuals.

Now consider a second simple argument:

$$(2)\qquad \dfrac{\text{All } F\text{'s are } G\text{'s}}{\text{All non-}G\text{'s are non-}F\text{'s}}$$

Translated into logical notation this argument becomes

$$\dfrac{\forall x(Fx\supset Gx)}{\forall x(\sim Gx\supset\sim Fx)}$$

An informal proof would run as follows:

Let a be an arbitrary object.
Suppose a is an F.
Since all F's are G's, a is a G.
Now suppose a is not a G. Contradiction.
We no longer suppose a is an F: a is not an F.
So *if* a is a non-G *then* a is a non-F.
But a was arbitrary.
Thus all non-G's are non-F's.

In logical notation the pattern of proof is

$$\dfrac{\dfrac{\dfrac{\dfrac{\dfrac{{\scriptstyle(1)}\dfrac{}{Fa}\qquad \dfrac{\forall x(Fx\supset Gx)}{Fa\supset Ga}}{Ga}\qquad \dfrac{}{\sim Ga}{\scriptstyle(2)}}{\divideontimes}{\scriptstyle(1)}}{\sim Fa}{\scriptstyle(2)}}{\sim Ga\supset\sim Fa}}{\forall x(\sim Gx\supset\sim Fx)}$$

At step (1), having reached $\divideontimes$ from the assumption Fa and certain others, we chose to retain the latter and conclude $\sim Fa$, thereby discharging the assumption Fa. This was an application of the

Rule of Reductio ad Absurdum, or $\sim$-Introduction

Given a proof of ※ from φ and certain other premisses we may immediately infer $\sim\varphi$. This conclusion does not depend on φ, but only on the other premisses:

$$\dfrac{\begin{array}{c}\overline{\quad\varphi\quad}^{\,(i)}\\ \vdots \\ ※\end{array}}{\sim\varphi}\,(i)$$

In applying this rule there does not *have* to be an assumption of the form φ to be discharged.

Now consider a third simple argument:

(3) Everything is either F or G
All F's are H's
All G's are H's
―――――――――――――
Everything is an H

Translated into logical notation this argument becomes

$$\dfrac{\begin{array}{l}\forall x(Fx \vee Gx)\\ \forall x(Fx \supset Hx)\\ \forall x(Gx \supset Hx)\end{array}}{\forall x\, Hx}$$

An informal proof would run as follows:

Let a be an arbitrary object.
Since everything is either F or G, a is either F or G.
Case (i) : a is F. Since all F's are H's, a is an H.
Case (ii): a is G. Since all G's are H's, a is an H.
Since a is F or G we have a is an H independently of the assumptions for Case (i) and Case (ii).
But a was arbitrary.
Thus everything is an H.

In logical notation the pattern of argument is

$$\dfrac{\dfrac{\dfrac{\forall x(Fx \vee Gx)}{Fa \vee Ga} \qquad \dfrac{{}^{(1)}\overline{\;Fa\;} \quad \dfrac{\forall x(Fx \supset Hx)}{Fa \supset Ha}}{Ha} \qquad \dfrac{{}^{(1)}\overline{\;Ga\;} \quad \dfrac{\forall x(Gx \supset Hx)}{Ga \supset Ha}}{Ha}}{Ha}\,(1)}{\forall x Hx}$$

At the step marked (1), having concluded *Ha* in both the case where *Fa* and the case where *Ga*, we conclude *Ha* and discharge the assumptions *Fa* and *Ga* in the respective subproofs. This step is an application of the

Rule of Proof by Cases, or ∨-Elimination

$$\dfrac{\varphi\vee\psi \qquad \begin{matrix}\overline{\varphi}^{\,(i)}\\ \vdots\\ \theta\end{matrix} \qquad \begin{matrix}\overline{\psi}^{\,(i)}\\ \vdots\\ \theta\end{matrix}}{\theta}\,(i)$$

Consider now a fourth and final argument:

(4) Something is an *F*
All *F*'s are *G*'s
Something is a *G*

Translated into logical notation this becomes

$$\dfrac{\begin{matrix}\exists x\, Fx\\ \forall x(Fx\supset Gx)\end{matrix}}{\exists x\, Gx}$$

An informal proof would run as follows:

Something is an *F*. Let us call it *a*.
Since all *F*'s are *G*'s, *a* is a *G*.
Thus something is a *G* (viz. *a*).
All we assumed about *a* was that it was an *F* – i.e., *a* was an arbitrary *F*. Our last conclusion is also independent of *a*.
So, since *some*thing is an *F*, that conclusion holds independently of the assumption that *a* is an *F*.

In logical notation the pattern of argument is

$$\dfrac{\exists x Fx \qquad \dfrac{\dfrac{{}^{(1)}\overline{Fa} \qquad \dfrac{\forall x(Fx\supset Gx)}{Fa\supset Ga}}{Ga}}{\exists x Gx}}{\exists x Gx}\,(1)$$

The final step discharges the assumption *Fa*. It is an application of the

Rule of ∃-Elimination

$$\dfrac{\exists x\varphi(x) \qquad \begin{array}{c} \overline{\varphi(a)}^{\,(i)} \\ \vdots \\ \psi \end{array}}{\psi}\,(i)$$

In applying the rule we must ensure that

(i) a does not occur in $\exists x\varphi(x)$

(ii) a does not occur in ψ

(iii) a does not occur in any assumption, other than $\varphi(a)$, on which the upper occurrence of ψ depends.

These are the proof-theoretic conditions for a's being an 'arbitrary' F and for the conclusion ψ in the subproof on the right to be independent of a. If these conditions are met then by appropriate substitutions of any given term t we can obtain from that subproof a proof of ψ from $\varphi(t)$ and the other premisses.

This suggests another analogy, this time between ∃ and ∨. Suppose again that there are only two individuals, called 0 and 1. Suppose we have a proof of ψ from $\varphi(a)$ and certain other premisses, with a satisfying the conditions above. Then by appropriate substitutions we can obtain a proof of ψ from $\varphi(0)$ and those other premisses, and a proof of ψ from $\varphi(1)$ and the other premisses. With $\exists x\varphi(x)$ equivalent to $\varphi(0)\vee\varphi(1)$ we have the analogy

$$\dfrac{\exists x\varphi(x) \qquad \begin{array}{c} \overline{\varphi(a)}^{\,(i)} \\ \vdots \\ \psi \end{array}}{\psi}\,(i) \quad \leftrightarrow \quad \dfrac{\varphi(0)\vee\varphi(1) \qquad \begin{array}{c} {}^{(i)}\overline{\varphi(0)} \\ \vdots \\ \psi \end{array} \qquad \begin{array}{c} \overline{\varphi(1)}^{\,(i)} \\ \vdots \\ \psi \end{array}}{\psi}\,(i)$$

Once again the analogy extends, by multiple ∨-eliminations, to the case where the domain consists of any *finite* number of named individuals.

We have so far stated introduction and elimination rules for ∼, &, ∨, ⊃, ∃ and ∀. These, however, will not suffice for the proof of the following obviously valid argument (given our definition of validity, *not* the intuitions of entailment theorists such as Anderson and Belnap):

$$\dfrac{\begin{array}{c} \varphi \\ \sim\varphi \end{array}}{\psi}$$

By adopting the

Absurdity Rule

$$\frac{\text{※}}{\varphi}$$

(*ex falso quodlibet*; *pace* Anderson, Belnap, et al.), we can give the proof

$$\dfrac{\dfrac{\varphi \quad \sim\varphi}{\text{※}}}{\psi}$$

The absurdity rule also has another conspicuous application in the proof of the *disjunctive syllogism*

$$\frac{\begin{array}{c}\varphi\vee\psi \\ \sim\varphi\end{array}}{\psi}$$

The proof is as follows:

$$\dfrac{\varphi\vee\psi \qquad \dfrac{\dfrac{\overset{(1)}{\overline{\varphi}} \quad \sim\varphi}{\text{※}}}{\psi} \qquad \overline{\psi}^{\,(1)}}{\psi}\,(1)$$

Note that in the extreme right hand subproof ψ stands as both assumption and conclusion. The single occurrence of ψ is a proof of itself from itself. In its role as subordinate conclusion it is brought down as the main conclusion of proof by cases. In its role as an assumption for proof by cases it is simultaneously discharged.

Finally, how do we prove the logical truth $\varphi\vee\sim\varphi$? We need to prove it from no assumptions at all. Thus we require a proof whose conclusion is $\varphi\vee\sim\varphi$ and whose assumptions have all been discharged in the course of reaching that conclusion.

An obvious answer is to adopt the

Law of Excluded Middle

$$\frac{}{\varphi\vee\sim\varphi}$$

as an axiom scheme. Any substitution instance trivially constitutes a proof of itself from no assumptions (hence the inference stroke with nothing written above it). A second possibility would be to adopt the

Rule of Dilemma

$$\dfrac{\begin{matrix}\dfrac{}{\varphi}{}^{(i)} \\ \vdots \\ \psi\end{matrix} \qquad \begin{matrix}\dfrac{}{\sim\varphi}{}^{(i)} \\ \vdots \\ \psi\end{matrix}}{\psi}{}^{(i)}$$

by which we can construct the proof

$$\dfrac{\dfrac{\dfrac{}{\varphi}{}^{(1)}}{\varphi\vee\sim\varphi} \qquad \dfrac{\dfrac{}{\sim\varphi}{}^{(1)}}{\varphi\vee\sim\varphi}}{\varphi\vee\sim\varphi}{}^{(1)}$$

Without either excluded middle or dilemma we can at least prove ※ from $\sim(\varphi\vee\sim\varphi)$ by means of rules already stated:

$$\dfrac{\dfrac{\dfrac{\dfrac{}{\varphi}{}^{(1)}}{\varphi\vee\sim\varphi} \quad \sim(\varphi\vee\sim\varphi)}{※}{}^{(1)}}{\dfrac{\sim\varphi}{\varphi\vee\sim\varphi}} \quad \sim(\varphi\vee\sim\varphi)$$
$$※$$

Thus by a terminal application of the
Rule of Classical Reductio ad Absurdum

$$\dfrac{\begin{matrix}\dfrac{}{\sim\varphi}{}^{(i)} \\ \vdots \\ ※\end{matrix}}{\varphi}{}^{(i)}$$

we would have the desired result. Alternatively, one could apply $\sim$-introduction once more to obtain $\sim\sim(\varphi\vee\sim\varphi)$, thereby discharging the only assumption $\sim(\varphi\vee\sim\varphi)$, and then apply the
Rule of Double Negation

$$\dfrac{\sim\sim\varphi}{\varphi}$$

to obtain the desired result.

Any proof constructed as a tree of immediate inferences according to the rules stated above is valid, in the sense that if all its undischarged assumptions are true then its conclusion is true also. The validity of each rule above (except, perhaps, the Absurdity Rule) derives from the classical meanings of the logical operators. Not to accept any of these rules as valid is not to understand the classical meaning of the logical operator concerned. Not to accept an accumulation of valid steps as amounting overall to a valid argument is not to understand the notion of a (classically) valid argument.

4.2 Rules of inference as inductive clauses in a definition of proof. In Chapter 1 we discussed the general conditions that a piece of discourse must satisfy in order to count as a proof of a conclusion from certain premisses. The proof should be composed of finitely many steps of inference, each in accordance with one of a fixed set of rules of inference that are obviously valid. At each step we must be able effectively to determine which rule, if any, has been correctly applied. Starting with the premisses one would infer intermediate conclusions, which could then be used as premisses for further applications of rules of inference. One might also, as seen in the previous section, introduce assumptions 'for the sake of argument' that are to be discharged at some later step in the proof. By drawing intermediate inferences in this way, some of which may discharge earlier judiciously chosen assumptions, we eventually infer the overall conclusion to be established. The conclusion will depend on the undischarged assumptions of the proof. These should be among the premisses of the argument whose validity is to be established.

An important feature of this process is that every intermediate conclusion is itself the 'overall' conclusion of the subproof at whose last step it was inferred. Thus the process of constructing proofs is *cumulative*. Proofs $\Pi_1, \ldots, \Pi_n$ of $\varphi_1, \ldots, \varphi_n$, respectively, turn any proof Π of ψ from $\varphi_1, \ldots, \varphi_n$ into a proof of ψ from (at most) the combined premisses of $\Pi_1, \ldots, \Pi_n$:

$$\begin{array}{c}
\underbrace{\begin{array}{ccc} \Pi_1 & \ldots & \Pi_n \\ (\varphi_1) & & (\varphi_n) \end{array}} \\
\Pi \\
\psi
\end{array}$$

This transitivity of proof is nowhere better illustrated than in mathematical theories, where previously proved theorems are used as premisses in the proofs of new ones. Indeed, were it not for transitivity of proof the deductive fabric of mathematics would disintegrate.

Given that proofs may thus be built up from smaller proofs, it becomes important to keep account of the premisses on which any conclusion depends. We can do this if we know how each rule of inference determines the premisses its conclusion depends on. These premisses can be determined once we know which premisses support the intermediate conclusions that serve as premisses for the application of that rule.

Moreover, which rule is being applied, and that it is correctly applied, must be determined only by structural conditions on the subproofs whose conclusions are the premisses for, and on the conclusion of, the application of that rule. It must be possible effectively to determine whether these conditions hold, otherwise we shall not in general be able effectively to recognise a proof as such when we see one.

Because each application of a rule of inference forms a new proof from proofs already constructed, a rule of inference can be understood as a clause in an inductive definition of proof. Let us use the notation $\mathscr{P}(\Pi, \varphi, \Delta)$ to mean 'Π is a proof of φ depending on the set Δ of premisses'. The obvious basis clause is

$$\mathscr{P}(\varphi, \varphi, \{\varphi\}).$$

The general form of a rule of inference is that of an inductive clause:

$$\text{If} \quad \left\{ \begin{array}{l} \mathscr{P}(\Pi_1, \varphi_1, \Delta_1) \\ \vdots \\ \mathscr{P}(\Pi_n, \varphi_n, \Delta_n) \\ \text{and} \\ \mathscr{F}(\Pi_1, \ldots, \Pi_n, \varphi) \end{array} \right\} \quad \text{then} \quad \mathscr{P}\left(\frac{\Pi_1 \ldots \Pi_n}{\varphi}, \varphi, f(\Pi_1, \ldots, \Pi_n, \varphi)\right)$$

Here n, $\mathscr{F}$ and f depend on the rule in question. In the previous section we stated rules for which n was 1, 2 or 3. $\mathscr{F}$ is an effectively determinable condition (perhaps the null condition) on $\Pi_1, \ldots, \Pi_n, \varphi$. Examples are the conditions on the name involved in applications of $\forall$-introduction or $\exists$-elimination. $f(\Pi_1, \ldots, \Pi_n, \varphi)$ is the effectively determinable set of premisses on which the new conclusion φ depends. In many cases it is just $\Delta_1 \cup \ldots \cup \Delta_n$, but in other cases it will be the result of subtracting discharged premisses in the appropriate way. Details will emerge below. The new proof

$$\frac{\Pi_1 \ldots \Pi_n}{\varphi}$$

is the result of writing down $\Pi_1, \ldots, \Pi_n$ so that their conclusions are on the same horizontal line, drawing a horizontal inference stroke beneath them and writing φ below the stroke. More abstractly, since we wish to be able to speak of proofs that might never be written down,

$$\frac{\Pi_1 \ \ldots \ \Pi_n}{\varphi}$$

may be thought of as an abstract mathematical entity like the ordered sequence $(\Pi_1, \ldots, \Pi_n, \varphi)$ or the labelled tree

$$\begin{array}{c} \Pi_1 \ldots \Pi_n \\ \diagdown \ \diagup \\ \varphi \end{array}$$

If we wish specifically to mention the premisses and conclusions we might write

$$\frac{\begin{array}{ccc} \Delta_1 & & \Delta_n \\ \Pi_1 & \ldots & \Pi_n \\ \varphi_1 & & \varphi_n \end{array}}{\varphi}$$

instead of

$$\frac{\Pi_1 \ldots \Pi_n}{\varphi}$$

When $f(\Pi_1, \ldots, \Pi_n, \varphi)$ is simply the union $\Delta_1 \cup \ldots \cup \Delta_n$ of all the premisses of the subordinate proofs $\Pi_1, \ldots, \Pi_n$ the rule may be stated graphically as

$$\frac{\varphi_1 \ldots \varphi_n}{\varphi} \quad \text{where } \mathscr{F}$$

and where $\mathscr{F}$ is the null condition it is not mentioned. When $f(\Pi_1, \ldots, \Pi_n, \varphi)$ is more complicated as a result of discharge of certain assumptions, then a similar graphic statement of the rule is possible (as we have seen in the previous section) using 'discharge strokes' over the relevant assumptions.

If $\mathscr{P}(\Sigma, \psi, \Gamma)$, $\psi \in \Delta$ and $\mathscr{P}(\Pi, \varphi, \Delta)$ then $\begin{array}{c} \Sigma \\ (\psi) \\ \Pi \end{array}$ will be the proof obtained by writing the proof Σ above each initial (undischarged) occurrence of ψ in Π, so that ψ stands as the conclusion of a copy of Σ at each such occurrence:

$$\begin{array}{c} \Gamma \quad \Gamma \\ \Sigma \quad \Sigma \\ \ldots \psi \ldots \psi \ldots \\ \Pi \\ \varphi \end{array}$$

Obviously then we have that the overall result, viz. $\overset{\Sigma}{\underset{\Pi}{(\psi)}}$, is a proof of φ from the set of assumptions $\Gamma \cup (\Delta \backslash \{\psi\})$. If $\psi \notin \Delta$, then $\overset{\Sigma}{\underset{\Pi}{(\psi)}}$ is defined simply to be Π. The definition of $\overset{\Sigma}{\underset{\Pi}{(\psi)}}$ will be useful in subsequent discussion of various transformations of proofs.

4.3 The rules of section 1 construed in the manner of section 2. Let us now examine how each of the rules of inference stated above exhibits the general form just discussed. We use the notation φ^x_t for the result of substituting the closed term t at every free occurrence of the variable x in φ. φ^a_x is the result of replacing a at every occurrence in φ by a variable x that is not bound by any quantifier in φ which has a within its scope.

&-Introduction

If Π_1 is a proof of φ_1 depending on the set of assumptions Δ_1, and if Π_2 is a proof of φ_2 depending on the set of assumptions Δ_2, then

$$\frac{\Pi_1 \quad \Pi_2}{\varphi_1 \& \varphi_2}$$

is a proof of $\varphi_1 \& \varphi_2$ depending on the set of assumptions $\Delta_1 \cup \Delta_2$. Graphically, this rule (which is really a clause in the inductive definition of proof) may be stated as

$$\frac{\varphi_1 \quad \varphi_2}{\varphi_1 \& \varphi_2}$$

$\vee$-Introduction

(i) If Π is a proof of φ depending on the set of assumptions Δ, then $\dfrac{\Pi}{\varphi \vee \psi}$ is a proof of $\varphi \vee \psi$ depending on the set of assumptions Δ.

(ii) If Π is a proof of ψ depending on the set of assumptions Δ, then $\dfrac{\Pi}{\varphi \vee \psi}$ is a proof of $\varphi \vee \psi$ depending on the set of assumptions Δ.

Graphically: $\dfrac{\varphi}{\varphi \vee \psi} \qquad \dfrac{\psi}{\varphi \vee \psi}$

For the statement of the remaining rules let us use the convenient abbreviation $\mathscr{P}(\Pi, \varphi, \Delta)$ for ‘Π is a proof of φ depending on the set of assumptions Δ’. Where there are more than one ‘if ...’ in the statement of the rule, we shall write the relevant conditions in a column contained in braces.

⊃-Introduction

If $\mathscr{P}(\Pi, \varphi, \Delta)$ then $\mathscr{P}(\frac{\Pi}{\psi \supset \varphi}, \psi \supset \varphi, \Delta \backslash \{\psi\})$

Graphically:

$$\frac{\begin{matrix}(\psi)\\ \Delta\\ \Pi\\ \varphi\end{matrix}}{\psi \supset \varphi} \qquad \text{or} \qquad \frac{\begin{matrix}\overline{}^{\,(i)}\\ \psi\\ \vdots\\ \varphi\end{matrix}}{\psi \supset \varphi}{\scriptstyle (i)}$$

∼-Introduction

If $\mathscr{P}(\Pi, ⋇, \Delta)$ then $\mathscr{P}(\frac{\Pi}{\sim\varphi}, \sim\varphi, \Delta \backslash \{\varphi\})$

Graphically:

$$\frac{\begin{matrix}(\varphi)\\ \Delta\\ \Pi\\ ⋇\end{matrix}}{\sim\varphi} \qquad \text{or} \qquad \frac{\begin{matrix}\overline{}^{\,(i)}\\ \varphi\\ \vdots\\ ⋇\end{matrix}}{\sim\varphi}{\scriptstyle (i)}$$

∃-Introduction

If $\mathscr{P}(\Pi, \varphi^x_\iota, \Delta)$ then $\mathscr{P}(\frac{\Pi}{\exists x\varphi}, \exists x\varphi, \Delta)$

Graphically: $\frac{\varphi^x_\iota}{\exists x\varphi}$

∀-Introduction

If $\left\{\begin{array}{l}\mathscr{P}(\Pi, \varphi, \Delta)\\ a \text{ does not occur in any}\\ \text{member of } \Delta\end{array}\right\}$ then $\mathscr{P}(\frac{\Pi}{\forall x\varphi^a_x}, \forall x\varphi^a_x, \Delta)$

Graphically: $\frac{\varphi}{\forall x\varphi^a_x}$

where a does not occur in any
assumption on which φ depends

Absurdity Rule

If $\mathscr{P}(\Pi, ⋇, \Delta)$ then $\mathscr{P}(\frac{\Pi}{\varphi}, \varphi, \Delta)$

Graphically: $\frac{⋇}{\varphi}$

∼-Elimination

If $\left\{\begin{array}{l}\mathscr{P}(\Pi_1, \varphi, \Delta_1)\\ \mathscr{P}(\Pi_2, \sim\varphi, \Delta_2)\end{array}\right\}$ then $\mathscr{P}(\frac{\Pi_1\,\Pi_2}{⋇}, ⋇, \Delta_1 \cup \Delta_2)$

Graphically: $\frac{\varphi \quad \sim\varphi}{⋇}$

&-Elimination

(i) If $\mathscr{P}(\Pi, \varphi \& \psi, \Delta)$ then $\mathscr{P}(\frac{\Pi}{\varphi}, \varphi, \Delta)$

(ii) If $\mathscr{P}(\Pi, \varphi \& \psi, \Delta)$ then $\mathscr{P}(\frac{\Pi}{\psi}, \psi, \Delta)$

Graphically: $\dfrac{\varphi \& \psi}{\varphi} \quad \dfrac{\varphi \& \psi}{\psi}$

∨-Elimination

$$\text{If} \left\{ \begin{array}{l} \mathscr{P}(\Pi_1, \varphi \vee \psi, \Delta_1) \\ \mathscr{P}(\Pi_2, \theta, \Delta_2) \\ \mathscr{P}(\Pi_3, \theta, \Delta_3) \end{array} \right\} \text{ then } \mathscr{P}(\frac{\Pi_1\ \Pi_2\ \Pi_3}{\theta}, \theta, \Delta_1 \cup (\Delta_2 \setminus \{\varphi\}) \cup (\Delta_3 \setminus \{\psi\}))$$

Graphically:

$$\dfrac{\begin{array}{ccc} & (\varphi) & (\psi) \\ \Delta_1 & \Delta_2 & \Delta_3 \\ \Pi_1 & \Pi_2 & \Pi_3 \\ \varphi \vee \psi & \theta & \theta \end{array}}{\theta} \quad \text{or} \quad \dfrac{\begin{array}{ccc} & \overline{\varphi}^{(i)} & \overline{\psi}^{(i)} \\ & \vdots & \vdots \\ \varphi \vee \psi & \theta & \theta \end{array}}{\theta}(i)$$

⊃-Elimination

$$\text{If} \left\{ \begin{array}{l} \mathscr{P}(\Pi_1, \varphi, \Delta_1) \\ \mathscr{P}(\Pi_2, \varphi \supset \psi, \Delta_2) \end{array} \right\} \text{ then } \mathscr{P}(\frac{\Pi_1\ \Pi_2}{\psi}, \psi, \Delta_1 \cup \Delta_2)$$

Graphically: $\dfrac{\varphi \quad \varphi \supset \psi}{\psi}$

∃-Elimination

$$\text{If} \left\{ \begin{array}{l} \mathscr{P}(\Pi_1, \exists x\varphi, \Delta_1) \\ \mathscr{P}(\Pi_2, \psi, \Delta_2) \\ \text{a does not occur in} \\ \exists x\varphi, \psi \text{ or } \Delta_2 \setminus \{\varphi^x_a\} \end{array} \right\} \text{ then } \mathscr{P}(\frac{\Pi_1\ \Pi_2}{\psi}, \psi, \Delta_1 \cup (\Delta_2 \setminus \{\varphi^x_a\}))$$

Graphically:

$$\dfrac{\begin{array}{cc} & (\varphi^x_a) \\ \Delta_1 & \Delta_2 \\ \Pi_1 & \Pi_2 \\ \exists x\varphi & \psi \end{array}}{\psi} \quad \text{or} \quad \dfrac{\begin{array}{cc} & \overline{\varphi^x_a}^{(i)} \\ & \vdots \\ \exists x\varphi & \psi_{(i)} \end{array}}{\psi}$$

where a does not occur in $\exists x\varphi, \psi$ or any assumption other than φ^x_a on which the upper occurrence of ψ depends.

∀-Elimination

If $\mathscr{P}(\Pi, \forall x\varphi, \Delta)$ then $\mathscr{P}(\dfrac{\Pi}{\varphi^x_t}, \varphi^x_t, \Delta)$

Graphically: $\dfrac{\forall x\varphi}{\varphi^x_t}$

Law of Excluded Middle

$\mathscr{P}(\varphi \vee \sim\varphi, \varphi \vee \sim\varphi, \emptyset)$. Graphically: $\dfrac{}{\varphi \vee \sim\varphi}$

Dilemma

If $\left\{ \begin{matrix} \mathscr{P}(\Pi_1, \psi, \Delta_1) \\ \mathscr{P}(\Pi_2, \psi, \Delta_2) \end{matrix} \right\}$ then $\mathscr{P}(\dfrac{\Pi_1 \; \Pi_2}{\psi}, \psi, (\Delta_1 \backslash \{\varphi\}) \cup (\Delta_2 \backslash \{\sim\varphi\}))$

Graphically: $\dfrac{\begin{matrix} (\varphi) & (\sim\varphi) \\ \Delta_1 & \Delta_2 \\ \Pi_1 & \Pi_2 \\ \psi & \psi \end{matrix}}{\psi}$ or $\dfrac{\begin{matrix} \overline{\varphi}^{(i)} & \overline{\sim\varphi}^{(i)} \\ \vdots & \vdots \\ \psi & \psi \end{matrix}}{\psi}{}^{(i)}$

Classical Reductio ad Absurdum

If $\mathscr{P}(\Pi, ※, \Delta)$ then $\mathscr{P}(\dfrac{\Pi}{\varphi}, \varphi, \Delta \backslash \{\sim\varphi\})$

Graphically: $\dfrac{\begin{matrix} (\sim\varphi) \\ \Delta \\ \Pi \\ ※ \end{matrix}}{\varphi}$ or $\dfrac{\begin{matrix} \overline{\sim\varphi}^{(i)} \\ \vdots \\ ※ \end{matrix}}{\varphi}{}^{(i)}$

Double Negation

If $\mathscr{P}(\Pi, \sim\sim\varphi, \Delta)$ then $\mathscr{P}(\dfrac{\Pi}{\varphi}, \varphi, \Delta)$

Graphically: $\dfrac{\sim\sim\varphi}{\varphi}$

Note that no formula with free variables can occur in a proof. Proofs are tree-like arrays of *sentences*, in which all variables are bound. We restrict the basis clause in the definition of proof to sentences; likewise with the law of excluded middle. Any term introduced by ∀-elimination is to be closed. It follows that no formula with free variables can ever occur in a proof. The inductive definition of proof is naturally completed by a closure clause to the effect that nothing is a proof unless its being so follows from the basis clause and the clauses that 'are' the rules of inference stated above.

4.4 Remarks on discharging assumptions. The rules which permit discharge of assumptions are $\sim$-*I*, $\supset$-*I*, $\vee$-*E*, $\exists$-*E*, classical reductio and dilemma. An important point to make is that discharge is a *permissible*, not an obligatory operation when applying one of these rules. Thus for example

$$\frac{\psi}{\varphi\supset\psi}$$

is a proof consisting of one step of $\supset$-*I* at which no assumption of the form φ is discharged. Likewise the final step of the proof

$$\frac{\dfrac{\psi \qquad \sim\psi}{\text{※}}}{\sim\varphi}$$

might be regarded as an application of $\sim$-*I* at which no assumption of the form φ is discharged. Equally it might be regarded as an application of the absurdity rule. Equally it might be regarded as an application of classical reductio at which no assumption of the form $\sim\sim\varphi$ is discharged.

A second important point is that one may discharge an assumption which is simultaneously a premiss for the application of the rule in question. We saw this in the earlier proof of disjunctive syllogism. An even simpler example is

$$\frac{\overline{\varphi}^{\,(1)}}{\varphi\supset\varphi}\,{\scriptstyle(1)}$$

In this proof of $\varphi\supset\varphi$ from no assumptions the application of $\supset$-*I* discharges the assumption φ, which is also the premiss for that application of $\supset$-*I*.

When a proof is being written down, and discharge strokes are being inscribed and numbered so as to show the step at which the discharge is effected, one indicates the discharge of an assumption at all its presently undischarged occurrences. Thus in the proof

$$\frac{\dfrac{\dfrac{{}^{(1)}\overline{\varphi} \qquad \varphi\supset\psi}{\psi} \qquad \dfrac{{}^{(1)}\overline{\varphi} \qquad \varphi\supset\theta}{\theta}}{\psi\,\&\,\theta}}{\varphi\supset(\psi\,\&\,\theta)}\,{\scriptstyle(1)}$$

the final application of $\supset$-*I* discharges φ at the two occurrences indicated. Discharge strokes do not, strictly, form part of the proof proper. Proofs have been defined as tree-like arrays of occurrences of sentences without any mention of discharge strokes in the definition.

These strokes are added to the proof when it is written down merely as a mnemonic device to help keep account of the assumptions on which the conclusion depends.

There is an obvious analogy between stage-by-stage justifications of the grammaticality of formulae, keeping track of which occurrences of variables are free, and the stage-by-stage justifications of the 'proofhood' of tree-like arrays of formulae, keeping track of the assumptions on which the conclusion depends. When all the variables in a formula are bound we have a sentence. When all the assumptions in a proof have been discharged we have a proof of a *theorem*. Simple examples of proofs of theorems are those given above for $\varphi \supset \varphi$ and $\varphi \vee \sim\varphi$. Another is

$$\dfrac{\dfrac{\overline{\quad}^{\,(1)} \atop \psi}{\varphi \supset \psi}}{\psi \supset (\varphi \supset \psi)}\,{}^{(1)}$$

4.5 Intuitionistic and classical logic. The introduction rules allow one to infer a conclusion in which one introduces a dominant occurrence of the logical operator concerned. By means of an introduction rule one reasons directly towards a more complex conclusion. The elimination rules, on the other hand, allow one to reason away from a complex premiss involving a dominant occurrence of the operator concerned. This premiss is called the *major* premiss for the elimination.

The introduction and elimination rules, together with the absurdity rule, constitute what is known as *intuitionistic* logic. By confining ourselves to these rules in the inductive definition of proof we obtain a definition of *intuitionistic* proof. We write $\Delta \vdash_I \varphi$ as an abbreviation of 'There is an intuitionistic proof of φ depending on a subset of Δ'.

If we broaden our definition of proof by allowing as an extra clause in the inductive definition any one of the four rules

(i) excluded middle
(ii) dilemma
(iii) classical reductio
(iv) double negation

we obtain a definition of *classical* proof. Exactly what counts as a classical proof will of course depend on exactly which one of rules (i)–(iv) is adopted. It might therefore be appropriate to talk of classical proof in each of the senses (i), (ii), (iii) and (iv). These differences, however, are unimportant in the light of the following fact:

(c) If there is a classical proof of φ from Δ in any one of the senses (i)–(iv) then there is a classical proof of φ from Δ in any one of the other senses.

We may therefore introduce $\Delta \vdash_C \varphi$ as an abbreviation of 'There is a classical proof of φ depending on a subset of Δ' without bothering to specify which of the four classical negation rules have been incorporated into the system.

The result (c) may be established as follows. First, excluded middle yields dilemma:

$$\dfrac{\dfrac{}{\varphi\vee\sim\varphi}\qquad \begin{array}{c}\overline{\varphi}^{\,(i)}\\ \vdots\\ \psi\end{array}\qquad \begin{array}{c}\overline{\sim\varphi}^{\,(i)}\\ \vdots\\ \psi\end{array}}{\psi}\,(i)$$

Secondly, dilemma yields classical reductio:

$$\dfrac{\dfrac{\begin{array}{c}\overline{\sim\varphi}^{\,(i)}\\ \vdots\\ \divideontimes\end{array}}{\varphi}\qquad \overline{\varphi}^{\,(i)}}{\varphi}\,(i)$$

Thirdly, classical reductio yields double negation:

$$\dfrac{\dfrac{{}^{(i)}\overline{\sim\varphi}\qquad \sim\sim\varphi}{\divideontimes}}{\varphi}\,(i)$$

Finally, to bring the chain of derivability full circle, double negation yields the law of excluded middle:

$$\dfrac{\dfrac{\dfrac{\dfrac{\dfrac{\dfrac{\overline{\varphi}^{\,(1)}}{\varphi\vee\sim\varphi}\qquad \overline{\sim(\varphi\vee\sim\varphi)}^{\,(2)}}{\divideontimes}}{\sim\varphi}\,(1)}{\varphi\vee\sim\varphi}\qquad \overline{\sim(\varphi\vee\sim\varphi)}^{\,(2)}}{\divideontimes}}{\sim\sim(\varphi\vee\sim\varphi)}\,(2)}{\varphi\vee\sim\varphi}$$

These schemata provide obvious ways of transforming a classical proof in any of the senses (i)–(iv) into a classical proof in any of the other senses.

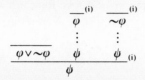

When there is a classical (intuitionistic) proof of φ from Δ we say that φ is classically (intuitionistically) deducible from Δ. Obviously if a conclusion is intuitionistically deducible from certain premisses then it is classically deducible from them, since every intuitionistic proof counts as a classical proof according to our definition. The converse, however, does not hold in general. Some conclusions are classically but not intuitionistically deducible from certain premisses. We are not yet in a position to demonstrate this. At this stage it could only be a plausible conjecture made on the basis of some experience of trying to construct intuitionistic and classical proofs. Such experience might lead one strongly to believe that, for example, there is no intuitionistic proof of the law of excluded middle. This is indeed the case, but in order to demonstrate it conclusively we need first to provide a soundness proof for the intuitionistic system with respect to its own semantics. We shall then be able to provide a counterexample to the law of excluded middle within the intuitionistic semantics. This will show via soundness that the law of excluded middle is indeed not intuitionistically provable. These results will be given in a subsequent chapter. For the present the reader must take it on trust that the classical deducibility relation properly extends the intuitionistic one.

4.6 Some simple proofs – mimicking truth tables, and dualities. We recall the truth tables for $\sim$, &, $\vee$ and $\supset$. These truth tables may be mimicked within intuitionistic logic as follows. Replace each occurrence of T in a table by the formula to which it is assigned, and replace each occurrence of F by the negation of the formula to which it is assigned. The tables then become

$\varphi/{\sim}{\sim}\varphi$	$\varphi,\ \psi/\ \ \varphi\,\&\,\psi$	$\varphi,\ \psi/\ \ \varphi\vee\psi$	$\varphi,\ \psi/\ \ \varphi\supset\psi$
${\sim}\varphi/\ {\sim}\varphi$	$\varphi,{\sim}\psi/{\sim}(\varphi\,\&\,\psi)$	$\varphi,{\sim}\psi/\ \ \varphi\vee\psi$	$\varphi,{\sim}\psi/{\sim}(\varphi\supset\psi)$
	${\sim}\varphi,\ \psi/{\sim}(\varphi\,\&\,\psi)$	${\sim}\varphi,\ \psi/\ \ \varphi\vee\psi$	${\sim}\varphi,\ \psi/\ \ \varphi\supset\psi$
	${\sim}\varphi,{\sim}\psi/{\sim}(\varphi\,\&\,\psi)$	${\sim}\varphi,{\sim}\psi/{\sim}(\varphi\vee\psi)$	${\sim}\varphi,{\sim}\psi/\ \ \varphi\supset\psi$

Each of these arguments is intuitionistically provable. Dropping trivial and redundant ones, and those requiring for their proof only one application of an introduction rule, and suppressing mention of unnecessary premisses, we have the following as the remaining arguments requiring proofs consisting of more than one step:

$\varphi/{\sim}{\sim}\varphi$	$\varphi,{\sim}\psi/{\sim}(\varphi\supset\psi)$
${\sim}\psi/{\sim}(\varphi\,\&\,\psi)$	${\sim}\varphi/\varphi\supset\psi$
${\sim}\varphi,{\sim}\psi/{\sim}(\varphi\vee\psi)$	

The following are intuitionistic proofs of these arguments, respectively:

$$\dfrac{\dfrac{[\varphi]^{(1)} \quad \sim\varphi}{\divideontimes}}{\sim\sim\varphi}\,(1)
\qquad\qquad
\dfrac{\dfrac{\dfrac{\varphi \quad [\varphi\supset\psi]^{(1)}}{\psi} \quad \sim\psi}{\divideontimes}}{\sim(\varphi\supset\psi)}\,(1)$$

$$\dfrac{\dfrac{\dfrac{[\varphi\,\&\,\psi]^{(1)}}{\psi} \quad \sim\psi}{\divideontimes}}{\sim(\varphi\,\&\,\psi)}\,(1)
\qquad\qquad
\dfrac{\dfrac{\dfrac{[\varphi]^{(1)} \quad \sim\varphi}{\divideontimes}}{\psi}}{\varphi\supset\psi}\,(1)$$

$$\dfrac{\dfrac{[\varphi\vee\psi]^{(2)} \quad \dfrac{[\varphi]^{(1)} \quad \sim\varphi}{\divideontimes} \quad \dfrac{[\psi]^{(1)} \quad \sim\psi}{\divideontimes}}{\divideontimes}\,(1)}{\sim(\varphi\vee\psi)}\,(2)$$

The analogies between & and ∀ and between ∨ and ∃ are strikingly brought out in the proofs of the following so-called 'dual' statements of deducibility:

$$\begin{array}{ll}
\sim(\varphi\,\&\,\psi) \vdash_C \sim\varphi\vee\sim\psi & \sim\forall x\varphi \vdash_C \exists x\sim\varphi \\
\sim\varphi\vee\sim\psi \vdash_I \sim(\varphi\,\&\,\psi) & \exists x\sim\varphi \vdash_I \sim\forall x\varphi \\
\sim(\varphi\vee\psi) \vdash_I \sim\varphi\,\&\sim\psi & \sim\exists x\varphi \vdash_I \forall x\sim\varphi \\
\sim\varphi\,\&\sim\psi \vdash_I \sim(\varphi\vee\psi) & \forall x\sim\varphi \vdash_I \sim\exists x\varphi
\end{array}$$

Their proofs are as follows:

$$\dfrac{\dfrac{\dfrac{\dfrac{\dfrac{[\sim\varphi]^{(1)}}{\sim\varphi\vee\sim\psi} \quad [\sim(\sim\varphi\vee\sim\psi)]^{(3)}}{\divideontimes}}{\varphi}\,(1) \quad \dfrac{\dfrac{\dfrac{[\sim\psi]^{(2)}}{\sim\varphi\vee\sim\psi} \quad [\sim(\sim\varphi\vee\sim\psi)]^{(3)}}{\divideontimes}}{\psi}\,(2)}{\varphi\,\&\,\psi} \quad \sim(\varphi\,\&\,\psi)}{\dfrac{\divideontimes}{\sim\varphi\vee\sim\psi}\,(3)}$$

$$\dfrac{\dfrac{\dfrac{\dfrac{\dfrac{\dfrac{[\sim\varphi^x_a]^{(1)}}{\exists x\sim\varphi} \quad [\sim\exists x\sim\varphi]^{(2)}}{\divideontimes}}{\varphi^x_a}\,(1)}{\forall x\varphi} \quad \sim\forall x\varphi}{\divideontimes}}{\exists x\sim\varphi}\,(2)$$

$$\dfrac{\dfrac{\sim\varphi\vee\sim\psi \quad \dfrac{\dfrac{[\varphi\,\&\,\psi]^{(2)}}{\varphi} \quad [\sim\varphi]^{(1)}}{\divideontimes} \quad \dfrac{\dfrac{[\varphi\,\&\,\psi]^{(2)}}{\psi} \quad [\sim\psi]^{(1)}}{\divideontimes}}{\divideontimes}\,(1)}{\sim(\varphi\,\&\,\psi)}\,(2)
\qquad
\dfrac{\dfrac{\exists x\sim\varphi \quad \dfrac{\dfrac{[\forall x\varphi]^{(2)}}{\varphi^x_a} \quad [\sim\varphi^x_a]^{(1)}}{\divideontimes}}{\divideontimes}\,(1)}{\sim\forall x\varphi}\,(2)$$

$$\dfrac{\dfrac{\dfrac{\dfrac{\overline{\varphi}^{\,(1)}}{\varphi\vee\psi}\qquad \sim(\varphi\vee\psi)}{\text{※}}{\scriptstyle(1)}}{\sim\varphi}\qquad \dfrac{\dfrac{\dfrac{\overline{\psi}^{\,(2)}}{\varphi\vee\psi}\qquad \sim(\varphi\vee\psi)}{\text{※}}{\scriptstyle(2)}}{\sim\psi}}{\sim\varphi\,\&\sim\psi}
\qquad\qquad
\dfrac{\dfrac{\dfrac{\dfrac{\overline{\varphi^x_a}^{\,(1)}}{\exists x\varphi}\qquad \sim\exists x\varphi}{\text{※}}{\scriptstyle(1)}}{\sim\varphi^x_a}}{\forall x\sim\varphi}$$

$$\dfrac{\dfrac{\overline{\varphi\vee\psi}^{\,(2)}\qquad \dfrac{\overline{\varphi}^{\,(1)}\qquad \dfrac{\sim\varphi\,\&\sim\psi}{\sim\varphi}}{\text{※}}\qquad \dfrac{\overline{\psi}^{\,(1)}\qquad \dfrac{\sim\varphi\,\&\sim\psi}{\sim\psi}}{\text{※}}}{\text{※}}{\scriptstyle(1)}\ \ {\scriptstyle(2)}}{\sim(\varphi\vee\psi)}
\qquad\qquad
\dfrac{\dfrac{\overline{\exists x\varphi}^{\,(2)}\qquad \dfrac{\overline{\varphi^x_a}^{\,(1)}\qquad \dfrac{\forall x\sim\varphi}{\sim\varphi^x_a}}{\text{※}}{\scriptstyle(1)}}{\text{※}}{\scriptstyle(2)}}{\sim\exists x\varphi}$$

4.7 Expressive completeness and interderivability of rules. It is well known that in classical logic one needs only $\sim$, one of $\vee$, & and $\supset$, and one of $\exists$ and $\forall$ for expressive completeness. A set of connectives and quantifiers is expressively complete if all truth functions and both $\forall$ and $\exists$ are definable in terms of them. Let us take, for example, $\sim$, & and $\exists$. The other operators may be defined as follows:

$$\begin{aligned}
\varphi\vee\psi &=_{df} \sim(\sim\varphi\,\&\sim\psi)\\
\varphi\supset\psi &=_{df} \sim(\varphi\,\&\sim\psi)\\
\forall x\varphi &=_{df} \sim\exists x\sim\varphi
\end{aligned}$$

A simple truth tabular computation shows that the first two definitions are in order. Moreover, it is easily shown that any truth function (not just the two binary ones defined) is definable in terms of $\sim$ and &. With the definitions just given, the introduction and elimination rules for $\vee$, $\supset$ and $\forall$ become

$\vee$-*I*: $$\dfrac{\varphi}{\sim(\sim\varphi\,\&\sim\psi)}\qquad \dfrac{\psi}{\sim(\sim\varphi\,\&\sim\psi)}$$

$\vee$-*E*: $$\dfrac{\sim(\sim\varphi\,\&\sim\psi)\qquad \begin{matrix}\overline{\varphi}^{\,(i)}\\ \vdots\\ \theta\end{matrix}\qquad \begin{matrix}\overline{\psi}^{\,(i)}\\ \vdots\\ \theta\end{matrix}}{\theta}{\scriptstyle(i)}$$

$\supset$-*I*: $$\dfrac{\begin{matrix}\overline{\varphi}^{\,(i)}\\ \vdots\\ \psi\end{matrix}}{\sim(\varphi\,\&\sim\psi)}{\scriptstyle(i)}$$

$\supset$-*E*: $$\dfrac{\varphi\qquad \sim(\varphi\,\&\sim\psi)}{\psi}$$

$\forall$-*I*: $\dfrac{\varphi}{\sim\exists x{\sim}\varphi^a_x}$ $\qquad$ $\forall$-*E*: $\dfrac{\sim\exists x{\sim}\varphi}{\varphi^x_t}$

where a does not occur
in any assumption
on which φ depends.

These may be derived using the rules for $\sim$, & and $\exists$ as follows:

$\vee$-*I*:

$$\dfrac{\dfrac{\varphi \qquad \dfrac{\overline{\sim\varphi\,\&\,\sim\psi}^{\,(1)}}{\sim\varphi}}{\text{※}}{\scriptstyle(1)}}{\sim(\sim\varphi\,\&\,\sim\psi)} \qquad \dfrac{\dfrac{\psi \qquad \dfrac{\overline{\sim\varphi\,\&\,\sim\psi}^{\,(1)}}{\sim\psi}}{\text{※}}{\scriptstyle(1)}}{\sim(\sim\varphi\,\&\,\sim\psi)}$$

$\vee$-*E*:

$$\dfrac{\dfrac{\sim(\sim\varphi\,\&\,\sim\psi) \qquad \dfrac{\dfrac{\dfrac{\begin{array}{c}\overline{\varphi}^{\,(1)}\\ \vdots\\ \theta\end{array} \quad \overline{\sim\theta}^{\,(3)}}{\text{※}}}{\sim\varphi}{\scriptstyle(1)} \qquad \dfrac{\dfrac{\begin{array}{c}\overline{\psi}^{\,(2)}\\ \vdots\\ \theta\end{array} \quad \overline{\sim\theta}^{\,(3)}}{\text{※}}}{\sim\psi}{\scriptstyle(2)}}{\sim\varphi\,\&\,\sim\psi}}{\text{※}}}{\theta}{\scriptstyle(3)}$$

$\supset$-*I*:

$$\dfrac{\dfrac{\begin{array}{c}\dfrac{\overline{\varphi\,\&\,\sim\psi}^{\,(1)}}{\varphi}\\ \vdots\\ \psi\end{array} \qquad \dfrac{\overline{\varphi\,\&\,\sim\psi}^{\,(1)}}{\sim\psi}}{\text{※}}}{\sim(\varphi\,\&\,\sim\psi)}{\scriptstyle(1)}$$

$\supset$-*E*:

$$\dfrac{\dfrac{\dfrac{\varphi \qquad \overline{\sim\psi}^{\,(1)}}{\varphi\,\&\,\sim\psi} \qquad \sim(\varphi\,\&\,\sim\psi)}{\text{※}}}{\psi}{\scriptstyle(1)}$$

$\forall$-*I*:

$$\dfrac{\dfrac{{\scriptstyle(2)}\,\overline{\exists x{\sim}\varphi^a_x} \qquad \dfrac{\begin{array}{c}\vdots\\ \varphi\end{array} \quad \overline{\sim\varphi}^{\,(1)}}{\text{※}}{\scriptstyle(1)}}{\text{※}}}{\sim\exists x{\sim}\varphi^a_x}{\scriptstyle(2)}$$

$\forall$-*E*:

$$\dfrac{\dfrac{\dfrac{\overline{\sim\varphi^x_t}^{\,(1)}}{\exists x{\sim}\varphi} \qquad \sim\exists x{\sim}\varphi}{\text{※}}}{\varphi^x_t}{\scriptstyle(1)}$$

In the derivation of $\forall$-*I* the name a satisfies the conditions for the application of $\exists$-*E* that occurs in the derivation. Note that the derivations of $\vee$-*E*, $\supset$-*E* and $\forall$-*E* involve application of the classical reductio rule.

These derivations show that if in any true classical deducibility statement all occurrences of the defined operators $\vee$, $\supset$ and $\forall$ are eliminated by means of their definitions in terms of $\sim$, & and $\exists$, then the transformed deducibility statement remains true by virtue of a proof which contains no applications of the rules for $\vee$, $\supset$ and $\forall$. Such a proof can obviously be determined from any which contains applications of the latter rules, by applying the derivations above.

The reader may obtain similar results for all the other expressively complete combinations of logical operators. A question that naturally arises is whether it is possible to use just one connective and one quantifier to define the others. The answer is affirmative. The best known connective for this purpose is the *Sheffer stroke.* $\varphi|\psi$ means 'Not both φ and ψ' and has the truth table

φ	ψ	$\varphi\|\psi$
T	T	F
T	F	T
F	T	T
F	F	T

The introduction and elimination rules for stroke, stated graphically, are

$$|\text{-}I \quad \begin{array}{c} \underbrace{{}^{(i)}\overline{\varphi} \qquad \overline{\psi}^{(i)}} \\ \vdots \\ ※ \\ \hline \varphi|\psi \end{array}{}^{(i)} \qquad\qquad |\text{-}E: \quad \frac{\varphi \quad \varphi|\psi \quad \psi}{※}$$

Moreover, since stroke is to be the *only* connective from which all others, including negation, are to be defined, we adopt the reductio rule

$$\begin{array}{c} \overline{\varphi|\varphi}^{(i)} \\ \vdots \\ ※ \\ \hline \varphi \end{array}{}^{(i)}$$

Instead of using either $\exists$ or $\forall$ together with stroke to obtain an expressively complete set of operators for classical logic, one may use a quantifier version of the stroke so as to introduce a symmetry between the propositional and quantificational parts of the system. $\varphi(x)\,|_x\,\psi(x)$ will mean 'Nothing is both φ and ψ'. The introduction and elimination rules for the quantifier-stroke are

$$\begin{array}{c} \underbrace{{}^{(i)}\overline{\varphi^x_a} \qquad \overline{\psi^x_a}^{(i)}} \\ \vdots \\ ※ \\ \hline \varphi\,|_x\,\psi \end{array}{}^{(i)} \qquad\qquad \frac{\varphi^x_t \quad \varphi\,|_x\,\psi \quad \psi^x_t}{※}$$

where a does not
occur in any assumptions
other than φ^x_a or ψ^x_a on
which ※ depends;

The definitions of the other usual operators in terms of the connective-stroke and quantifier-stroke are as follows:

$$\begin{aligned}
\sim\varphi &=_{df} \varphi|\varphi \\
\varphi \& \psi &=_{df} (\varphi|\psi)|(\varphi|\psi) \\
\varphi \vee \psi &=_{df} (\varphi|\varphi)|(\psi|\psi) \\
\varphi \supset \psi &=_{df} \varphi|(\psi|\psi) \\
\exists x\varphi &=_{df} (\varphi x \,{}^{\mid}_{x}\, \varphi x)|(\varphi x \,{}^{\mid}_{x}\, \varphi x) \\
\forall x\varphi &=_{df} (\varphi x|\varphi x) \,{}^{\mid}_{x}\, (\varphi x|\varphi x)
\end{aligned}$$

The reader should derive the introduction and elimination rules for the defined operators using only the rules above for the connective- and quantifier-strokes. It is important to realize that reduction to these primitives is possible only in the classical case. In the intuitionistic system none of $\sim$, &, $\vee$, $\supset$, $\exists$ and $\forall$ can be defined in terms of the others. Although we do not prove this strictly here, note how we used classical reductio in deriving the rules for the defined connectives above. This is a strong hint that in intuitionistic logic the required derivations are not forthcoming. The obvious advantage of the strokes in the classical case is that when one proves general results about the system by induction on the complexity of formulae or by induction on the complexity of proofs there are fewer cases to consider in the inductive step, if the strokes are taken as the only means of building up formulae and the five rules above are taken as the only means of building up proofs. The disadvantage, however, is that it is very difficult to read formulae in the stroke notation and to grasp immediately what their truth conditions are.

4.8 Reasons for restrictions on quantifier rules. In this section we show why it is necessary to state the condition on $\forall$-*I* and $\exists$-*E* so carefully. First we consider

$$\forall\text{-}I: \quad \frac{\varphi}{\forall x \varphi^{a}_{x}}$$

where a does not occur in any assumption on which φ depends.

The substitution of x for a must be uniform, otherwise the following 'proof' could be constructed:

$$\cfrac{\cfrac{\cfrac{\forall x Lxx}{Laa}}{\forall y Lay}}{\forall x \forall y Lxy} \quad \leftarrow \text{ non-uniform substitution of the variable } y \text{ for } a.$$

Secondly, if a were allowed to occur in an assumption on which φ depends, the following 'proof' could be constructed:

$$\dfrac{\exists xFx \qquad \dfrac{\overline{\;Fa\;}^{\,(1)}}{\forall xFx}\;\leftarrow \text{violation occurs here.}}{\forall xFx}\,{\scriptstyle (1)}$$

Now we consider

$$\exists\text{-}E: \quad \dfrac{\exists x\varphi \qquad \begin{matrix}\overline{\;\varphi^x_a\;}^{\,(i)}\\ \vdots \\ \psi\end{matrix}}{\psi}\,{\scriptstyle (i)}$$

where (I) a must not occur in $\exists x\varphi$, (II) a must not occur in ψ, and (III) a must not occur in any assumption other than φ^x_a on which the upper occurrence of ψ depends. We shall construct three 'proofs' of invalid arguments, with each proof violating just one of the conditions (I)-(III):

$$\dfrac{\dfrac{\forall y\exists x\, y<x}{\exists x\, a<x} \qquad \dfrac{\overline{\;a<a\;}^{\,(1)}}{\exists y\, y<y}}{\exists y\, y<y}\,{\scriptstyle (1)} \quad \leftarrow \text{violation of (I)}$$

$$\dfrac{\dfrac{\exists xFx \qquad \overline{\;Fa\;}^{\,(1)}}{Fa}\,{\scriptstyle (1)} \leftarrow \text{violation of (II)}}{\forall xFx}$$

$$\dfrac{\exists xGx \qquad \dfrac{\exists xFx \qquad \dfrac{\dfrac{\overline{\;Fa\;}^{\,(1)} \quad \overline{\;Ga\;}^{\,(2)}}{Fa\,\&\,Ga}}{\exists x(Fx\,\&\,Gx)}}{\exists x(Fx\,\&\,Gx)}\,{\scriptstyle (1)}}{\exists x(Fx\,\&\,Gx)}\,{\scriptstyle (2)} \quad \text{violation of (III)}$$

The reader will easily find counterexamples to the three invalid arguments 'proved' here. Because of these 'proofs' we see that the conditions stated on ∀-*I* and ∃-*E* are necessary in order that these rules be truth preserving. In section 11 we shall see that they are sufficient, by proving the soundness of the deductive system for first order classical logic of which these rules are a part.

4.9 Substitutions in proofs. When a name occurs in subproofs in the way required for application of ∀-*I* or ∃-*E* we say that it occurs *parametrically*. We also say that it is the *parameter* for the application of the rule in question.

An application of the rule

$$\frac{\begin{matrix}\Pi\\ \varphi\end{matrix}}{\forall x\varphi^a_x}$$

is said to *close* all occurrences of a in Π. Likewise an application of the rule

$$\frac{\begin{matrix}\\ \Pi_1\\ \exists x\varphi\end{matrix} \qquad \begin{matrix}(\varphi^x_a)\\ \Pi_2\\ \psi\end{matrix}}{\psi}$$

is said to close all occurrences of a in Π_2.

Any occurrence of a name in a proof Π which has not been closed by an application of $\forall$-I or $\exists$-E in Π is said to be *free* in Π. Henceforth Π^a_t will be understood as the result of replacing a at all its *free* occurrences in Π by the term t (understood not to contain any variables).

Suppose Π contains closed occurrences of a. For example:

$$\dfrac{\exists xFx \qquad \dfrac{\dfrac{{}^{(1)}\dfrac{}{Fa} \qquad \dfrac{\forall x(Fx\supset Gx)}{Fa\supset Ga}}{Ga}}{\exists xGx}{}_{(1)}}{\exists xGx}$$

If we replace a at all its closed occurrences in Π by a name b not occurring in Π the result is a proof of the same conclusion from the same undischarged assumptions:

$$\dfrac{\exists xFx \qquad \dfrac{\dfrac{{}^{(1)}\dfrac{}{Fb} \qquad \dfrac{\forall x(Fx\supset Gx)}{Fb\supset Gb}}{Gb}}{\exists xGx}{}_{(1)}}{\exists xGx}$$

In general this is because by the definitions above there can be no closed occurrence of a name in the conclusion or in any undischarged assumption in any proof. We shall write $\Pi(a/b)$ for the result of replacing a at all its closed occurrences in Π by a name b understood not to occur in Π. Just as $\forall x\varphi(x)$ is a mere notational variant of $\forall y\varphi(y)$, so $\Pi(a/b)$ is a mere notational variant of Π, as our example above shows. If a has no closed occurrence in Π, then $\Pi(a/b)$ is simply Π.

Suppose $a_1, \ldots, a_n$ are all the names occurring in a closed term t.

Suppose distinct new names $b_1, \ldots, b_n$ occurring neither in t nor in Π are chosen to replace $a_1, \ldots, a_n$ respectively at any of their closed occurrences in Π. The resulting proof, $\Pi(a_1/b_1)\ldots(a_n/b_n)$, we shall simply call Πt. Thus Πt is any proof like Π except that no name in t has closed occurrences in Πt. Πt proves the same conclusion from the same undischarged assumptions as does Π. Note that Πt is not uniquely defined for given Π and t; we are using the notation Πt as a metaparameter over a class of proofs obtainable from Π by substitutions of the kind described.

The thrust of all these definitions is to be able to prove that proofs are 'schematic' in their free names, in the sense given by the following Lemma. The proof of the Lemma below is far more complicated than the simple point it is intended to demonstrate. These complications are the inevitable price of rigour in discussion of syntactical substitutions.

Lemma. If $\mathscr{P}(\Pi, \varphi, \Delta)$ and u is a closed term then $\mathscr{P}((\Pi u)^b_u, \varphi^b_u, \Delta^b_u)$.

Proof. We need consider only the case where b does occur free in Π. We proceed by induction on the complexity of Π. The basis step is obvious. In the inductive step we consider Π by cases according to the rule of inference last applied. For all rules except the quantifier rules the result is immediate from the inductive hypothesis, since term substitutions distribute across connectives. Let us now consider the rules (i) $\forall$-*E*, (ii) $\exists$-*I*, (iii) $\forall$-*I* and (iv) $\exists$-*E* in that order:

(i) Suppose Π is
$$\begin{array}{c}\Delta\\ \Sigma\\ \forall x\varphi\\ \hline \varphi^x_t\end{array}$$
. Then Πu^b_u is
$$\begin{array}{c}\Delta^b_u\\ (\Sigma u)^b_u\\ (\forall x\varphi)^b_u\\ \hline (\varphi^x_t)^b_u\end{array}$$

Now $(\forall x\varphi)^b_u$ is $\forall x(\varphi^b_u)$, and $(\varphi^x_t)^b_u$ is $(\varphi^b_u)^x_{t^b_u}$. Thus $(\Pi u)^b_u$ is

$$\begin{array}{c}\Delta^b_u\\ (\Sigma u)^b_u\\ \forall x(\varphi^b_u)\\ \hline (\varphi^b_u)^x_{t^b_u}\end{array}$$

By inductive hypothesis applied to $(\Sigma u)^b_u$ and by the correctness of the final application of $\forall$-*E* we have $\mathscr{P}((\Pi u)^b_u, (\varphi^x_t)^b_u, \Delta^b_u)$.

(ii) Suppose Π is
$$\begin{array}{c}\Delta\\ \Sigma\\ \varphi^x_t\\ \hline \exists x\varphi\end{array}$$
. By reasoning as in (i), $\mathscr{P}((\Pi u)^b_u, \exists x\varphi^b_u, \Delta^b_u)$.

(iii) Suppose Π is

$$\begin{array}{c}\Delta\\ \Sigma\\ \dfrac{\varphi}{\forall x\varphi^a_x}\end{array}$$

. Note that the final application of $\forall$-I closes a in Σ. Thus Πu is

$$\begin{array}{c}\Delta\\ \Sigma u\\ \dfrac{\varphi^a_c}{\forall x\varphi^{ac}_{cx}}\end{array}$$

, where c is chosen so as not to occur in u or in Π, and therefore occurs parametrically in Σu. So $(\Pi u)^b_u$ is

$$\begin{array}{c}\Delta^b_u\\ (\Sigma u)^b_u\\ \dfrac{\varphi^{ab}_{cu}}{(\forall x\varphi^{ac}_{cx})^b_u}\end{array}$$

. Since c does not occur in u, ψ^{cb}_{xu} is ψ^{bc}_{ux}, whence $(\forall x\varphi^{ac}_{cx})^b_u$ is $\forall x(\varphi^{ab}_{cu})^c_x$. Thus $(\Pi u)^b_u$ is

$$\begin{array}{c}\Delta^b_u\\ (\Sigma u)^b_u\\ \dfrac{\varphi^{ab}_{cu}}{\forall x(\varphi^{ab}_{cu})^c_x}\end{array}$$

By inductive hypothesis applied to $(\Sigma u)^b_u$ and by the correctness of the final application of $\forall$-I we have $\mathscr{P}((\Pi u)^b_u, (\forall x\varphi^a_x)^b_u, \Delta^b_u)$.

(iv) Suppose Π is

$$\begin{array}{cc} & (\varphi^x_a)\\ \Delta_1 & \Delta_2\\ \Sigma_1 & \Sigma_2\\ \multicolumn{2}{c}{\dfrac{\exists x\varphi \qquad \psi}{\psi}}\end{array}$$

. Note that the final application of $\exists$-E closes a in Σ_2. Thus Πu is

$$\begin{array}{cc} & (\varphi^{xa}_{ac})\\ \Delta_1 & \Delta_2\\ \Sigma_1 u & \Sigma_2 u\\ \multicolumn{2}{c}{\dfrac{\exists x\varphi \qquad \psi}{\psi}}\end{array}$$

, where c is chosen so as not to occur in u or Π, and therefore occurs parametrically in $\Sigma_1 u$ and $\Sigma_2 u$. So $(\Pi u)^b_u$ is

$$\begin{array}{cc} & (\varphi^{xb}_{cu})\\ \Delta_{1u}^{\,b} & \Delta_{2u}^{\,b}\\ (\Sigma_1 u)^b_u & (\Sigma_2 u)^b_u\\ \multicolumn{2}{c}{\dfrac{\exists x\varphi^b_u \qquad \psi^b_u}{\psi^b_u}}\end{array}$$

Now since c does not occur in u, φ^{xb}_{cu} is φ^{bx}_{uc}. Thus $(\Pi u)^b_u$ is

$$\dfrac{\begin{matrix} & (\varphi^{bx}_{uc}) \\ \Delta^{b}_{1u} & \Delta^{b}_{2u} \\ (\Sigma_1 u)^b_u & (\Sigma_2 u)^b_u \\ \exists x\varphi^b_u & \psi^b_u \end{matrix}}{\psi^b_u}$$

By inductive hypothesis applied to by $(\Sigma_1 u)^b_u$ and $(\Sigma_2 u)^b_u$ and the correctness of the final application of $\exists$-E we have $\mathscr{P}((\Pi u)^b_u, \psi^b_u, \Delta^b_u)$.

This completes the proof of the Lemma.

We recall the discussion in Section 1 of the analogy between & and $\forall$ and between $\vee$ and $\exists$. We spoke there of substituting terms 'in an appropriate way' for names within a proof. The Lemma above explains what this informal expression means. Suppose we have a proof Π containing a name a. The result of 'appropriately substituting' a term t for the name a in the proof Π is just $(\Pi t)^a_t$. That is, we 'clear' the proof Π of closed occurrences of names occurring in the term t. This gives Πt. We then substitute the term t for all *free* occurrences of the name a in Πt. This gives the result $(\Pi t)^a_t$. The Lemma tells us that the result is a proof of the conclusion concerned from the premisses concerned, as claimed for the purpose of establishing the analogies.

4.10 Reduction procedures. Any proof ending with an application of an elimination rule can be reduced to a simpler proof if that elimination occurs immediately after a corresponding introduction. The following statement of *reduction procedures* for the logical operators will make it clear why this is so:

$$\dfrac{\dfrac{\begin{matrix}\Pi_1 & \Pi_2 \\ \varphi_1 & \varphi_2\end{matrix}}{\varphi_1 \& \varphi_2}}{\varphi_i} \qquad \rightarrow \qquad \begin{matrix}\Pi_i \\ \varphi_i\end{matrix}$$

$$\dfrac{\dfrac{\begin{matrix}\Pi \\ \varphi_i\end{matrix}}{\varphi_1 \vee \varphi_2} \quad \begin{matrix}(\varphi_1) \\ \Sigma_1 \\ \theta\end{matrix} \quad \begin{matrix}(\varphi_2) \\ \Sigma_2 \\ \theta\end{matrix}}{\theta} \qquad \rightarrow \qquad \begin{matrix}\Pi \\ (\varphi_i) \\ \Sigma_i \\ \theta\end{matrix}$$

$$\dfrac{\begin{matrix}\Pi_1 \\ \varphi\end{matrix} \quad \dfrac{\begin{matrix}(\varphi) \\ \Pi_2 \\ \psi\end{matrix}}{\varphi \supset \psi}}{\psi} \qquad \rightarrow \qquad \begin{matrix}\Pi_1 \\ (\varphi) \\ \Pi_2 \\ \psi\end{matrix}$$

$$\dfrac{\begin{array}{c}\Pi_1\\ \varphi\end{array} \quad \dfrac{\begin{array}{c}(\varphi)\\ \Pi_2\\ ※\end{array}}{\sim\varphi}}{※} \quad \rightarrow \quad \begin{array}{c}\Pi_1\\ (\varphi)\\ \Pi_2\\ ※\end{array}$$

$$\dfrac{\dfrac{\begin{array}{c}\Pi_1\\ \varphi^x_t\end{array}}{\exists x\varphi} \quad \begin{array}{c}(\varphi^x_a)\\ \Pi_2\\ \psi\end{array}}{\psi} \quad \rightarrow \quad \begin{array}{c}\Pi_1\\ (\varphi^x_t)\\ (\Pi_2 t)^a_t\\ \psi\end{array}$$

$$\dfrac{\dfrac{\begin{array}{c}\Pi\\ \varphi\end{array}}{\forall x\varphi^a_x}}{\varphi^a_t} \quad \rightarrow \quad \begin{array}{c}(\Pi t)^a_t\\ \varphi^a_t\end{array}$$

By the Lemma above, the last two reducts on the right are indeed proofs as claimed.

The reduction procedures for the Sheffer strokes are

$$\dfrac{\begin{array}{c}\Pi_1\\ \varphi\end{array} \quad \dfrac{\begin{array}{c}\underbrace{(\varphi)\quad(\psi)}\\ \Sigma\\ ※\end{array}}{\varphi|\psi} \quad \begin{array}{c}\Pi_2\\ \psi\end{array}}{※} \quad \rightarrow \quad \begin{array}{c}\underbrace{\begin{array}{cc}\Pi_1 & \Pi_2\\ (\varphi) & (\psi)\end{array}}\\ \Sigma\\ ※\end{array}$$

$$\dfrac{\begin{array}{c}\Pi_1\\ \varphi^x_t\end{array} \quad \dfrac{\begin{array}{c}\underbrace{(\varphi^x_a)\quad(\psi^x_a)}\\ \Sigma\\ ※\end{array}}{\varphi \mid_x \psi} \quad \begin{array}{c}\Pi_2\\ \psi^x_t\end{array}}{※} \quad \rightarrow \quad \begin{array}{c}\underbrace{\begin{array}{cc}\Pi_1 & \Pi_2\\ (\varphi^x_t) & (\psi^x_t)\end{array}}\\ (\Sigma t)^a_t\\ ※\end{array}$$

The reduction procedures apply to proofs of the form

$$\dfrac{\dfrac{\Pi}{\varphi}{\scriptstyle (I)} \qquad \Sigma_1 \ldots \Sigma_n}{\psi}{\scriptstyle (E)}$$

to produce a proof of ψ from (at most) the combined premisses of $\Pi, \Sigma_1, \ldots, \Sigma_n$. If, instead of the application of an I-rule as indicated we have an application of the absurdity rule then if ψ is ※ the reduct will simply be Π; and if ψ is not ※, the reduct will be $\dfrac{\Pi}{\psi}$. The general form of a reduct will be written as $\nu(\Pi, \varphi, \Sigma_i, \psi)$ or, for brevity, as $\nu(\Pi, \vec{\Sigma})$.

One school of thought in the philosophy of logic holds that an introduction rule is constitutive of the meaning of its logical operator. This meaning, it is maintained, is specified by stating the conditions under which one may 'directly' infer a conclusion with that operator dominant. Because of the reduction procedures, the elimination rules are justified on the grounds that by using them one cannot infer from directly established statements any conclusion that one could not directly establish without using the elimination rules. The reduction procedures ensure that the elimination rules conservatively extend the introduction rules: that is, they ensure that direct proofs of the premisses of an elimination can be transformed into a direct proof of its conclusion. Therefore if one sees no need to justify the introduction rules, taking them as constitutive of the meanings of the logical operators, the task of justifying the rules of intuitionistic logic is complete. This discussion of course requires further explanation of what is meant by 'direct', but that would involve too lengthy a digression. The reader is referred to the appropriate items in the bibliography.

4.11 Soundness of classical logic. Other philosophers of logic, however, regard the meaning of an operator as consisting in the contribution it makes to determining the *truth conditions* of any sentence in which it occurs. The classical assumption is that any sentence is either *true* or *false* (but not both) in any situation about which it can be interpreted as saying something, even though it may in principle be impossible effectively to determine which is the case. The justification of the classical rules of inference consists in a demonstration that they are *truth preserving*: given any classical proof, if all its undischarged assumptions are true then its conclusion is true also; that is, the conclusion is a logical consequence of the undischarged assumptions.

Before giving a precise account of this result, let us look more closely at the definition of logical consequence. Recall that models were defined in 3.5 as possessing non-empty domains, and as assigning referents to all and only certain 'distinguished' names. The set of distinguished names can vary from model to model. In defining truth of a sentence in a model we required that every name occurring in the sentence be distinguished for the model concerned. Since, moreover, function signs are taken always to represent operations everywhere defined in the domain, there is no place in our semantical account for 'non-denoting' terms in the sentences involved.

When every name occurring in a sentence φ is distinguished for a model $\mathfrak{A}$, we say that $\mathfrak{A}$ is *for* φ, and this of course can be the case whether or not φ is true in $\mathfrak{A}$. When $\mathfrak{A}$ is for every member of Δ we likewise say that $\mathfrak{A}$ is for Δ.

$\mathfrak{A}$ must be for φ before the question of the truth of falsity of φ in $\mathfrak{A}$ arises. When φ is true in $\mathfrak{A}$ we say that $\mathfrak{A}$ is a model *of* φ. When $\mathfrak{A}$ is a model of every member of Δ we likewise say that $\mathfrak{A}$ is a model of Δ. Obviously any model *of* Δ is a model *for* Δ.

If a name a is not distinguished for $\mathfrak{A}$ we may *extend* $\mathfrak{A}$ to a model $\mathfrak{A}_a$ by assigning a some referent α in the domain of $\mathfrak{A}$. The name a thereby becomes distinguished for the model $\mathfrak{A}_a$. Likewise we may extend models with respect to any set of hitherto undistinguished names. Extensions of a model $\mathfrak{A}$ simply 'deal with more names' than $\mathfrak{A}$. The domain remains the same as before, as does the specification of operations for function signs and extensions for predicates. Trivially, every model extends itself; and is extended by any extension of any extension. The following two facts about extensions are also easily proved by induction on φ:

(i) If $\mathfrak{A}$ is a model of φ, so is every extension of $\mathfrak{A}$.
(ii) If $\mathfrak{A}$ is for φ, and some extension of $\mathfrak{A}$ is a model of φ, then $\mathfrak{A}$ is a model of φ.

We shall appeal to these facts about extensions throughout the soundness proof below.

We now define logical consequence as follows:

$\Delta \models \varphi$ iff for every model $\mathfrak{A}$ of Δ, every extension of $\mathfrak{A}$ for φ is a model of φ.

Classical Soundness Theorem. If $\mathscr{P}(\Pi, \varphi, \Delta)$ then $\Delta \models \varphi$.
Proof. By induction on the complexity of Π. The basis step is obvious. In the inductive step we argue by cases according to the rule of inference applied last in Π. We shall give the reasoning for the two 'difficult' quantifier rules, $\forall$-*I* and $\exists$-*E*, and for the classical rule of dilemma. The others will be left to the reader.
$\forall$-*I*. Suppose Π is

$$\begin{array}{c}\Delta\\ \Sigma\\ \psi\\ \hline \forall x \psi^a_x\end{array}$$

Suppose $\mathfrak{A}$ is a model of Δ and $\mathfrak{B}$ is any extension of $\mathfrak{A}$ for $\forall x\psi^a_x$. We show that $\mathfrak{B}$ is a model of $\forall x\psi^a_x$.

Let β be an arbitrary individual in the domain. Let b be a name undistinguished for $\mathfrak{B}$. Extend $\mathfrak{B}$ to $\mathfrak{B}_b$ by letting b denote β. Since a does not occur in Δ (for correctness of $\forall$-*I*) we have by the previous

Lemma that $\mathscr{P}((\Sigma b)^a_b, \psi^a_b, \Delta)$. By inductive hypothesis applied to $(\Sigma b)^a_b$ we have that $\Delta \models \psi^a_b$. Now $\mathfrak{B}_b$ is a model of Δ and for ψ^a_b. Hence $\mathfrak{B}_b$ is a model of ψ^a_b. Since b does not occur in ψ^a_x, β satisfies ψ^a_x in $\mathfrak{B}$. But β was arbitrary. So $\mathfrak{B}$ is a model of $\forall x \psi^a_x$.

$\exists$-*E*. Suppose Π is

$$\dfrac{\begin{matrix} & (\psi^x_a) \\ \Delta_1 & \Delta_2 \\ \Sigma_1 & \Sigma_2 \\ \exists x\psi & \varphi \end{matrix}}{\varphi} \qquad \text{where } \Delta = \Delta_1 \cup (\Delta_2 \backslash \psi^x_a)$$

Suppose $\mathfrak{A}$ is a model of Δ and $\mathfrak{B}$ is any extension of $\mathfrak{A}$ for φ. We show that $\mathfrak{B}$ is a model of φ.

Let $\mathfrak{C}$ be any extension of $\mathfrak{B}$ for $\exists x\psi$. By inductive hypothesis applied to Σ_1 we have that $\Delta_1 \models \exists x\psi$. Hence $\mathfrak{C}$ is a model of $\exists x\psi$. Thus some individual in the domain satisfies ψ in $\mathfrak{C}$. Call it β. Let b be a name undistinguished for $\mathfrak{C}$. Extend $\mathfrak{C}$ to $\mathfrak{C}_b$ by letting b denote β. So $\mathfrak{C}_b$ is a model of ψ^x_b. By conditions on a for correctness of $\exists$-*E*, a does not occur in φ. Hence by the previous Lemma we have that $\mathscr{P}((\Sigma_2 b)^a_b, \varphi, \Delta^a_{2b})$. By inductive hypothesis applied to $(\Sigma_2 b)^a_b$ we have that $\Delta^a_{2b} \models \varphi$. By conditions on a for correctness of $\exists$-*E*, $\Delta^a_{2b} = (\Delta_2 \backslash \psi^x_a) \cup \{\psi^x_b\}$. Now $\mathfrak{C}_b$ is a model for this set and is also for φ. Hence $\mathfrak{C}_b$ is a model of φ. Finally $\mathfrak{C}_b$ extends $\mathfrak{B}$, and $\mathfrak{B}$ is a model for φ. Thus $\mathfrak{B}$ is a model of φ.

Dilemma. Suppose Π is

$$\dfrac{\begin{matrix} (\psi) & (\sim\psi) \\ \Delta_1 & \Delta_2 \\ \Sigma_1 & \Sigma_2 \\ \varphi & \varphi \end{matrix}}{\varphi} \qquad \text{where } \Delta = (\Delta_1 \backslash \psi) \cup (\Delta_2 \backslash \sim\psi)$$

Suppose $\mathfrak{A}$ is a model of Δ and $\mathfrak{B}$ is any extension of $\mathfrak{A}$ for φ. We show that $\mathfrak{B}$ is a model of φ.

Let $\mathfrak{C}$ be any extension of $\mathfrak{B}$ for ψ (and thus for $\sim\psi$). There are now two cases to consider.

(1) $\mathfrak{C}$ is a model of ψ. Then $\mathfrak{C}$ is a model of Δ_1. By inductive hypothesis applied to Σ_1 we have that $\Delta_1 \models \varphi$. Hence, since $\mathfrak{C}$ is a model for φ, $\mathfrak{C}$ is a model of φ. Since $\mathfrak{C}$ extends $\mathfrak{B}$ and $\mathfrak{B}$ is a model for φ, it follows that $\mathfrak{B}$ is a model of φ.

(2) $\mathfrak{C}$ is not a model of ψ. Then $\mathfrak{C}$ is a model of $\sim\psi$. So $\mathfrak{C}$ is a model of Δ_2. By similar reasoning as in (1) it follows that $\mathfrak{B}$ is a model of φ.

Thus $\mathfrak{B}$ is a model of φ.

Note that we use non-intuitionistic reasoning in the metalanguage only in the case for dilemma. There we use the rule of dilemma itself in the metalanguage. In all other cases the metalinguistic reasoning is intuitionistic. Moreover in each case we *use* the rule concerned in the very metalinguistic reasoning carried out to establish its soundness. For example, in the case for ∀-*I* we used ∀-*I* in the metalanguage ('Let β be an arbitrary individual .... But β was arbitrary ...'). The reader will have no difficulty in locating metalinguistic uses of the other rules in the reasoning concerning each of them. So it appears that we establish the soundness of our rules of inference by using those very rules in the metalanguage, and doing so, moreover, in a conspicuously 'one-to-one' fashion. For a discussion of the philosophical difficulties thereby engendered for a *justification of deduction* the reader is referred to papers of that title by Dummett and Haack.

4.12 Harmony and containment. Can one specify a meaning for a logical operator by laying down arbitrary introduction and elimination rules? An affirmative answer is too strong a claim to be attributed even to those who maintain that it is *only* from their introduction and elimination rules that logical operators derive their meanings.

Consider the connective × governed by the sole introduction rule

$$\frac{\varphi}{\varphi \times \psi}$$

Intuition inclines one to say that this rule alone must confer upon '$\ldots \times \psi$' the force of a superfluous rhetorical flourish. The introduction rule must make $\varphi \times \psi$ equivalent to φ. Can we make explicit a general principle underlying this intuition? I think so, and would propose the following *Principle of Harmony*:

> Introduction and elimination rules for a logical operator λ must be formulated so that a sentence with λ dominant expresses the *strongest* proposition which can be inferred from the stated premisses when the conditions for λ-introduction are satisfied; while it expresses the *weakest* proposition which can feature in the way required for λ-elimination.

Some clarification of terminology is required here. The proposition expressed by φ is the class of sentences interdeducible with φ. Since interdeducibility is an equivalence relation, logical relations between propositions are induced in an obvious way from logical relations between their members. The strongest proposition which has property F is the one among those with property F which implies them all. The weakest proposition which has property F is the one among those with property F which is implied by any of them. For brevity we may identify sentences with the propositions they express; no confusion will arise.

It is easy to establish the following illustrations of our harmony principle:

(&) $\varphi \& \psi$ is the strongest proposition implied by $\{\varphi, \psi\}$.
$\varphi \& \psi$ is the weakest proposition which implies φ and implies ψ.

($\vee$) $\varphi \vee \psi$ is the strongest proposition implied by φ and implied by ψ.
$\varphi \vee \psi$ is the weakest proposition which implies θ when φ implies θ and ψ implies θ.

($\supset$) $\varphi \supset \psi$ is the strongest proposition implied by $\Delta \backslash \{\varphi\}$ when Δ implies ψ.
$\varphi \supset \psi$ is the weakest proposition which, with φ, implies ψ.

($\sim$) $\sim\varphi$ is the strongest proposition implied by $\Delta \backslash \{\varphi\}$ when Δ implies ⁎.
$\sim\varphi$ is the weakest proposition which, with φ, implies ⁎.

($\forall$) $\forall x \varphi^a_x$ is the strongest proposition implied by Δ when Δ implies φ parametrically in a.
$\forall x \varphi$ is the weakest proposition which, for all t, implies φ^x_t.

($\exists$) $\exists x \varphi$ is the strongest proposition which, for any t, is implied by φ^x_t.
$\exists x \varphi$ is the weakest proposition which, with $\Delta \backslash \{\varphi^x_a\}$, implies ψ when Δ implies ψ parametrically in a.

For each logical operator the verification of the first claim depends on a consideration of the elimination rule, while the verification of the second claim depends on a consideration of the introduction rule.

Let us illustrate this in the case of $\supset$.

Verification of first claim. $\varphi \supset \psi$ is the strongest proposition implied by $\Delta \backslash \{\varphi\}$ when Δ implies ψ.

For, suppose θ is any proposition that is implied by $\Delta \backslash \{\varphi\}$ when Δ implies ψ. By $\supset$-E φ, $\varphi \supset \psi$ imply ψ. Thus we would have that $\varphi \supset \psi$ implies θ. Thus $\varphi \supset \psi$ is strongest in the respect claimed.

Verification of second claim. $\varphi \supset \psi$ is the weakest proposition that, with φ, implies ψ.

For, suppose θ is any proposition that, with φ, implies ψ. Then, by $\supset$-I, θ implies $\varphi \supset \psi$. Thus $\varphi \supset \psi$ is weakest in the respect claimed.

Similar illustrations for the other operators are left to the reader.

How does our harmony principle bear on the operator $\times$ discussed above? With its introduction rule the principle would declare that $\varphi \times \psi$ is the strongest proposition implied by φ. Since φ implies itself, we would have that $\varphi \times \psi$ implies φ. In order therefore for both the inferences $\dfrac{\varphi}{\varphi \times \psi}$ and $\dfrac{\varphi \times \psi}{\varphi}$ to be valid the truth table for $\times$ would have to be

φ	ψ	$\varphi \times \psi$
T	T	T
T	F	T
F	T	F
F	F	F

It would therefore be quite illegitimate, given the introduction rule for $\times$, arbitrarily to specify the elimination rule

$$\frac{\varphi \times \psi}{\psi}$$

since the second line of the truth table shows it to be invalid.

Another way of arriving at this conclusion is to observe that the elimination rule just mentioned cannot conservatively extend the introduction rule given earlier. For $\overline{0=0}$ is a direct proof of $0=0$. But the proof

$$\cfrac{\cfrac{0=0}{(0=0)\times(0=1)}}{0=1}$$

offers no way of transforming the former direct proof of the premiss into a direct proof of the conclusion. There is no reduction procedure for $\times$.

The reduction procedures help to explicate the philosophical maxim that the conclusion of a proof is 'contained' in the premisses: contained, as Frege observed, not as roof beams are contained in a house but as a plant is contained in the seed from which it grows. We shall establish below the precise proof theoretical result that we need, namely the normalization theorem. Very roughly, by repeated application of the reduction procedures any proof can be converted into one in so-called 'normal form'. In a normal form proof no sentence occurs as the conclusion of an introduction and as the major premiss of an immediate elimination. Speaking figuratively, in the 'upper half' of a normal form proof one uses elimination rules to 'unpack' the information contained in the premisses, which is re-arranged in the 'lower half' by means of the introduction rules to yield the conclusion.

The internal structure of each of a set of premisses – the configuration of logical operators and non-logical expressions in each of them – determines the class of normal form proofs of conclusions that follow from them. We saw earlier in Chapter 2 how sentential structure may conveniently be represented by means of tree diagrams. Moreover, we have seen in this Chapter how proofs may be understood as tree-like arrays of sentence occurrences. The macroscopic proof tree is determined by the microscopic sentential trees of the premisses and conclusion. Frege's metaphor is therefore heightened by the analogy with the way in which the microstructure of genes determines the possible features of the adult organism that will develop from them. Biologists talk metaphorically of the maturing organism 'expressing' its genetic information. Even for a nihilist the individual life is at least a passage to a conclusion!

4.13 Identity and extensionality. The identity predicate = has its own special and important meaning which requires us to specify two rules of inference.

Reflexivity of identity

$\mathscr{P}(t=t, t=t, \emptyset)$. Graphically: $\overline{t=t}$

Substitutivity of identicals

$$\text{If}\left\{\begin{array}{l}\mathscr{P}(\Pi_1, \varphi, \Delta_1)\\ \mathscr{P}(\Pi_2, t=u, \Delta_2)\\ \varphi^t_u \text{ is } \psi^t_u\\ t, u \text{ are closed terms}\end{array}\right\} \quad \text{then} \quad \mathscr{P}\left(\frac{\Pi_1 \quad \Pi_2}{\psi}, \psi, \Delta_1 \cup \Delta_2\right)$$

Graphically: $\dfrac{\varphi \quad t=u}{\psi}$, where ψ results from φ by intersubstitution of the closed terms t and u.

The last condition may also be expressed by saying that φ and ψ are t-u variants of one another.

As special cases of substitutivity we have $\dfrac{t=u \quad t=u}{u=t}$ which we abbreviate to $\dfrac{t=u}{u=t}$ (symmetry of identity); and $\dfrac{t=u \quad u=s}{t=s}$ (transitivity of identity).

The deductive power of first order logic with identity is not impaired if we restrict substitutivity of identicals to *atomic* sentences φ. If we wish to effect a substitution in a complex sentence we simply 'break it down' to atomic sentences by means of elimination rules, make appropriate substitutions in these atomic sentences by means of the restricted rule of substitutivity, and then 'build up' to the desired complex result by means of introduction rules.

Substitutivity of identicals is a *principle of extensionality* for closed terms. The extension of a closed term is the object it denotes. The extension of a function sign is the operation on objects which it represents. The extension of a predicate is the set of (sequences of) objects of which it holds. The extension of a sentence is its truth value. All these extensions depend, of course, on the interpretation or model in question. *Co-extensive* expressions have the same extension.

A connective which is useful in discussions of co-extensiveness is the *biconditional* $\equiv$. It may be taken as primitive, or defined in terms of others. The usual definition is

$$\varphi \equiv \psi =_{df} (\varphi \supset \psi) \,\&\, (\psi \supset \varphi).$$

The truth table for $\equiv$ is

φ	ψ	$\varphi \equiv \psi$
T	T	T
T	F	F
F	T	F
F	F	T

which obviously shows that $\varphi \equiv \psi$ expresses agreement in truth value of φ and ψ. The deductive rules for $\equiv$, primitive or derived, are stated graphically thus:

$$\equiv\text{-}I \quad \frac{\begin{matrix} {}^{(i)}\overline{\ \varphi\ } & \overline{\ \psi\ }^{(i)} \\ \vdots & \vdots \\ \psi & \varphi \end{matrix}}{\varphi \equiv \psi}{}_{(i)} \qquad\qquad \equiv\text{-}E \quad \frac{\varphi \quad \varphi \equiv \psi}{\psi} \qquad \frac{\psi \quad \varphi \equiv \psi}{\varphi}$$

When co-extensiveness of expressions is secured by a set Δ of sentences we say that the expressions are co-extensive relative to Δ. For example:

(1) The closed terms t and u are co-extensive relative to Δ if and only if $\Delta \vdash t = u$.

(2) The one-place functions f and g are co-extensive relative to Δ if and only if $\Delta \vdash \forall x f(x) = g(x)$.

(3) The one-place predicates F and G are co-extensive relative to Δ if and only if $\Delta \vdash \forall x F(x) \equiv G(x)$.

(4) The sentences φ and ψ are co-extensive relative to Δ if and only if $\Delta \vdash \varphi \equiv \psi$. This holds if and only if $\Delta, \varphi \vdash \psi$ and $\Delta, \psi \vdash \varphi$. For this reason we also say that φ and ψ are interdeducible relative to Δ. We write $\varphi \overset{\Delta}{\dashv\vdash} \psi$.

The principle of extensionality for expressions in general, roughly stated, is that if two expressions co-extensive relative to Δ are 'substituted' for one another in any expression then the latter is co-extensive (relative to Δ) with the result. It will suffice to state and prove this principle only in the case where the host expression is a sentence. So the principle we are concerned to establish is

> If two expressions co-extensive relative to Δ are 'substituted' for one another in a sentence φ then the result is interdeducible with φ relative to Δ.

I have said 'substituted' because this can be a complicated operation when the expressions involved are complex and substitution takes place within a quantified context. We shall now provide some definitions that enable us to talk precisely about substituting expressions for one another within larger expressions.

Let $t(x_1, \ldots, x_n)$ be a term with just the variables $x_1, \ldots, x_n$ free. Suppose $t_1, \ldots, t_n$ are terms (not necessarily distinct and not necessarily closed). Let $t(t_1, \ldots, t_n)$, abbreviated to $t(\vec{t})$, be the result of simultaneously replacing $x_1, \ldots, x_n$ at all free occurrences in t by $t_1, \ldots, t_n$ respectively.

We say $t(\vec{x})$ occurs in an expression E if and only if for some $\vec{t}$ $t(\vec{t})$ is a subterm of E. We also say that $t(\vec{x})$ occurs in E by virtue of $\vec{t}$. For example, $f(x,g(x,y))$ occurs in the formula $F(x,y,g(f(f(x),g(f(x),h(y)))))$ by virtue of $\vec{t} = \langle f(x),h(y)\rangle$, where $\vec{x} = \langle x,y\rangle$.

Likewise when $\varphi(x_1, \ldots, x_n)$ is a formula with just $x_1, \ldots, x_n$ free we say $\varphi(\vec{x})$ occurs in E by virtue of $\vec{t}$ if and only if $\varphi(\vec{t})$ is a subformula of E.

Obviously when t is closed, t occurs in E if and only if t is a closed subterm of E. We can say t occurs in E by virtue of the empty sequence $\emptyset$. Likewise when φ is a sentence, φ occurs in E if and only if φ is a subsentence of E. We can say φ occurs in E by virtue of $\emptyset$.

Suppose φ and ρ are alike except that one may have occurrences of $u(\vec{t})$ where the other has occurrences of $t(\vec{t})$, and vice versa. We say φ and ρ are t-u variants with respect to $\vec{t}$. We also say that they result from one another by intersubstituting $t(\vec{t})$ and $u(\vec{t})$. Likewise φ and ρ may be ψ-θ variants.

When $x_1, \ldots, x_n$ are the free variables of t and u let $\forall\vec{x}\, t=u$ be the sentence $\forall x_1 \ldots \forall x_n t = u$. When $n=0$, i.e. when t and u are closed, then it is just the sentence $t=u$. Likewise we may define $\forall\vec{x}\, \psi \equiv \theta$. If t and u have the same free variables then t and u are co-extensive relative to Δ if and only if $\Delta \vdash \forall\vec{x}\, t = u$. Likewise if ψ and θ have the same free variables then ψ and θ are co-extensive relative to Δ if and only if $\Delta \vdash \forall\vec{x}\, \psi \equiv \theta$.

The following theorem is a precise version of the principle of extensionality stated informally above.

Theorem

(I) Suppose t and u are co-extensive relative to Δ and that one of them

occurs in the sentence φ by virtue of $\vec{t}$. Then φ is interdeducible relative to Δ with any of its t-u variants with respect to $\vec{t}$.
(II) Suppose ψ and θ are co-extensive relative to Δ and that one of them occurs in the sentence φ by virtue of $\vec{t}$. Then φ is interdeducible relative to Δ with any of its ψ-θ variants with respect to $\vec{t}$.
Proof. By induction on φ.
Basis. φ is an atomic sentence. Then t or u occurs in φ by virtue of *closed* $\vec{t}$.
(I) Suppose ρ is a t-u variant of φ with respect to $\vec{t}$. Then by

$$\cfrac{\varphi \qquad \cfrac{\begin{matrix}\Delta\\ \vdots\\ \forall\vec{x}\ \ t=u\end{matrix}}{t(\vec{t})=u(\vec{t})}\text{(multiple }\forall\text{-}E)}{\rho}\text{(substitutivity of identicals)}$$

and a similar proof of the converse we have $\varphi \dashv\vdash^{\Delta} \rho$.
(II) ψ or θ occurs in φ by virtue of $\vec{t}$ only because φ is either $\psi(\vec{t})$ or $\theta(\vec{t})$. So by the proof

$$\cfrac{\psi(\vec{t}) \qquad \cfrac{\begin{matrix}\Delta\\ \vdots\\ \forall\vec{x}\ \ \psi\equiv\theta\end{matrix}}{\psi(\vec{t})\equiv\theta(\vec{t})}\text{(multiple }\forall\text{-}E)}{\theta(\vec{t})}$$

and a similar proof of the converse, φ is interdeducible relative to Δ with any of its ψ-θ variants with respect to $\vec{t}$.
Inductive Step. For part (II) we suppose without loss of generality that φ is neither $\psi(\vec{t})$ nor $\theta(\vec{t})$ since in those cases one could simply repeat the reasoning for Basis (II). We perform the inductive step for parts (I) and (II) by structurally identical arguments. Suppose ρ is a variant of φ. (We need not bother to specify whether it is a t-u variant or a ψ-θ variant.)

Suppose φ is $\varphi_1 \& \varphi_2$. Then ρ is $\rho_1 \& \rho_2$, for variants ρ_1, ρ_2 of φ_1, φ_2 respectively with respect to $\vec{t}$. By the proof

$$\cfrac{\begin{matrix}\underbrace{\Delta,\ \cfrac{\varphi_1\&\varphi_2}{\varphi_1}}\\ \vdots\text{(by IH)}\\ \rho_1\end{matrix} \qquad \begin{matrix}\underbrace{\Delta,\ \cfrac{\varphi_1\&\varphi_2}{\varphi_2}}\\ \vdots\text{(by IH)}\\ \rho_2\end{matrix}}{\rho_1\&\rho_2}$$

and a similar proof of the converse we have $\varphi \dashv\vdash^{\Delta} \rho$. When φ is $\sim\varphi_1$, $\varphi_1 \vee \varphi_2$, $\varphi_1 \supset \varphi_2$ the argument is similar, using elimination rules, inductive hypothesis, and introduction rules appropriately.

Now suppose φ is $\forall x\eta$. We are considering variants with respect to $\bar{t}$ of the form $\forall x\xi$, where ξ is a variant of η with respect to $\bar{t}$. Let a be a name occurring neither in Δ nor in φ. Then ξ^x_a is a variant of η^x_a with respect to $\bar{t}^x_a$. Moreover, if t occurs in $\forall x\eta$ by virtue of $\bar{t}$ then t occurs in η^x_a by virtue of $\bar{t}^x_a$. Likewise if ψ occurs in $\forall x\eta$ by virtue of $\bar{t}$ then ψ occurs in η^x_a by virtue of $\bar{t}^x_a$. Thus by IH η^x_a is interdeducible with ξ^x_a relative to Δ. By the proof

$$
\begin{array}{c}
\underbrace{\Delta,\ \dfrac{\forall x\eta}{\eta^x_a}} \\
\vdots \\
\dfrac{\xi^x_a}{\forall x\xi}
\end{array}
$$

and a similar proof of the converse we have $\forall x\eta \overset{\Delta}{\dashv\vdash} \forall x\xi$.

Finally suppose φ is $\exists x\eta$. We are considering variants with respect to $\bar{t}$ of the form $\exists x\xi$, where ξ is a variant of η with respect to $\bar{t}$. Let a be a name occurring neither in Δ nor in φ. By reasoning as in the previous case, η^x_a is interdeducible with ξ^x_a relative to Δ. By the proof

$$
\dfrac{\exists x\eta \qquad \begin{array}{c} \underbrace{\Delta,\ \overline{\eta^x_a}^{\,(1)}} \\ \vdots \\ \dfrac{\xi^x_a}{\exists x\xi} \end{array}}{\exists x\xi}\,{\scriptstyle (1)}
$$

and a similar proof of the converse we have $\exists x\eta \overset{\Delta}{\dashv\vdash} \exists x\xi$. This completes the proof of the theorem.

Note that we required substitutivity of identicals only for atomic sentences (in Basis (I)). Note also that $\vdash$ may be read as classical or intuitionistic deducibility throughout.

4.14 Some simple proofs. In this section we shall provide proofs of some simple arguments in order to illustrate further the rules of inference given above. First we provide the proof promised in 3.8 for the argument

> Everyone has either fooled someone
> or been fooled by someone
> Everyone who has fooled someone
> has fooled himself

Everyone who has been fooled by
someone has fooled himself
___
Everyone has both fooled someone
and been fooled by him

We shall use the following translation into logical notation, observing the maxim of shallow analysis:

$$\dfrac{\begin{array}{l}\forall x(Gx \vee Hx)\\ \forall x(Gx \supset Fxx)\\ \forall x(Hx \supset Fxx)\end{array}}{\forall x \exists y(Fxy \,\&\, Fyx)}$$

The proof is as follows:

$$\dfrac{\dfrac{\dfrac{\forall xGx \vee Hx}{Ga \vee Ha} \quad \dfrac{\dfrac{\dfrac{\overset{(1)}{\overline{Ga}} \quad \dfrac{\forall xGx \supset Fxx}{Ga \supset Faa}}{Faa} \quad \dfrac{\overset{(1)}{\overline{Ga}} \quad \dfrac{\forall xGx \supset Fxx}{Ga \supset Faa}}{Faa}}{Faa \,\&\, Faa}}{\exists yFay \,\&\, Fya} \quad \dfrac{\dfrac{\dfrac{\overset{(1)}{\overline{Ha}} \quad \dfrac{\forall xHx \supset Fxx}{Ha \supset Faa}}{Faa} \quad \dfrac{\overset{(1)}{\overline{Ha}} \quad \dfrac{\forall xHx \supset Fxx}{Ha \supset Faa}}{Faa}}{Faa \,\&\, Faa}}{\exists yFay \,\&\, Fya}}{\exists yFay \,\&\, Fya}\,(1)}{\forall x \exists yFxy \,\&\, Fyx}$$

This proof illustrates the one shortcoming of the 'tree' proofs in our system of natural deduction – that of 'sideways spread' as a result of re-writing a sentence each time it is appealed to as a premiss for the application of a rule. For example, the sentence *Faa* is proved 'twice over' in each of the sub-proofs for proof by cases. But this is a small price to pay for the undeniable advantage of perspicuity, which tree proofs enjoy over the linear proofs of other systems. The latter, because of their complicated marginal annotations, are much more difficult to take in at a glance.

Consider now the argument

(1) Someone loves everyone
(2) Not everyone loves himself
___
(3) There are at least two individuals, one of whom loves the other

Translated into logical notation it becomes

(1) $\exists x \forall y Lxy$
(2) $\sim\forall x Lxx$
___
(3) $\exists x \exists y(\sim x = y \,\&\, Lxy)$

We shall provide for this argument three different versions of informal reasoning and the corresponding formal proof which conclusively establishes its validity.

Version I

Someone loves everyone (1). Let a be such an individual. So for arbitrary b, Lab ... (i). Suppose there is no individual other than a. Then for arbitrary b, $a=b$. Thus by substitution in (i), Lbb (for arbitrary b). But not everyone loves himself (2). Contradiction. Therefore there is some individual other than a. Let c be such an individual. By (i), Lac. Thus there are at least two individuals (namely a and c), one of whom loves the other.

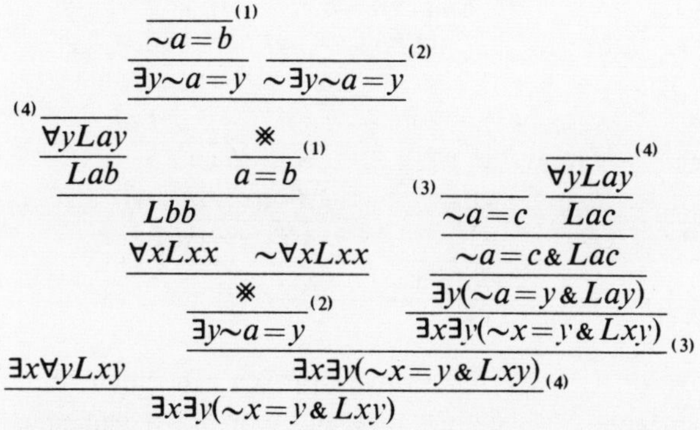
∼a=b
∃y∼a=y
∼∃y∼a=y
∀yLay
Lab
※
a=b
Lbb
∀xLxx
∼∀xLxx
∃y∼a=y
∼a=c
Lac
∼a=c&Lac
∃y(∼a=y&Lay)
∃x∃y(∼x=y&Lxy)
∃x∀yLxy
∃x∃y(∼x=y&Lxy)

Version II

Suppose for reductio that it is not the case that there are at least two individuals, one of whom loves the other ... (i). Someone loves everyone (1). Let a be such an individual. So for arbitrary b, Lab ... (ii). If b is distinct from a, then there *are* at least two individuals, one of whom loves the other, contradicting (i). Thus b is identical to a. Hence by substitution in (ii), Lbb (for arbitrary b). But not everyone loves himself (2). Contradiction. Thus there are at least two individuals, one of whom loves the other.

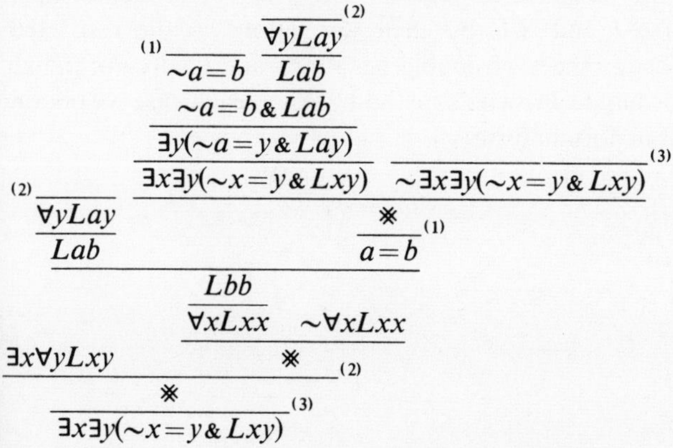
∀yLay
∼a=b
Lab
∼a=b&Lab
∃y(∼a=y&Lay)
∃x∃y(∼x=y&Lxy)
∼∃x∃y(∼x=y&Lxy)
∀yLay
Lab
※
a=b
Lbb
∀xLxx
∼∀xLxx
∃x∀yLxy
※
※
∃x∃y(∼x=y&Lxy)

Version III

Someone loves everyone (1). Let *a* be such an individual. Then in particular *Laa*. Since not everyone loves himself (2), it follows that someone does not love himself. Let *b* be such an individual. Since *Laa* and not-*Lbb*, *a* is distinct from *b*. Since also *Lab*, it follows that there are at least two individuals, one of whom loves the other.

$$
\dfrac{\exists x\forall yLxy \qquad \dfrac{\dfrac{\dfrac{\dfrac{\dfrac{\dfrac{\dfrac{\overline{\sim Lcc}^{\,(1)}}{\exists x{\sim}Lxx} \quad \overline{\sim\exists x{\sim}Lxx}^{\,(2)}}{\text{※}}}{Lcc}{\scriptstyle(1)}}{\forall xLxx} \quad \sim\forall xLxx}{\text{※}}}{\exists x{\sim}Lxx}{\scriptstyle(2)} \qquad \dfrac{\dfrac{\dfrac{\dfrac{\dfrac{\dfrac{\dfrac{\overline{\forall yLay}^{\,(5)}}{Laa} \quad \overline{a=b}^{\,(3)}}{Lbb} \quad \overline{\sim Lbb}^{\,(4)}}{\text{※}}}{\sim a=b}{\scriptstyle(3)} \quad \dfrac{\overline{\forall yLay}^{\,(5)}}{Lab}}{\sim a=b \,\&\, Lab}}{\exists y(\sim a=y \,\&\, Lay)}}{\exists x\exists y(\sim x=y \,\&\, Lxy)}}{\exists x\exists y(\sim x=y \,\&\, Lxy)}{\scriptstyle(4)}}{\exists x\exists y(\sim x=y \,\&\, Lxy)}{\scriptstyle(5)}
$$

In his book *Natural Deduction* Prawitz proves a normalization theorem for classical logic based on ※, ⊃, & and ∀, with $\sim\varphi$ defined as $\varphi\supset$※, $\varphi\vee\psi$ defined as $(\sim\varphi)\supset\psi$, and $\exists x\varphi$ defined as $\sim\forall x\sim\varphi$. The reader will have derived the introduction and elimination rules for ∨ and ∃ using only the rules for ※, (∼), ⊃, & and ∀ in section 7 above, on the basis of the definitions just given for ∨ and ∃. In the language based on ※, (∼), & and ∀ the argument above becomes

(1) $\sim\forall x{\sim}\forall yLxy$

(2) $\sim\forall xLxx$

(3) $\sim\forall x\forall y{\sim}(\sim x=y \,\&\, Lxy)$

If in the three proofs above we replace $\exists x$ by $\sim\forall x\sim$ and replace each application of ∃-*I* and ∃-*E* by their derivations in the restricted system, drop occurrences of double negations and finally normalize the result according to Prawitz's method, then in each case we obtain the same proof in normal form:

$$\dfrac{\dfrac{\dfrac{\dfrac{\dfrac{\dfrac{\dfrac{\dfrac{[\forall yLay]^{(2)}}{Lab} \quad \dfrac{\dfrac{\dfrac{[\sim a=b]^{(1)} \quad \dfrac{[\forall yLay]^{(2)}}{Lab}}{\sim a=b\,\&\,Lab} \quad \dfrac{\dfrac{[\forall x\forall y\sim(\sim x=y\,\&\,Lxy)]^{(3)}}{\forall y\sim(\sim a=y\,\&\,Lay)}}{\sim(\sim a=b\,\&\,Lab)}}{\text{※}}}{a=b}\,{}^{(1)}}{Lbb}}{\forall xLxx} \quad \sim\forall xLxx}{\text{※}}}{\sim\forall yLay}\,{}^{(2)}}{\forall x\sim\forall yLxy} \quad \sim\forall x\sim\forall yLxy}{\text{※}}}{\sim\forall x\forall y\sim(\sim x=y\,\&\,Lxy)}\,{}^{(3)}$$

This would cast some doubt on Prawitz's conjecture that two formal proofs (in his system) represent the same process of reasoning if and only if they normalize to the same result. For, Versions I, II, and III intuitively appear to represent different processes of reasoning, yet, as just remarked, their formalizations in Prawitz's system normalize to the same result. This is part of the reason why we shall subsequently prove normalization in a different manner from Prawitz, for a classical system with all the logical operators $\sim$, $\vee$, &, $\supset$, $\exists$ and $\forall$ primitive. It remains, of course, as tentative a conjecture as ever that two formal proofs of the system represent the same process of reasoning if and only if they normalize to the same result.

To the best of my knowledge no-one has yet succeeded in counting or classifying distinct proofs (in normal form) of the same conclusion from the same premisses. Nor has anyone produced a satisfactory measure of *depth of proof*, understood as a measure of the profundity of the process of reasoning which the proof represents. These are two areas where future investigation may yield interesting results.

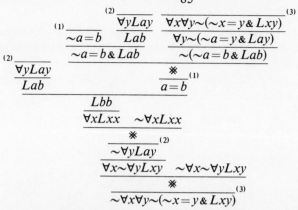

CHAPTER 5

Propositional metalogic

5.1
Propositional logic vs. first order logic *p.88*
5.2
Compactness of classical consequence *p.89*
5.3
Classical completeness via truth sets *p.90*
5.4
Normalization of proofs *p.94*
5.5
Classical completeness via disjunctive normal forms *p.98*
5.6
A direct proof of classical completeness *p.101*
5.7
Classical completeness via Henkin's method *p.103*
5.8
Kripke semantics for intuitionistic logic *p.106*

5.1 Propositional logic vs. first order logic. Arguments are valid by virtue of the logical structure of their premisses and conclusions. When the logical structure concerned arises from connections rather than quantifications we may talk of *propositional* arguments. We saw in 2.1 that the validity of the argument

$$\frac{\begin{array}{l}\text{Either someone is rich or everyone is bald}\\ \text{Not everyone is bald}\end{array}}{\text{Someone is rich}}$$

depends only on *connections*:

$$\frac{\begin{array}{c}\varphi \vee \psi\\ \sim\psi\end{array}}{\varphi}$$

and that the quantifications did not have to be taken into account when showing that the argument was valid. By contrast the valid argument

$$\frac{\begin{array}{l}\text{Either someone is rich or everyone is bald}\\ \text{Everyone is not bald}\end{array}}{\text{Someone is rich}}$$

cannot be shown to be valid without revealing at least this much quantificational structure:

$$\frac{\begin{array}{c}\varphi \vee \forall x \psi x\\ \forall x \sim \psi x\end{array}}{\varphi}$$

To prove this argument we have to attend to the logical behaviour of the quantifier 'everyone'. Arguments whose validity or invalidity can be established only by attending to the behaviour of quantifiers are called first order, or quantificational arguments.

In this chapter we shall develop the metatheory of *propositional* logic, in order to introduce the reader to results that are easier to understand and prove in this simpler setting than are the corresponding results for first order logic.

In propositional logic, as we saw from the example above, the validity (or invalidity) of arguments is due to the structure of *connection* alone. In our example the sentences 'Someone is rich' and 'Everyone is bald' were not subjected to logical analysis. In the context of the argument they were treated as *atoms*.

In propositional logic we therefore have the following simplified definition of *sentence*:

(i) Any atom is a sentence.
(ii) If φ and ψ are sentences then so are $\sim\varphi$, $\varphi \vee \psi$, $\varphi \,\&\, \psi$ and $\varphi \supset \psi$.
(iii) Nothing is a sentence unless its being so follows from (i) and (ii).

We shall use the notation $A, B, C, \dots$ for atoms. It will be assumed that the atoms are given in a countably infinite list $A_0, A_1, A_2, \dots$. Exactly what these atoms are is unimportant; all that matters is the logical purpose they serve.

Our analysis of truth conditions is commensurately simplified. As we are no longer enquiring into the structure of quantified or atomic sentences, we discard the detailed account of their truth or falsity depending on the relational structure on a domain of individuals. All we do now to specify a situation or model is specify which atoms are true and which are false.

A *truth value assignment* assigns to each atom a truth value T or F. We shall use the notation τ, ρ, σ, ... for truth value assignments. $\tau(\varphi)$, the truth value of a (complex) sentence φ under the assignment τ, is defined inductively in the obvious way:

$$\begin{aligned}
\tau(\sim\varphi) &= \sim(\tau(\varphi))\\
\tau(\varphi \vee \psi) &= \vee(\tau(\varphi), \tau(\psi))\\
\tau(\varphi \,\&\, \psi) &= \&(\tau(\varphi), \tau(\psi))\\
\tau(\varphi \supset \psi) &= \supset(\tau(\varphi), \tau(\psi))
\end{aligned}$$

On the right hand side of these defining equations $\sim$, $\vee$, $\&$ and $\supset$ represent the mappings of truth values given by the respective truth tables. If $\tau(\varphi) = T$ we say τ satisfies φ. If τ satisfies every member of Δ we say τ satisfies Δ. φ is a *logical consequence* of Δ ($\Delta \vDash \varphi$) if and only if every assignment which satisfies Δ satisfies φ. φ is a *logical truth* if and only if every assignment satisfies φ.

The notions of proof and deducibility are defined by using only the rules of inference for absurdity and the connectives. As in the case of first order logic we may distinguish between intuitionistic and classical logic by reference to the classical rules of negation.

5.2 Compactness of classical consequence. The first result we shall prove is that logical consequence is *compact*: if φ is a logical consequence of Δ then φ is a logical consequence of some finite subset of Δ. What we shall actually prove is the following equivalent statement:
Compactness Theorem. If every finite subset of Δ is satisfiable then Δ is satisfiable.
(Remember that φ is a logical consequence of Δ iff $\Delta \cup \{\sim\varphi\}$ is not satisfiable.)

Proof. τ_n will be a partial assignment of truth values to just the first n atoms in the list $A_0, A_1, A_2, \ldots$ of all atoms. As a special case τ_0 is the null assignment. An assignment is *total* if it assigns every atom a truth value. Our aim is to use the assumption that every finite subset of Δ is satisfiable to construct a total assignment which satisfies Δ. Consider now the property P of a partial assignment τ_n defined as follows:

$P(\tau_n)$: For every finite subset Φ of Δ there is a total assignment which agrees with τ_n on $A_0, \ldots, A_{n-1}$ and satisfies Φ.

Obviously $P(\tau_0)$ is the assumption just mentioned. This accomplishes the basis step of our inductive construction of the desired assignment. Now suppose we have constructed τ_n so that $P(\tau_n)$. We show how to construct τ_{n+1} so that $P(\tau_{n+1})$. Suppose $\tau_n(A_n/T)$ has property P; then we take it for τ_{n+1}. Otherwise we take $\tau_n(A_n/F)$, which we now show to have property P if $\tau_n(A_n/T)$ does not:

Since not-$P(\tau_n(A_n/T))$ there is some finite subset Γ, say, of Δ which is not satisfied by any total assignment that agrees with $\tau_n(A_n/T)$ on $A_0, \ldots, A_n \ldots$ (1). Now let Φ be an arbitrary finite subset of Δ. Since $(\Gamma \cup \Phi)$ is finite, by $P(\tau_n)$ there is a total assignment τ, say, which agrees with τ_n on $A_0, \ldots, A_{n-1}$ and satisfies Γ and satisfies Φ. Now suppose for reductio ad absurdum that $\tau(A_n) = T$. Then τ agrees with $\tau_n(A_n/T)$ on $A_0, \ldots, A_n$ and satisfies Γ, contrary to (1). Since τ is total we must therefore have $\tau(A_n) = F$. Thus τ agrees with $\tau_n(A_n/F)$ on $A_0, \ldots, A_n$ and satisfies Φ. Hence there is an assignment which agrees with $\tau_n(A_n/F)$ on $A_0, \ldots, A_n$ and satisfies Φ. But Φ was an arbitrary finite subset of Δ. Hence for every finite subset Φ of Δ there is a total assignment that agrees with $\tau_n(A_n/F)$ on $A_0, \ldots, A_n$ and satisfies Φ, i.e. $P(\tau_n(A_n/F))$.

We are therefore able to construct a sequence $\tau_0, \tau_1, \tau_2, \ldots$ where each τ_{n+1} agrees with τ_n on $A_0, \ldots, A_{n-1}$, and each τ_n has property P. Now let τ be the total assignment that agrees with all the τ_n's. We show that τ satisfies Δ. For, let φ be an arbitrary member of Δ. φ has only finitely many atoms. Suppose A_k is the last of these to appear in the list. We have $P(\tau_{k+1})$, i.e. for every finite subset Φ of Δ there is a total assignment that agrees with τ_{k+1} on $A_0, \ldots, A_k$ and satisfies Φ. Now $\{\varphi\}$ is finite. So there is a total assignment that agrees with τ_{k+1} on $A_0, \ldots, A_k$ and satisfies φ. This assignment assigns to the atoms of φ the same values as does τ_{k+1}, and therefore the same values as does τ. Hence τ satisfies φ.

5.3 Classical completeness via truth sets. In Chapter 2 we saw an example of a meta-deduction of a conclusion of the form 'φ is true in $\mathfrak{A}'$ from the basic information about $\mathfrak{A}$. This deduction used clauses in the definition of satisfaction. In the propositional case we can likewise give examples of meta-deductions of conclusions of the form 'φ is true/false under τ' from the basic information about τ. These deductions would use clauses in the definition of truth.

But in the propositional case the meta-deductions can be mimicked in the object language. For the basic information about any assignment:

$$\tau(A)=T, \quad \tau(B)=F, \text{ etc. } \ldots$$

can be expressed in the object language:

$$A \qquad , \quad \sim B \qquad , \text{ etc. } \ldots;$$

and the conclusion

$$\varphi \text{ is true under } \tau (\varphi \text{ is false under } \tau)$$

can likewise be expressed in the object language:

$$\varphi \qquad\qquad\qquad (\sim\varphi).$$

Let us define $\underline{\tau}$, the truth set of τ, by the condition:

> $A \in \underline{\tau}$ iff $\tau(A)=T$, $\sim A \in \underline{\tau}$ iff $\tau(A)=F$, and only atoms or negations of atoms occur in $\underline{\tau}$.

Implicit in 4.6, where we mimicked the truth tables in intuitionistic logic, is the inductive proof of the following theorem:

Truth Set Theorem

(I) If $\tau(\varphi)=T$ then $\underline{\tau} \vdash \varphi$

(II) If $\tau(\varphi)=F$ then $\underline{\tau} \vdash \sim\varphi$

where $\vdash$ represents *intuitionistic* deducibility.

Proof. By induction on φ.

Basis. Result obviously holds for atomic φ by definition of $\underline{\tau}$.

Inductive step. By cases according to the dominant connective in φ.

Case (i): $\varphi = \sim\psi$

(I) Suppose $\tau(\sim\psi)=T$. Then $\tau(\psi)=F$. By IH(II) $\underline{\tau} \vdash \sim\psi$.

(II) Suppose $\tau(\sim\psi)=F$. Then $\tau(\psi)=T$. By IH(I) $\underline{\tau} \vdash \psi$. By the proof schema

$$\dfrac{\dfrac{\begin{matrix}\underline{\tau}\\ \Pi\\ \psi\end{matrix} \qquad \overline{\sim\psi}^{\,(1)}}{\divideontimes}}{\sim\sim\psi}\,(1)$$

we have $\underline{\tau} \vdash \sim(\sim\psi)$.

Case (ii): $\varphi = \psi \,\&\, \theta$

(I) Suppose $\tau(\psi \,\&\, \theta) = T$. Then $\tau(\psi) = T$ and $\tau(\theta) = T$. By IH(I) $\underline{\tau} \vdash \psi$ and $\underline{\tau} \vdash \theta$. By &-*I* $\underline{\tau} \vdash \psi \,\&\, \theta$.

(II) Suppose $\tau(\psi \,\&\, \theta) = F$. Then $\tau(\psi) = F$ or $\tau(\theta) = F$. Suppose without loss of generality that $\tau(\psi) = F$. By IH(II) $\underline{\tau} \vdash \sim\psi$. By virtue of the proof schema

$$\dfrac{\dfrac{\begin{array}{c}\underline{\tau}\\ \Pi\\ \sim\psi\end{array} \qquad \dfrac{\overline{\psi \,\&\, \theta}^{\,(1)}}{\psi}}{\divideontimes}}{\sim(\psi \,\&\, \theta)}\,(1)$$

we have $\underline{\tau} \vdash \sim(\psi \,\&\, \theta)$.

Case (iii): $\varphi = \psi \vee \theta$

(I) Suppose $\tau(\psi \vee \theta) = T$. Then $\tau(\psi) = T$ or $\tau(\theta) = T$. Suppose without loss of generality that $\tau(\psi) = T$. By IH(I) $\underline{\tau} \vdash \psi$. By $\vee$-*I* $\underline{\tau} \vdash \psi \vee \theta$.

(II) Suppose $\tau(\psi \vee \theta) = F$. Then $\tau(\psi) = F$ and $\tau(\theta) = F$. By IH(II) $\underline{\tau} \vdash \sim\psi$ and $\underline{\tau} \vdash \sim\theta$. By the proof schema

$$\dfrac{\dfrac{{}^{(2)}\overline{\psi \vee \theta} \qquad \dfrac{{}^{(1)}\overline{\psi} \quad \begin{array}{c}\underline{\tau}\\ \Pi_1\\ \sim\psi\end{array}}{\divideontimes} \qquad \dfrac{{}^{(1)}\overline{\theta} \quad \begin{array}{c}\underline{\tau}\\ \Pi_2\\ \sim\theta\end{array}}{\divideontimes}}{\divideontimes}\,(1)}{\sim(\psi \vee \theta)}\,(2)$$

we have $\underline{\tau} \vdash \sim(\psi \vee \theta)$.

Case (iv): $\varphi = \psi \supset \theta$

(I) Suppose $\tau(\psi \supset \theta) = T$. Then $\tau(\psi) = F$ or $\tau(\theta) = T$.

Suppose $\tau(\psi) = F$. By IH(II) $\underline{\tau} \vdash \sim\psi$. By the proof schema

$$\dfrac{\dfrac{\dfrac{{}^{(1)}\overline{\psi} \quad \begin{array}{c}\underline{\tau}\\ \Pi\\ \sim\psi\end{array}}{\divideontimes}}{\theta}}{\psi \supset \theta}\,(1)$$

we have $\underline{\tau} \vdash \psi \supset \theta$.

Now suppose $\tau(\theta) = T$. By IH(I) $\underline{\tau} \vdash \theta$. By $\supset$-*I* $\underline{\tau} \vdash \psi \supset \theta$.

(II) Suppose $\tau(\psi \supset \theta) = F$. Then $\tau(\psi) = T$ and $\tau(\theta) = F$. By IH(I) $\underline{\tau} \vdash \psi$ and by IH(II) $\underline{\tau} \vdash \sim\theta$. By the proof schema

$$\dfrac{\dfrac{\begin{matrix}\underline{\tau}\\ \Pi_1\\ \psi\end{matrix} \quad \dfrac{}{\psi\supset\theta}{}^{(1)}}{\theta} \qquad \begin{matrix}\underline{\tau}\\ \Pi_2\\ \sim\theta\end{matrix}}{\dfrac{\divideontimes}{\sim(\psi\supset\theta)}{}^{(1)}}$$

we have $\underline{\tau} \vdash \sim(\psi\supset\theta)$.

Note that the proof schemata displayed in the inductive step correspond to the 'non-trivial' proofs displayed in 4.6, where we mimicked the truth tables. An inspection of our proof of the last theorem reveals that the proofs of φ or $\sim\varphi$ from $\underline{\tau}$ involve as premisses only such atoms or negations of such atoms as occur in φ itself. Thus the theorem holds with τ_φ in place of $\underline{\tau}$, where τ_φ is defined in the obvious way by including the condition that the atoms involved occur in φ. The ability thus to 'decide' by means of our rules of inference whether a given sentence φ is true or false given the truth value of each atom in φ suggests that the rules are powerful enough to prove any valid argument. We have not yet, however, appealed to the classical negation rules. Indeed, classical completeness follows from the Truth Set Theorem only after the following lemma, whose proof appeals conspicuously to the presence of the rule of dilemma.

A truth set over a set of atoms contains, for each A in that set exactly one of A or $\sim A$, and nothing else. Henceforth $\vdash$ represents classical deducibility.

Lemma on Dilemma. If $\Delta \nvdash \varphi$ then for any finite set $\mathscr{A}$ of atoms occurring in (Δ,φ) there is some truth set Θ over $\mathscr{A}$ such that $\Delta, \Theta \nvdash \varphi$.

Proof. By induction on the number of atoms in $\mathscr{A}$, given the hypothesis of the Lemma.

Basis. Suppose $\mathscr{A} = \emptyset$. Then $\emptyset$ is a truth set over $\mathscr{A}$ and $\Delta, \emptyset \nvdash \varphi$.

Induction step. Suppose $\mathscr{A} = \{A_1, \ldots, A_n, A_{n+1}\}$. By inductive hypothesis let Θ be a truth set over $\{A_1, \ldots, A_n\}$ such that $\Delta, \Theta \nvdash \varphi$. If $\Delta, \Theta, A_{n+1} \vdash \varphi$ and $\Delta, \Theta, \sim A_{n+1} \vdash \varphi$ then by dilemma $\Delta, \Theta \vdash \varphi$. So either $\Delta, \Theta, A_{n+1} \nvdash \varphi$ or $\Delta, \Theta, \sim A_{n+1} \nvdash \varphi$. (Θ, A_{n+1}) and $(\Theta, \sim A_{n+1})$ are the required truth sets respectively.

Completeness Theorem (*Weak Version*). If $\Delta \vDash \varphi$ and only finitely many atoms occur in (Δ,φ) then $\Delta \vdash \varphi$.

Proof. Suppose only finitely many atoms occur in (Δ,φ) and $\Delta \nvdash \varphi$. We show $\Delta \nvDash \varphi$. By the preceding lemma let Θ be a truth set over the finitely many atoms concerned, such that $\Delta, \Theta \nvdash \varphi$. Define τ by the condition $\tau(A) = T$ iff $A \in \Theta$. We show τ satisfies Δ but not φ. Let ψ be an arbitrary member of Δ. Suppose for reductio ad absurdum that $\tau(\psi)=F$. By the truth set theorem $\Theta \vdash \sim\psi$, whence $\Delta, \Theta \vdash$ ※ and $\Delta, \Theta \vdash \varphi$. But $\Delta, \Theta \nvdash \varphi$. Thus $\tau(\psi)=T$. Moreover, since $\Delta, \Theta \nvdash \varphi$ certainly $\Theta \nvDash \varphi$; hence by the truth set theorem $\tau(\varphi)=F$.

Completeness Theorem (*Strong Version*). If $\Delta \vDash \varphi$ then $\Delta \vdash \varphi$.

Proof. Suppose $\Delta \vDash \varphi$. By compactness φ is a logical consequence of a finite subset of Δ, which obviously involves only finitely many atoms. By the preceding theorem $\Delta \vdash \varphi$.

5.4 Normalization of proofs. By means of the transformation

$$\begin{array}{c} \begin{array}{cc} {}^{(1)}\overline{\quad\psi\quad} & \overline{\quad\sim\psi\quad}^{(1)} \\ \Pi_1 & \Pi_2 \\ \theta & \theta \end{array} {}_{(1)} \\ \hline (\theta) \\ \Sigma \\ \varphi \end{array} \quad \rightarrow \quad \begin{array}{c} \begin{array}{cc} {}^{(1)}\overline{\quad\psi\quad} & \overline{\quad\sim\psi\quad}^{(1)} \\ \Pi_1 & \Pi_2 \\ (\theta) & (\theta) \\ \Sigma & \Sigma \\ \varphi & \varphi \end{array} {}_{(1)} \\ \hline \varphi \end{array}$$

all applications of dilemma may be driven downwards so that any proof of φ can be turned into one in which all applications of dilemma have φ as conclusion. This leads to the following result.

Inconsistency Theorem. If $\Delta \vdash_C$ ※ then $\Delta \vdash_I$ ※.

Proof. Take a proof of ※ from Δ in which all applications of dilemma have been driven downwards so as to have ※ as conclusion. Now the schema

$$\begin{array}{c} \begin{array}{cc} {}^{(1)}\overline{\quad\psi\quad} & \overline{\quad\sim\psi\quad}^{(1)} \\ \Pi_1 & \Pi_2 \\ \text{※} & \text{※} \end{array} {}_{(1)} \\ \hline \text{※} \end{array}$$

is intuitionistically derivable:

$$\begin{array}{c} \overline{\quad\psi\quad}^{(1)} \\ \Pi_1 \\ \text{※} \\ \hline \sim\psi \; {}^{(1)} \\ \Pi_2 \\ \text{※} \end{array}$$

Therefore by replacing all applications of the former by applications of the latter we obtain an intuitionistic proof of ※ from Δ.

Note that we have proved the inconsistency theorem only for *propositional* logic. It does not hold for first order logic.

In applications of dilemma:

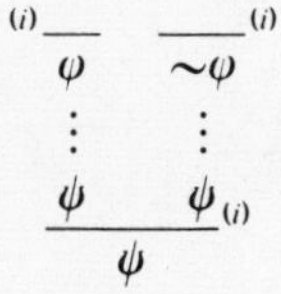

$$\dfrac{\begin{matrix} {}^{(i)}\overline{\quad\varphi\quad} & \overline{\quad\sim\varphi\quad}^{(i)} \\ \vdots & \vdots \\ \psi & \psi \end{matrix}}{\psi}\,(i)$$

I shall speak simply of discharging φ. In our proof of completeness we needed only such applications of dilemma as discharged atomic sentences. Thus we established the classical completeness of a system of deductive rules whose only rule besides those of intuitionistic logic is a rule of dilemma permitting discharge only of atomic sentences. The full classical strength of this system for propositional logic can also be appreciated from the following transformations on proofs. These transformations need only be applied finitely many times to convert any proof that contains applications of dilemma discharging complex sentences, into a proof whose applications of dilemma discharge only atomic sentences.

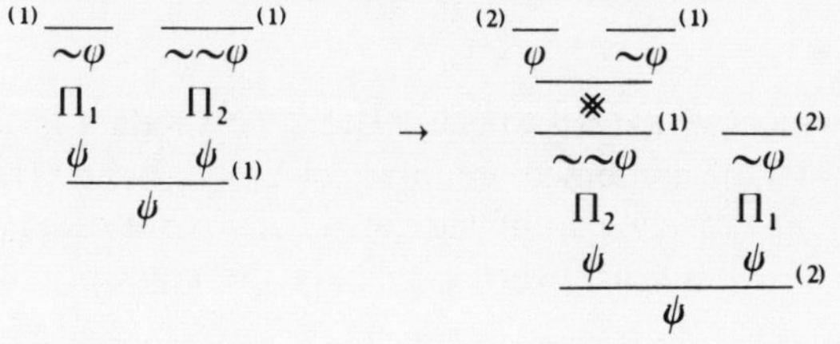

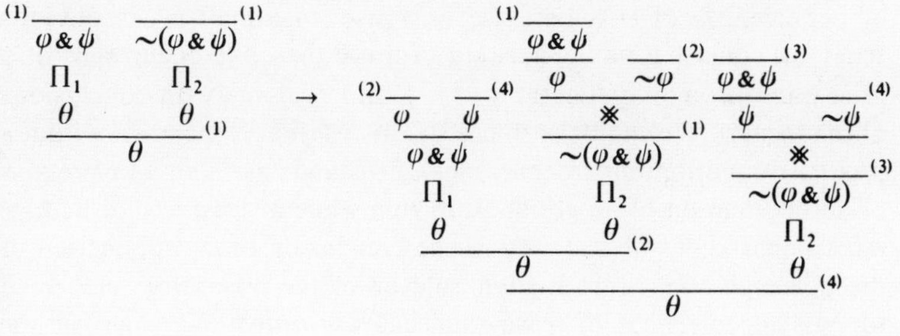

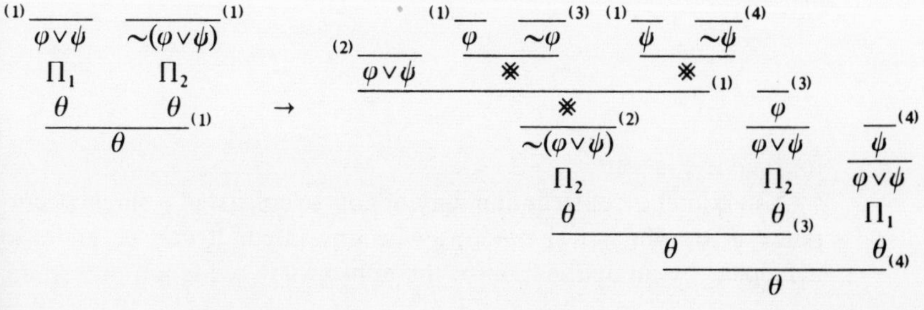

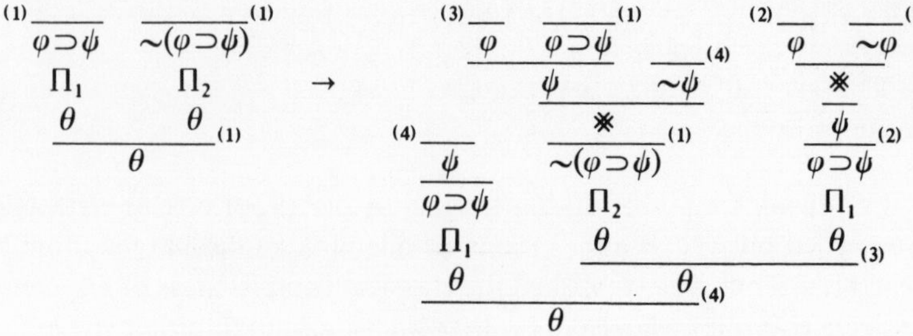

Once a proof has been transformed into one in which applications of dilemma discharge only atomic sentences, one can complete the *normalization* of the original proof by successively applying reduction procedures. The reader will recall the reduction procedures for the connectives from 4.10. They apply to proofs of the form

$$\dfrac{\dfrac{\Pi}{\varphi}\,(c\text{-}I \text{ or absurdity rule}) \quad \Sigma_1 \ldots \Sigma_n}{\psi}\,(c\text{-}E)$$

to produce a reduct which we agreed to call $\nu(\Pi, \vec{\Sigma})$. This reduct is a proof of ψ from (at most) the combined premisses of $\Sigma_1, \ldots, \Sigma_n$ and Π. In a proof of the form just displayed, the indicated occurrence of φ is said to be *maximal*. It disappears when we apply the appropriate reduction procedure.

A φ-constellation within a proof tree is a locally maximal subtree of occurrences of φ (where we now use 'maximal' in its obvious sense). φ-constellations consisting of more than one occurrence of φ arise only through applications of $\vee$-*E* and dilemma with conclusions of the form φ. We shall say that a φ-constellation is maximal within a proof if its bottommost occurrence of φ stands as the major premiss of an application of an elimination rule while at least one of its topmost occurrences of φ stands as the conclusion of an application of the corresponding introduction rule or of the absurdity rule. Such topmost occurrences of φ we shall call *unwanted*. We shall use the notation

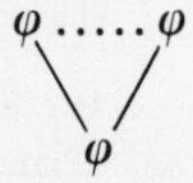

for φ-constellations.

A maximal φ-constellation may of course consist of a single occurrence of φ, which will obviously be unwanted. It can be made to disappear by an application of the appropriate reduction procedure.

This indeed is a special case of the following more general reduction procedure that applies to any maximal φ-constellation.

The general reduction procedure is applied within a proof to a fragment of the form

$$\begin{array}{ccc} \Pi_1 & & \Pi_m \\ \varphi & \cdots\cdots & \varphi \end{array}$$

$$\dfrac{\varphi \quad \Sigma_1 \ldots \Sigma_n}{\psi}(E)$$

in which the indicated φ-constellation is maximal. The procedure is in four stages.

(1) Take in turn each unwanted occurrence of φ standing as the conclusion of some Π_i. Replace $\begin{array}{c}\Pi_i\\ \varphi\end{array}$ by $\begin{array}{c}\iota(\Pi_i,\vec{\Sigma})\\ \varphi\end{array}$.

(2) Take in turn every other topmost occurrence of φ standing as the conclusion of some Π_j. Replace $\begin{array}{c}\Pi_j\\ \varphi\end{array}$ by

$$\begin{array}{l}\Pi_j\\ \dfrac{\varphi \quad \Sigma_1 \ldots \Sigma_n}{\psi}\end{array}$$

(3) Replace all remaining occurrences of φ in the constellation by occurrences of ψ. Note that all applications of $\vee$-E and dilemma within the whole proof remain correct.

(4) Take as result the fragment terminating with the occurrence of ψ which replaced the bottommost occurrence of φ in the old constellation.

The height of a φ-constellation within a proof is determined as the length of the branch running from the conclusion of the proof to the bottommost occurrence of φ in the constellation. The *degree* of a φ-constellation is that of φ, that is the number of occurrences of connectives in φ. The *degree* of a *proof* is the maximum degree of its maximal constellations. The *index* of a proof is the number of maximal constellations of maximum degree within the proof. The *order* of a proof is the ordered pair (degree, index). Orders can be well-ordered in the obvious way.

For the purposes of normalizing proofs, the order of a proof is a well-founded measure of its abnormality. How abnormal a proof is will be determined firstly by its degree (the maximum degree of its maximal constellations) and secondly by how many maximal constellations of maximum degree there are.

Application of our general reduction procedure to any maximal constellation of maximum degree *occurring no lower than any such other* within a proof obviously reduces the order of a proof. This is because no proof tree can contain a fragment of the form

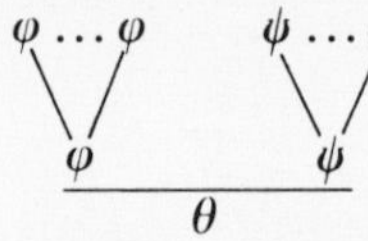

with φ and ψ distinct but of the same degree. Thus, by well-ordering of orders, only finitely many reductions are needed before no further reductions can be applied. The resulting proof is said to be in *normal form*. We have therefore established the following result.

Normalization Theorem. Any proof of φ from Δ can be effectively transformed into one in normal form. The latter is a proof of φ from a subset of Δ. If it is classical, then applications of dilemma discharge only atomic sentences.

5.5 Classical completeness via disjunctive normal forms. Suppose the sentence φ involves just the atoms $A_1, \ldots, A_n$. Suppose we do not know how φ has been built up from those atoms, but are told only what truth value φ has under each of the 2^n possible assignments of truth values to $A_1, \ldots, A_n$. Then we can find a sentence ψ involving just those atoms that is logically equivalent to φ. We do so as follows. First look at each row in the truth table for φ in which φ has value T. For each A_i write down A_i if A_i has value T in that row, but write down $\sim A_i$ if A_i has value F. Form the n-fold conjunction of what you have written down: that is, form the conjunction of all the members of the truth set of the assignment given by that row. When you have obtained in this way a conjunction for each row in which φ has value T, form the disjunction of those conjunctions. This disjunction is easily seen to have the same truth value as φ in every row of the truth table.

A more concise description of the procedure is as follows. For each assignment τ under which φ is true, form the conjunction of all the members of τ_φ. Then form the disjunction of those conjunctions. The result is logically equivalent to φ. If φ has value F in every row, simply take $A_1 \& \sim A_1$ as the disjunctive normal form.

Example. Suppose φ involves just the atoms A, B, and C and has the following truth table. We find ψ as indicated:

$$
\left.\begin{array}{llllll}
A & B & C & \varphi & & \\
T & T & T & F & & \\
T & T & F & T & \rightarrow \{A,B,{\sim}C\} & \rightarrow (A \,\&\, B \,\&\, {\sim}C) \\
T & F & T & T & \rightarrow \{A,{\sim}B,C\} & \rightarrow (A \,\&\, {\sim}B \,\&\, C) \\
T & F & F & F & & \\
F & T & T & T & \rightarrow \{{\sim}A,B,C\} & \rightarrow ({\sim}A \,\&\, B \,\&\, C) \\
F & T & F & F & & \\
F & F & T & F & & \\
F & F & F & T & \rightarrow \{{\sim}A,{\sim}B,{\sim}C\} & \rightarrow ({\sim}A \,\&\, {\sim}B \,\&\, {\sim}C)
\end{array}\right\}
\begin{array}{l}
(A \,\&\, B \,\&\, {\sim}C)\vee \\
\quad (A \,\&\, {\sim}B \,\&\, C)\vee \\
\quad ({\sim}A \,\&\, B \,\&\, C)\vee \\
\quad ({\sim}A \,\&\, {\sim}B \,\&\, {\sim}C)
\end{array}
$$

What we have established is the semantical equivalence of any sentence with some sentence having the form of a disjunction of conjunctions of atoms and negations of atoms. Sentences of this form are said to be in *disjunctive normal form.* What we wish now to establish, without appealing to completeness, is that any sentence is *classically interdeducible* with some sentence in disjunctive normal form.

First let us define precisely what it is for a sentence to be in disjunctive normal form.

(i) Any atom is a basic conjunction.
(ii) The negation of any atom is a basic conjunction.
(iii) If φ and ψ are basic conjunctions then so is $(\varphi \,\&\, \psi)$.
(iv) Any basic conjunction is a dnf.
(v) If φ and ψ are dnf's then so is $(\varphi \vee \psi)$.
(vi) Nothing is a basic conjunction or dnf unless its being so follows from (i)–(v).

A basic conjunction φ is maximal in a dnf ψ iff: φ is a subformula of ψ, but not of any other basic conjunction that is a subformula of ψ.

DNF Lemma 1. If φ and ψ are dnf's then $(\varphi \,\&\, \psi)$ is interdeducible with some dnf.

Proof. By induction on the combined degree of φ and ψ.

Basis. If φ and ψ are atoms then $(\varphi \,\&\, \psi)$ is a dnf by (i), (iii) and (iv).

Inductive step. If φ and ψ are basic conjunctions then $(\varphi \,\&\, \psi)$ is a dnf by (iii) and (iv). If φ is not a basic conjunction then it is of the form $\chi \vee \eta$ where χ and η are dnf's. Now $(\chi \vee \eta) \,\&\, \psi \dashv\vdash (\chi \,\&\, \psi) \vee (\eta \,\&\, \psi)$ ...(1). By IH $(\chi \,\&\, \psi)$ is interdeducible with some dnf, and $(\eta \,\&\, \psi)$ is interdeducible with some dnf. Thus $(\chi \,\&\, \psi) \vee (\eta \,\&\, \psi)$ is interdeducible with a disjunction of dnf's, which by (v) is a dnf. Thus by (1) $(\chi \vee \eta) \,\&\, \psi$ is interdeducible with some dnf. The reasoning is similar if ψ is not a basic conjunction.

DNF Lemma 2. If φ is a dnf then ${\sim}\varphi$ is interdeducible with some dnf.

Proof. By induction on φ. Note that

$\sim\sim A \dashv\vdash A$ . . . (1)

$\sim(\psi \vee \theta) \dashv\vdash \sim\psi \,\&\, \sim\theta$ . . . (2)

$\sim(\psi \,\&\, \theta) \dashv\vdash \sim\psi \vee \sim\theta$ . . . (3)

Basis. If φ is an atom then φ is a dnf by (ii) and (iv).
Inductive step. φ is of one of the three forms $\sim\psi$, $\psi \vee \theta$, $\psi \,\&\, \theta$. Suppose φ is $\sim\psi$. The only way for $\sim\psi$ to be a dnf is for ψ to be an atom. Then by (1), (i) and (iv) $\sim\varphi$ is interdeducible with a dnf. Suppose φ is $\psi \vee \theta$. The only way for $\psi \vee \theta$ to be a dnf is for both ψ and θ to be dnf's. By IH both $\sim\psi$ and $\sim\theta$ are interdeducible with dnf's. So $\sim\psi \,\&\, \sim\theta$ is interdeducible with a conjunction of dnf's, which by DNF Lemma 1 is interdeducible with a dnf. By (2) $\sim\varphi$ is interdeducible with a dnf. Suppose finally that φ is $\psi \,\&\, \theta$. The only way for $\psi \,\&\, \theta$ to be a dnf is for both ψ and θ to be basic conjunctions, hence dnf's. By IH both $\sim\psi$ and $\sim\theta$ are interdeducible with dnf's. So $\sim\psi \vee \sim\theta$ is interdeducible with a disjunction of dnf's, which is a dnf. So by (3) $\sim(\psi \,\&\, \theta)$ is interdeducible with a dnf.
DNF Lemma 3. If φ and ψ are dnf's then $\varphi \supset \psi$ is interdeducible with some dnf.
Proof. Since $\varphi \supset \psi \dashv\vdash \sim(\varphi \,\&\, \sim\psi)$, the result follows from the last two lemmata by intersubstitutivity of interdeducibles (cf. 4.13).
DNF Theorem. Any sentence is interdeducible with some dnf.
Proof. By induction, using intersubstitutivity, (v) and the last three lemmata.
Theorem-Completeness Theorem. If $\models \varphi$ then $\vdash \varphi$.
Proof. Suppose φ is true under every assignment. Let ψ be a dnf interdeducible with $\sim\varphi$ by the last theorem. For every assignment τ $\tau(\psi) = F$, whence every maximal basic conjunction in ψ is false under τ. Thus every maximal basic conjunction in ψ must have as conjuncts some atom and its negation; hence by &-eliminations and $\sim$-elimination, provably implies ※. Since ※ is thus deducible from every maximal basic conjunction in ψ it is, by $\vee$-eliminations, deducible from ψ. Thus $\sim\varphi \vdash$ ※. By classical reductio $\vdash \varphi$.

We are now in a position to prove once again the strong completeness result.
Completeness Theorem (*Strong Version*). If $\Delta \models \varphi$ then $\Delta \vdash \varphi$.
Proof. Suppose $\Delta \models \varphi$. Then by compactness φ is a logical consequence of finitely many members $\psi_1, \ldots, \psi_n$, say, of Δ. Thus $\models \psi_1 \supset (\psi_2 \supset (\ldots \supset \varphi) \ldots)$. By the previous theorem $\vdash \psi_1 \supset (\psi_2 \supset (\ldots \supset \varphi) \ldots))$. So by n steps of $\supset$-*E* $\psi_1, \ldots, \psi_n \vdash \varphi$.

We have now proved completeness by two different methods, respectively considering truth sets and disjunctive normal forms. Both methods of proof are constructive in that they implicitly provide methods of finding propositional proofs of valid arguments with finitely many premisses. These methods are implicit in the inductions involved in establishing the results above.

5.6 A direct proof of classical completeness. If, however, the reader were to try for himself to find a proof of a valid argument from finitely many premisses by following either of these methods he would follow a lengthy and roundabout route to a proof that is likely to be highly 'non-normal'. It is therefore worth providing here another constructive completeness proof, establishing directly that

For finite Δ, if $\Delta \vDash \varphi$ then $\Delta \vdash \varphi$

and encoding a method for finding proofs that parallels as closely as possible the sensible method that a competent user of the proof system is likely to employ in his search for a proof. This is the method of 'breaking down' the premisses and conclusion and accordingly 'breaking down' the problem of finding a proof into further subproblems of finding appropriate subproofs. For economy and novelty we confine our third constructive completeness proof to the system based on Sheffer's stroke.

First we define the *degree* of a sentence as follows.

(i) $d(A) = d(\divideontimes) = 0$
(ii) $d(\varphi|\varphi) = 1 + d(\varphi)$
(iii) $d(\varphi|\psi) = 2 + \max(d(\varphi), d(\psi))$, if φ is not the same sentence as ψ.

Let Δ be a finite set of sentences which does not contain $\divideontimes$. Then $\delta\Delta$ is 0 if Δ is empty, and is $\max\{d(\varphi)|\varphi\in\Delta\}$ otherwise. $\mu\Delta$ is the number of sentences of maximum degree in Δ. Let $+$ be a mapping that assigns to Δ a sentence of maximum degree in Δ that is of the form $\varphi|\varphi$ only if all sentences of maximum degree in Δ are of that form. Let Δ^- be $\Delta\backslash\{+\Delta\}$. Note that $\delta\Delta^- \leq \delta\Delta$. Now define a well-founded relation $\prec$ between finite arguments as follows: $\Gamma/\psi \prec \Delta/\varphi$ if and only if either (i) $\delta(\Gamma,\psi) < \delta(\Delta,\varphi)$, or (ii) $\delta(\Gamma,\psi) = \delta(\Delta,\varphi)$ and $d(\psi) < d(\varphi)$, or (iii) $\delta(\Gamma,\psi) = \delta(\Delta,\varphi)$ and $d(\psi) = d(\varphi)$ and $\mu\Gamma < \mu\Delta$.

For the purposes of our inductive proof which follows we may read '$\Gamma/\psi \prec \Delta/\varphi$' as '$\Gamma/\psi$ is a less complex argument than Δ/φ'. Our definition establishes that complexity is determined, in order of importance, by (i) overall maximum degree of sentences involved, (ii) degree of the conclusion, and (iii) number of premisses of maximum degree. Note that the least complex arguments are of the form $\emptyset/A$, with A atomic. The following Lemma shows how to break an argument down to less complex arguments.

Complexity Lemma

$$\left.\begin{array}{ll}\text{(I)} & \text{If } \varphi=\psi|\theta \text{ then } (\Delta,\psi,\theta)/\divideontimes \\ \text{(II)} & \text{If } +\Delta=\psi|\theta,\ \psi\neq\theta, \text{ then } \begin{cases}(\Delta^-,\psi|\psi)/\varphi\\(\Delta^-,\theta|\theta)/\varphi\end{cases} \\ \text{(III)} & \text{If } +\Delta=(\psi|\theta)|(\psi|\theta) \text{ then } (\Delta^-,\psi,\theta)/\varphi\end{array}\right\} \prec \Delta/\varphi$$

Proof. (I) by (i) if $\delta\Delta < d\varphi$
by (ii) if $\delta\Delta \geqslant d\varphi$
(II) and (III) by (iii) if $\delta\Delta \leqslant d\varphi$
by (i) if $\delta\Delta > d\varphi$ and $\delta\Delta^- < \delta\Delta$
by (iii) if $\delta\Delta > d\varphi$ and $\delta\Delta^- = \delta\Delta$

We are now in a position to prove another version of weak completeness.

Theorem. For finite Δ, if $\Delta \vDash \varphi$ then $\Delta \vdash \varphi$.

Proof. By induction on the well-founded relation defined above.

Basis. Obvious, since every atomic sentence can be falsified.

Inductive step. We consider Δ/φ according to the following cases:

(i) $\varphi=\psi|\theta$
(ii) $+\Delta=\psi|\theta, \psi\neq\theta$
(iii) $+\Delta=(\psi|\theta)|(\psi|\theta)$
(iv) Δ non-empty with every member of the form A or $A|A$ (A atomic) and $d\varphi=0$.

These cases are not mutually exclusive, but they are exhaustive, which is all we need for proof by cases.

Suppose $\Delta \vDash \varphi$. We show in cases (i)–(iv) that $\Delta \vdash \varphi$, given the inductive hypothesis that this result holds for less complex arguments.

Case (i). By the truth table $\Delta,\psi,\theta \vDash \divideontimes$. By Complexity Lemma (I) and IH $\Delta,\psi,\theta \vdash \divideontimes$. By $|$-I $\Delta \vdash \psi|\theta$.

Case (ii). By the truth table $\Delta^-,\psi|\psi \vDash \varphi$ and $\Delta^-,\theta|\theta \vDash \varphi$. By Complexity Lemma (II) and IH $\Delta^-,\psi|\psi \vdash \varphi$ and $\Delta^-,\theta|\theta \vdash \varphi$. By the proof schema

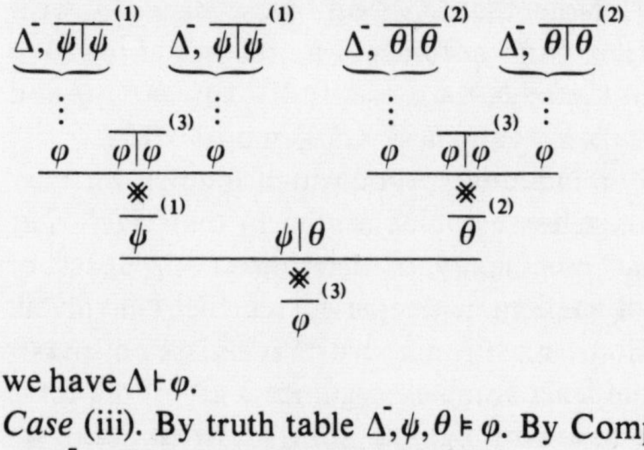

we have $\Delta \vdash \varphi$.

Case (iii). By truth table $\Delta^-,\psi,\theta \vDash \varphi$. By Complexity Lemma (III) and IH $\Delta^-,\psi,\theta \vdash \varphi$. By the proof schema

$$\dfrac{\dfrac{\dfrac{\begin{matrix}\underbrace{\Delta, \overline{\psi}^{(1)}, \overline{\theta}^{(1)}} \\ \vdots \\ \varphi\end{matrix} \quad \overline{\varphi|\varphi}^{(3)} \quad \begin{matrix}\underbrace{\Delta, \overline{\psi}^{(1)}, \overline{\theta}^{(1)}} \\ \vdots \\ \varphi\end{matrix}}{\text{※}}}{\psi|\theta}{\scriptstyle (1)} \quad (\psi|\theta)|(\psi|\theta) \quad \dfrac{\dfrac{\begin{matrix}\underbrace{\Delta, \overline{\psi}^{(2)}, \overline{\theta}^{(2)}} \\ \vdots \\ \varphi\end{matrix} \quad \overline{\varphi|\varphi}^{(3)} \quad \begin{matrix}\underbrace{\Delta, \overline{\psi}^{(2)}, \overline{\theta}^{(2)}} \\ \vdots \\ \varphi\end{matrix}}{\text{※}}}{\psi|\theta}{\scriptstyle (2)}}{\dfrac{\text{※}}{\varphi}{\scriptstyle (3)}}$$

we have $\Delta \vdash \varphi$.

Case (iv). Either $\varphi \in \Delta$ or for some atomic B $B \in \Delta$ and $B|B \in \Delta$. If $\varphi \in \Delta$ then obviously $\Delta \vdash \varphi$. If $B, B|B \in \Delta$ then, according as φ is ※ or not, by the proofs

$$\dfrac{B \quad B|B \quad B}{\text{※}} \qquad \dfrac{\dfrac{B \quad B|B \quad B}{\text{※}}}{\varphi}$$

we have $\Delta \vdash \varphi$.

5.7 Classical completeness via Henkin's method. Our three constructive proofs of completeness of classical logic establish only *weak* completeness:

for finite Δ, if $\Delta \vDash \varphi$ then $\Delta \vdash \varphi$.

We have an independent proof of the compactness theorem:

if $\Delta \vDash \varphi$ then for some finite $\Gamma \subseteq \Delta$, $\Gamma \vDash \varphi$.

Combining these two results we obtain strong completeness:

for all Δ if $\Delta \vDash \varphi$ then $\Delta \vdash \varphi$.

There is, however, a method of proving compactness and strong completeness simultaneously, due to Henkin. Henkin's method does not intrinsically codify a way of finding a proof of φ from finite Δ given that φ is a logical consequence of Δ. By contrast the constructive methods do more. They enable us to decide in general *whether* φ is a logical consequence of Δ, and, if so, to provide a proof. The disadvantage of the 'non-constructiveness' of Henkin's method is, however, outweighed by its elegance and the fact that it can be used to prove completeness of first order logic (for which constructive proofs of completeness are impossible). It is therefore worth illustrating Henkin's method in the simpler setting of propositional logic.

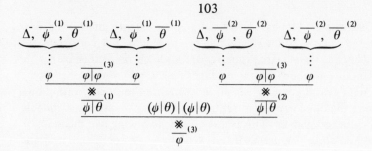

By a *maximal consistent set* of sentences I shall mean a set Δ with the following properties: (1) $\Delta \nvdash_I ※$ (Δ is consistent), and (2) for all φ either $\varphi \in \Delta$ or $(\sim\varphi) \in \Delta$ (Δ is maximal). A maximal consistent set obviously has the closure property (3) for all φ if $\Delta \vdash_I \varphi$ then $\varphi \in \Delta$.

'Henkin's method' has two stages. First one shows that every consistent set can be consistently maximalized. Secondly one shows that any maximal consistent set is satisfiable by a naturally definable truth value assignment. This is done by the following two theorems.

Maximalization Theorem. If $\Delta \nvdash_I ※$ then Δ is contained in some maximal consistent set.

Satisfiability Theorem. Every maximal consistent set is satisfiable.

Completeness follows immediately from these two theorems. For, if $\Delta \vDash \varphi$ then $(\Delta, \sim\varphi)$ is not satisfiable. Hence $\Delta, \sim\varphi \vdash_I ※$. Thus by classical reductio $\Delta \vdash_C \varphi$. Compactness of $\vDash$ follows from the obvious compactness of $\vdash_C$.

Proof of Maximalization Theorem. Suppose $\Delta \nvdash ※$. (Throughout this proof and the next $\vdash$ will mean $\vdash_I$.) Let $\varphi_0, \varphi_1, \varphi_2, \ldots$ be a list of all sentences. Inductively define a sequence $\Delta_0, \Delta_1, \Delta_2, \ldots$ of sets of sentences as follows.

$$\begin{aligned} \Delta_0 &= \Delta \\ \Delta_{n+1} &= \Delta_n, \varphi_n \text{ if } \Delta_n, \varphi_n \nvdash ※; \\ &\quad \Delta_n \text{ if } \Delta_n, \varphi_n \vdash ※ \end{aligned}$$

Obviously if Δ_n is consistent then so is Δ_{n+1}. Moreover Δ_0 is consistent. Thus by induction for all i Δ_i is consistent ... (0). Now let $\bar{\Delta}$ be $\cup_i \Delta_i$. Obviously Δ is contained in $\bar{\Delta}$. First we show that $\bar{\Delta}$ is consistent:

For, suppose $\bar{\Delta} \vdash ※$. Then there is a proof of ※ from finitely many premisses in $\bar{\Delta}$. Some Δ_k contains all these and is therefore inconsistent, contrary to (0) above. Thus $\bar{\Delta} \nvdash ※$.

Secondly we show that $\bar{\Delta}$ is maximal:

For, suppose neither φ nor $\sim\varphi$ is in $\bar{\Delta}$. Let φ occur in our list as φ_i and let $\sim\varphi$ occur as φ_j. Since φ_i is not in $\bar{\Delta}$ it is not in Δ_{i+1}, which therefore cannot be Δ_i, φ_i, whence the latter is inconsistent. Similarly Δ_j, φ_j is inconsistent. Let $m = \max(i,j)$. We have $\Delta_m, \varphi \vdash ※$ and $\Delta_m, \sim\varphi \vdash ※$. By the proof schema

$$
\begin{array}{c}
\underbrace{\Delta_m,\ \overline{\varphi}^{\,(1)}} \\
\vdots \\
\underline{\quad ※ \quad}{}^{(1)} \\
\underbrace{\Delta_m,\ \sim\varphi} \\
\vdots \\
※
\end{array}
$$

we have $\Delta_m \vdash ※$, contrary to (0). Thus for all φ either $\varphi \in \bar{\Delta}$ or $\sim\varphi \in \bar{\Delta}$.

Proof of Satisfiability Theorem. Let Δ be a maximal consistent set of sentences. Define a natural truth value assignment τ by the condition that $\tau(A) = T$ if and only if $A \in \Delta$. This accomplishes the basis of an inductive proof that $\tau(\varphi) = T$ if and only if $\varphi \in \Delta$. In the inductive step we consider φ by cases.

Case (i): $\varphi = \sim\psi$. Suppose $\tau(\sim\psi) = T$. Then $\tau(\psi) = F$. By IH $\psi \notin \Delta$. By maximality $(\sim\psi) \in \Delta$. Conversely suppose $(\sim\psi) \in \Delta$. By consistency $\psi \notin \Delta$. By IH $\tau(\psi) = F$. Thus $\tau(\sim\psi) = T$.

Case (ii): $\varphi = \psi \,\&\, \theta$. Suppose $\tau(\psi \,\&\, \theta) = T$. Then $\tau(\psi) = T$ and $\tau(\theta) = T$. By IH $\psi \in \Delta$ and $\theta \in \Delta$. By &-*I* $\Delta \vdash \psi \,\&\, \theta$. By closure $\psi \,\&\, \theta \in \Delta$. Conversely, suppose $\psi \,\&\, \theta \in \Delta$. By &-*E* $\Delta \vdash \psi$ and $\Delta \vdash \theta$. By closure $\psi \in \Delta$ and $\theta \in \Delta$. By IH $\tau(\psi) = T$ and $\tau(\theta) = T$. Thus $\tau(\psi \,\&\, \theta) = T$.

Case (iii): $\varphi = \psi \vee \theta$. Suppose $\tau(\psi \vee \theta) = T$. Then $\tau(\psi) = T$ or $\tau(\theta) = T$. Suppose $\tau(\psi) = T$. By IH $\psi \in \Delta$. By $\vee$-*I* $\Delta \vdash \psi \vee \theta$. By closure $\psi \vee \theta \in \Delta$. Similarly if $\tau(\theta) = T$ then $\psi \vee \theta \in \Delta$. Conversely, suppose $\psi \vee \theta \in \Delta$. If $(\sim\psi) \in \Delta$ and $(\sim\theta) \in \Delta$ then by $\sim$-*E* and $\vee$-*E* we have $\Delta \vdash ※$, contrary to assumption. So either $(\sim\psi) \notin \Delta$ or $(\sim\theta) \notin \Delta$. By maximality either $\psi \in \Delta$ or $\theta \in \Delta$. By IH either $\tau(\psi) = T$ or $\tau(\theta) = T$. Thus $\tau(\psi \vee \theta) = T$.

Case (iv): $\varphi = \psi \supset \theta$. Suppose $\tau(\psi \supset \theta) = T$. Then either $\tau(\psi) = F$ or $\tau(\theta) = T$. Suppose $\tau(\psi) = F$. By IH $\psi \notin \Delta$. By maximality $(\sim\psi) \in \Delta$. By the proof

$$
\dfrac{\dfrac{\dfrac{{}^{(1)}\overline{\psi} \quad \sim\psi}{※}}{\theta}}{\psi \supset \theta}\,{}^{(1)}
$$

we have $\Delta \vdash \psi \supset \theta$. By closure $\psi \supset \theta \in \Delta$.

Now suppose $\tau(\theta) = T$. By IH $\theta \in \Delta$. By $\supset$-*I* $\Delta \vdash \psi \supset \theta$. By closure $\psi \supset \theta \in \Delta$. Conversely, suppose $\psi \supset \theta \in \Delta$. If $\psi \in \Delta$ and $(\sim\theta) \in \Delta$ then by the proof

$$\dfrac{\dfrac{\psi \quad \psi \supset \theta}{\theta} \quad \sim\theta}{\text{※}}$$

we have $\Delta \vdash$ ※, contrary to assumption. So either $\psi \notin \Delta$ or $(\sim\theta) \notin \Delta$. If $\psi \notin \Delta$ then by IH $\tau(\psi) = F$ whence $\tau(\psi \supset \theta) = T$. If $(\sim\theta) \notin \Delta$ then by maximality $\theta \in \Delta$, whence by IH $\tau(\theta) = T$ and so $\tau(\psi \supset \theta) = T$.

We have a new proof of the Inconsistency Theorem as a corollary to the Maximalization and Satisfiability Theorems. Suppose $\Delta \nvdash_C$ ※. By soundness Δ is not satisfiable. Hence Δ is not contained in any maximal consistent set. Hence $\Delta \nvdash_I$ ※.

$\sim\sim\varphi$ is called the *double negation* of φ. Let $\sim\sim\Delta$ be the set of double negations of members of Δ.

Double Negation Theorem. If $\Delta \vdash_C \varphi$ then $\sim\sim\Delta \vdash_I \sim\sim\varphi$.

Proof. Suppose $\Delta \vdash_C \varphi$. Then $\sim\sim\Delta \vdash_C \varphi$. Thus $\sim\sim\Delta, \sim\varphi \vdash_C$ ※. By the Inconsistency Theorem $\sim\sim\Delta, \sim\varphi \vdash_I$ ※. Hence $\sim\sim\Delta \vdash_I \sim\sim\varphi$.

5.8 Kripke semantics for intuitionistic logic. Formally, the semantics for classical propositional logic is an algebra of truth functions over the set of two truth values T and F. It arises naturally from the philosophical assumption that every sentence is either true or false in any situation in which it is interpreted. Chapter 3 contained an exposition of classical first order semantics. We have yet to indicate how classical semantics differs from intuitionistic semantics. Indeed, whether there is any such thing as a satisfactory intuitionistic 'semantics' or whether, intuitionistically, there is any need for such a thing, is a question that raises considerable difficulties.

There are two senses of 'semantics' that it may be useful to distinguish. To each corresponds a different purpose in the project of providing a semantics for a language (endowed, perhaps, with a deductive system).

The first, which I shall call the *philosophical* sense, is the sense in which the semantics yields an explication of the truth conditions (for a particular conception of truth) of sentences of the language. A fundamental feature of such a semantics will be an account of the structure of reality, the form of world, of which the language may intelligibly speak. In the absence of such an account we need an argument justifying its omission, and an alternative account of what it is that makes language intelligible. Philosophical semantics would be integrated into general theories of meaning and ontology.

The second sense of 'semantics' I shall call the *algebraic* sense. In algebraic semantics we are concerned to define a suitable class of algebras, and a relation ρ between them and sentences of the language, so that we may define a conclusion to be a logical consequence of certain premisses if and only if every algebra bearing the relation ρ to all the premisses bears the relation ρ to the conclusion. We then try to establish soundness and completeness theorems showing that this consequence relation coincides exactly with some independently defined deducibility relation. Thus if we can find an algebra bearing relation ρ to all the premisses in Δ but not to the conclusion φ we know that φ cannot be deduced from Δ (soundness); and if φ cannot be deduced from Δ we do not have to survey all possible proofs to establish this, but can instead find some counterexemplary algebra as above (completeness). Initially, therefore, algebraic semantics provides no more nor less than necessary and sufficient conditions for deducibility.

It would, however, be a further mark in favour of a particular algebraic semantics if it incorporated in some recognizable and natural way the essential features of the preferred philosophical semantics. This would both help us understand why the completeness theorem held for the algebraic semantics, and would sharpen our intuitions in searches for counterexemplary algebras to invalid arguments. Moreover, it would serve to highlight any source of difficulty, obscurity or complexity in the philosophical semantics itself.

In classical semantics as set forth in Chapter 3 we have a paradigm of this algebraic encapsulation of the results of philosophical analysis. Whether the same can be said for extant intuitionistic semantics of the algebraic kind is less certain. In this section I shall set forth the best known of these, due to Kripke, and shall prove some results that may be of help in assessing how well it models intuitionistic truth conditions (or, as some may say, assertability conditions). The reader is reminded that we are dealing with the propositional case only.

A sentence φ is intuitionistically true, or assertable, just in case one has, or possesses an effective means for finding, a *canonical proof* of φ from present *atomic knowns*. An *atomic known* is either an atomic axiom (an atomic sentence assertable outright) such as $t=t$, or a rule of inference involving only atomic sentences, such as $\dfrac{t+1=u+1}{t=u}$ or $\dfrac{0=1}{\divideontimes}$. A *proof* of φ is an argument that can be effectively transformed into a *canonical proof* of φ; where a *canonical proof* of

(i) an atomic sentence is one built up from the atomic knowns

(ii) $\sim\psi$ consists in a method that, applied to any proof of ψ, would yield a proof of absurdity

(iii) $\psi \,\&\, \theta$ consists in a proof of ψ and a proof of θ

(iv) $\varphi \vee \theta$ consists in a proof of ψ or a proof of θ

(v) $\psi \supset \theta$ consists in a method that, applied to any proof of ψ, would yield a proof of θ.

Let us denote by i my present position in respect of atomic knowns. Let us use the expression '$i \Vdash \varphi$' ('i forces φ') to mean that in my present position I could assert φ if I were clever enough. That is, φ is assertable by virtue of a proof of φ from the present atomic knowns even though I might not have such a proof at present nor (what is essentially the same thing) knowingly possess an effective means for finding one. I shall denote by $[i]$ the set of all sentences forced at i.

Suppose my present position i might evolve into the future position j. This could involve 'intuiting' new atomic axioms or rules. We shall write '$j \geqslant i$' or '$i \leqslant j$' to express this. Since what is proven or provable is so for eternity, we ought to have $[i] \subseteq [j]$; and it will be proved below that we do.

Suppose that for all possible $j \geqslant i, j \nVdash \varphi$. A fundamental assumption underlying Kripke modelling is that this can be so only because φ is *presently* absurd, i.e. $i \Vdash \sim\varphi$. Likewise suppose that for all possible $j \geqslant i$, if $j \Vdash \psi$ then $j \Vdash \theta$. Another assumption is that this can be so only because θ is *presently* provable from ψ, i.e. $i \Vdash \psi \supset \theta$.

We are now in a position to consider Kripke's formalization of these intuitions about assertability or provability. An *index set I* contains all possible 'positions'. These positions, or *indices*, are partially ordered by a relation $\geqslant$ which, intuitively, is that of possible temporal succession. To each index $i \in I$ is assigned a set $\underline{i}$ of atomic sentences. These are all the atomic sentences forced at i. There is no distinction made within $\underline{i}$ between 'directly' known atomic axioms and those atomic sentences that are provable from atomic axioms by means of atomic rules, but that have not yet actually been so proved. This is one point at which the algebraic modelling does not incorporate a distinction that may be philosophically relevant or useful. Nor do we make any separate mention, in our characterization of i, of the atomic rules that are known to hold (or have been directly intuited) at i, as opposed to those atomic rules that are derivable, but not yet derived, therefrom. Indeed, what rules hold at i (either by being directly intuited or indirectly derivable) would only be gleaned from global consideration of I, $\geqslant$, and $\underline{j}$ for each $j \in I$.

We now have the ingredients for a Kripke model K. It consists of a set I with a partial ordering $\geqslant$ of its members. Each member is called an *index*. In addition there is a mapping _ which assigns to each $i \in I$ a set $\underline{i}$ of atomic sentences. This mapping satisfies the two conditions (1) for no $i \in I$ do we have $\divideontimes \in \underline{i}$, and (2) for all $i, j \in I$ if $j \geqslant i$ then $\underline{i} \subseteq \underline{j}$.

Blending these ingredients we write $K=(\{\underline{i}|i\in I\},\geqslant)$. We shall define $\sim\varphi$ as $\varphi\supset\divideontimes$ so that $\vee$, & and $\supset$ are our primitive connectives. Given $i\in I$ we now define what it is for i to force φ within K:

(1) $i \Vdash A$ iff $A\in\underline{i}$ (for A atomic)
(2) $i\Vdash\psi\vee\theta$ iff either $i\Vdash\psi$ or $i\Vdash\theta$
(3) $i\Vdash\psi\&\theta$ iff $i\Vdash\psi$ and $i\Vdash\theta$
(4) $i\Vdash\psi\supset\theta$ iff for all $j\geqslant i$, if $j\Vdash\psi$ then $j\Vdash\theta$
$[i]=_{df}\{\varphi|i\Vdash\varphi\}$

Subsequently the model K determining $\Vdash$ and [ ] must be understood from the context.

Given a set Δ we define $\underline{\Delta}$, the atomic closure of Δ, to be the set of all atomic sentences intuitionistically deducible from Δ. Henceforth $\vdash$ represents intuitionistic deducibility.

A set Δ is *intuitionistic* if and only if it satisfies the following three conditions:

(1) $\Delta\nvdash\divideontimes$ (Δ is consistent)
(2) for all φ, if $\Delta\vdash\varphi$ then $\varphi\in\Delta$ (Δ is closed)
(3) for all ψ, θ if $(\psi\vee\theta)\in\Delta$ then either $\psi\in\Delta$ or $\theta\in\Delta$ (Δ is disjunctive)

Note that atomic axioms are simply atomic rules with no premisses. If R is a collection of finitary atomic rules we shall let $\mathscr{P}_R$ and $\vdash_R$ be the notions of proof and deducibility that result from augmenting the stock of intuitionistic rules of inference by R. R-intuitionistic sets are defined as above with $\vdash_R$ in place of $\vdash$. There are corresponding obvious definitions of R-consistency, R-closure, etc.

Let I_R be the set of all R-intuitionistic sets. Define $\leqslant$ to be the subset relation, which is obviously a partial ordering. Note that if $\Delta\leqslant\Gamma$ then $\underline{\Delta}\subseteq\underline{\Gamma}$ but not conversely; for we can have two partially overlapping intuitionistic sets (differing with respect to the implications they contain) with a common atomic closure. Let $\natural_R$, the *natural model for* R, be the Kripke model $(\{\underline{\Delta}|\Delta\in I_R\},\geqslant)$. Here the mapping _ within the natural model simply assigns to each R-intuitionistic set (as index) its own atomic R-closure.

Within any Kripke model K let us define $\Delta\Vdash_i\varphi$ to mean that for all $j\geqslant i$, if $\Delta\subseteq[j]$ then $\varphi\in[j]$. Intuitively this means that from the index i onward within K as soon as all the members of Δ are forced, φ is forced also. We may read '$\Delta\Vdash_i\varphi$' as 'Δ forces φ by i'. We shall say that an atomic rule *holds* at i or that i *admits* the rule, if and only if its premisses force its conclusion by i. Note that if i admits a rule and $j\geqslant i$ then j admits that rule. It is obvious that any index in the natural model for R admits all the rules in R. The following statements are also clearly equivalent:

(i) for all K, for all i in K admitting R, if $\Delta \subseteq \lfloor i \rfloor$ then $\varphi \in \lfloor i \rfloor$

(ii) for all K, for all i in K admitting R, $\Delta \Vdash_i \varphi$

We shall use the common abbreviation $\Delta \vDash_R \varphi$, and say φ is an R-consequence of Δ. This is the semantical notion of consequence which we hope to match with R-deducibility by means of soundness and completeness results.

Eternity Lemma. In any Kripke model if $j \geqslant i$ then $\lfloor i \rfloor \subseteq \lfloor j \rfloor$ (intuitively, 'once forced, always forced').

Proof. By induction on φ, assuming $i \Vdash \varphi$.

Basis. If φ is atomic the result is immediate from the conditions on $\lfloor\_\rfloor$.

Inductive step. Consider φ by cases. Suppose $j \geqslant i$. For $\varphi = (\varphi \vee \theta)$ or $(\psi \,\&\, \theta)$ the result is immediate by IH and the definition of forcing. So suppose $\varphi = (\psi \supset \theta)$. Suppose $k \geqslant j$ and $k \Vdash \psi$. Then $k \geqslant i$ whence, since $i \Vdash \psi \supset \theta$, $k \Vdash \theta$. Thus $j \Vdash \psi \supset \theta$.

Soundness Theorem. If $\mathscr{P}_R(\Pi, \varphi, \Delta)$ then for any Kripke model K and any i in K admitting all the rules in R, $\Delta \Vdash_i \varphi$.

Proof. By induction on Π.

Basis. Obvious.

Inductive step. Suppose $\mathscr{P}_R(\Pi, \varphi, \Delta)$. Consider Π by cases according to the rule of inference last applied in Π. The reasoning in the case of the absurdity rule, &-*I*, &-*E*, $\vee$-*I*, and $\supset$-*E* is trivial. So we consider only the cases where the rule last applied in Π is (i) $\supset$-*I*, (ii) $\vee$-*E* or (iii) a rule in R.

(i) Π is

$$\begin{array}{c} (\psi) \\ \Gamma \\ \Sigma \\ \theta \\ \hline \psi \supset \theta \end{array} \qquad \text{where } \Delta = \Gamma \backslash \psi.$$

Suppose $\Delta \subseteq \lfloor j \rfloor, j \geqslant i$. We must show $j \Vdash \psi \supset \theta$. So suppose $k \geqslant j$ and $k \Vdash \psi$. Then $k \geqslant i$. By eternity lemma $\Delta \subseteq \lfloor k \rfloor$. Thus $\Gamma \subseteq \lfloor k \rfloor$. By IH applied to Σ, $k \Vdash \theta$. Thus $j \Vdash \psi \supset \theta$.

(ii) Π is

$$\begin{array}{ccc} & (\psi) & (\theta) \\ \Gamma & \Gamma_1 & \Gamma_2 \\ \Sigma & \Sigma_1 & \Sigma_2 \\ \psi \vee \theta & \chi & \chi \\ \hline & \chi & \end{array} \qquad \text{where } \Delta = \Gamma \cup (\Gamma_1 \backslash \psi) \cup (\Gamma_2 \backslash \theta).$$

Suppose $\Delta \subseteq \lfloor j \rfloor, j \geqslant i$. We must show $\chi \in \lfloor j \rfloor$. By IH applied to Σ, since $\Gamma \subseteq \lfloor j \rfloor$, $(\psi \vee \theta) \in \lfloor j \rfloor$. Hence $\psi \in \lfloor j \rfloor$ or $\theta \in \lfloor j \rfloor$. If $\psi \in \lfloor j \rfloor$ then $\Gamma_1 \subseteq \lfloor j \rfloor$ and by IH applied to Σ_1, $\chi \in \lfloor j \rfloor$. Similarly if $\theta \in \lfloor j \rfloor$ then $\chi \in \lfloor j \rfloor$.

(iii) Π is $\begin{array}{ccc} \Delta_1 & & \Delta_n \\ \Pi_1 & \ldots & \Pi_n \\ A_1 & & A_n \\ \hline & A & \end{array}$ where $\dfrac{A_1 \ldots A_n}{A}$ is a rule in R and $\Delta = \cup_i \Delta_i$.

Suppose $\Delta \subseteq \lfloor j \rfloor$ and $j \geqslant i$. By IH applied to each Π_i we have $A_i \in \lfloor j \rfloor$. Since i admits the rule we have $A \in \lfloor j \rfloor$.

Corollary 1. For any K, for any i in K admitting all the rules in R, if $[i] \vdash_R \varphi$ then $\varphi \in [i]$.

Corollary 2. For any K, for any i in K admitting all the rules in R, $\underline{i}$ is precisely the atomic R-closure of $[i]$. That is, one cannot deduce from the sentences forced at i any atomic sentence not forced at i.

In particular, since $\divideontimes \notin \underline{i}$ we have that $[i]$ is R-consistent. By Corollary 1 $[i]$ is R-closed. By definition of forcing, $[i]$ is disjunctive. Thus the set of sentences forced at any index admitting all the rules in R is an R-intuitionistic set.

Intuitionistic Maximalization Theorem. If $\Delta \nvdash_R \varphi$ then Δ is included in an R-intuitionistic set not containing φ.

Proof. By a Henkin construction. Let $\varphi_0, \varphi_1, \ldots$ be a list of all sentences. Let $\Delta_0 = \Delta$ and let

$$\Delta_{n+1} = \begin{cases} \Delta_n, \varphi_n & \text{if } \Delta_n, \varphi_n \nvdash_R \varphi \quad \ldots (1) \\ \Delta_n, \varphi_n \supset \varphi & \text{if } \Delta_n, \varphi_n \vdash_R \varphi \quad \ldots (2) \end{cases}$$

Finally let $\bar{\Delta} = \cup_i \Delta_i$. Obviously Δ is included in $\bar{\Delta}$. We now show $\bar{\Delta}$ is an R-intuitionistic set not containing φ.

First, suppose for reductio that we have $\bar{\Delta} \vdash_R \varphi$. Then φ is R-deducible from finitely many members of $\bar{\Delta}$.

So for some k, $\Delta_k \vdash_R \varphi$. Since $\Delta_0 \nvdash_R \varphi$, let Δ_{m+1} be the *first* member of the sequence $\Delta_0, \Delta_1, \ldots$ from which φ is R-deducible. Now suppose $\Delta_m, \varphi_m \nvdash_R \varphi$. Then $\Delta_{m+1} = \Delta_m, \varphi_m$ by (1) and so $\Delta_m, \varphi_m \vdash_R \varphi$. Thus $\Delta_m, \varphi_m \vdash_R \varphi$. By (2) $\Delta_{m+1} = \Delta_m, \varphi_m \supset \varphi$ and so $\Delta_m, \varphi_m \supset \varphi \vdash_R \varphi$. Also by $\supset$-I $\Delta_m \vdash_R \varphi_m \supset \varphi$. Hence $\Delta_m \vdash_R \varphi$, contrary to choice of m. Thus $\bar{\Delta} \nvdash_R \varphi$, whence $\varphi \notin \bar{\Delta}$ and $\bar{\Delta} \nvdash_R \divideontimes$. So we have shown that $\bar{\Delta}$ is R-consistent and does not contain φ.

We now show that $\bar{\Delta}$ is R-closed. Suppose $\bar{\Delta} \vdash_R \psi$. Let ψ appear as φ_k. Thus $(\varphi_k \supset \varphi) \notin \bar{\Delta}$. So by construction $\varphi_k \in \Delta_{k+1}$. Hence $\psi \in \bar{\Delta}$.

Finally we show that $\bar{\Delta}$ is disjunctive. Suppose $(\psi \vee \theta) \in \bar{\Delta}$. Then either $(\psi \supset \varphi) \notin \bar{\Delta}$ or $(\theta \supset \varphi) \notin \bar{\Delta}$; otherwise, by $\supset$-E and $\vee$-E we would have $\bar{\Delta} \vdash_R \varphi$. So by construction either $\psi \in \bar{\Delta}$ or $\theta \in \bar{\Delta}$.

Intuitionistic Satisfiability Theorem. For every index Δ in $\natural_R$ $\Delta = [\Delta]$.

Proof. We show $\Delta \Vdash \varphi$ iff $\varphi \in \Delta$ by induction on φ.

Basis. For $\varphi = \divideontimes$ the result holds trivially. For $\varphi = A$ the result holds since Δ is closed and so $\underline{\Delta} \subseteq \Delta$.

Inductive step. For the case where φ is $(\psi \vee \theta)$ or $(\psi \& \theta)$ the result is immediate by IH and the definitions of forcing and of R-intuitionistic set. Suppose finally that φ is $(\psi \supset \theta)$. Suppose $(\psi \supset \theta) \in \Delta$. Let $\Gamma \geqslant \Delta$. So $\Delta \subseteq \Gamma$ and $\underline{\Delta} \subseteq \underline{\Gamma}$. Suppose $\Gamma \Vdash \psi$. By IH $\psi \in \Gamma$. But $(\psi \supset \theta) \in \Gamma$ so $\theta \in \Gamma$. By IH $\Gamma \Vdash \theta$. So by definition of forcing, $\Delta \Vdash (\psi \supset \theta)$. Now suppose for the converse that $(\psi \supset \theta) \notin \Delta$. We show $\Delta \not\Vdash \psi \supset \theta$. Since Δ is R-closed, $\Delta \not\vdash_R \psi \supset \theta$. So $(\Delta, \psi) \not\vdash_R \theta$. By the maximalization theorem let Γ be an R-intuitionistic set including (Δ, ψ) but not containing θ. By IH $\Gamma \Vdash \psi$ but $\Gamma \not\Vdash \theta$. Moreover $\Gamma \geqslant \Delta$. Thus by definition of forcing, $\Delta \not\Vdash \psi \supset \theta$. This completes our proof.

Now suppose $\Delta \not\vdash_R \varphi$. By the maximalization theorem let Γ be an R-intuitionistic set including Δ but not containing φ. In the natural model for R we have $\Gamma = [\Gamma]$ by the satisfiability theorem. So in this model Γ forces every member of Δ but does not force φ. Thus we have shown

if $\Delta \not\vdash_R \varphi$ then for some index Γ in $\natural_R$ $\Delta \subseteq [\Gamma]$ but $\varphi \notin [\Gamma]$.

This immediately yields the following theorem.
Intuitionistic Completeness Theorem
Suppose that for any Kripke model K and for any index i in K admitting R, $\Delta \Vdash_i \varphi$. Then $\Delta \vdash_R \varphi$.

Note that we cannot strengthen the Completeness Theorem to

(α) For every K and for every index i in K if $\Delta \Vdash_i \varphi$ and R is the set of rules which hold at i, then $\Delta \vdash_R \varphi$.

Firstly, assuming R contains only finitary rules, (α) fails for infinite Δ because $\Vdash_i$ need not be compact. For, suppose I is the set $\{0, 1, 2, \ldots, \omega\}$ with the usual left-right ordering. Suppose for each n, $\underline{n} = \{A_1, \ldots, A_{n+1}\}$ and $\underline{\omega} = \{A_0, A_1, \ldots\}$. Then $\{A_i | i > 0\} \Vdash_0 A_0$; but for all n $\{A_1, \ldots, A_n\} \not\Vdash_0 A_0$.

Secondly, (α) fails even for finite Δ. Consider the model

$$\emptyset = \underline{0} \cdot \begin{array}{l} \diagup \ \cdot\underline{1} = \{A_0, A_1\} \\ \diagdown \ \cdot\underline{2} = \{A_0, A_2\} \end{array}$$

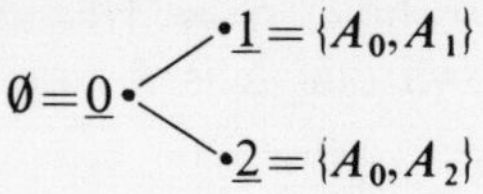

with $\leqslant$ from left to right. In this model $A_0 \Vdash_0 A_1 \vee A_2$. By considering the normal form of an R-proof of $A_1 \vee A_2$ from A_0, we see that one of the rules A_0/A_1 or A_0/A_2 would have to be used. But neither of these holds at 0.

The failure of (α) does raise a question mark over the feasibility of regarding any Kripke model as a satisfactory representation of what might be regarded as 'all possible intuitionistic states of affairs through time'. Perhaps it is only the natural model $\natural$ that can be so regarded. We do have the result

If for all i in $\natural_R$ $\Delta \Vdash_i \varphi$ then $\Delta \vdash_R \varphi$.

As a special case, taking R empty, we have

If for all i in $\natural$ $\Delta \Vdash_i \varphi$ then $\Delta \vdash \varphi$.

We shall end by showing that the law of excluded middle is not intuitionistically valid. A counterexemplary Kripke model for $A \vee {\sim} A$ is

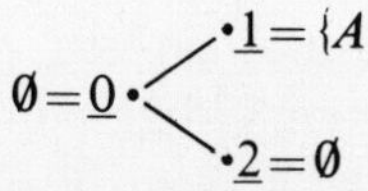

with $\leqslant$ from left to right. Here $0 \nVdash A \vee {\sim} A$.

CHAPTER 6

First order metalogic

6.1
Normalization and interpolation theorems *p.116*
6.2
Joint consistency and definability theorems *p.120*
6.3
Decidability of monadic logic *p.122*
6.4
Some major metatheorems via Henkin's method *p.125*
6.5
Corollaries to compactness *p.131*
6.6
Kripke semantics for first order intuitionistic logic *p.132*

6.1 Normalization and interpolation theorems. The normalization theorem extends to first order logic. We recall 5.4. Again we adopt dilemma as the only classical rule of negation. The difference now from the propositional case is that a proof can be transformed to one in which applications of dilemma discharge only atomic ***or quantified*** sentences. The proof of normalization then goes through as in the propositional case. As before applications of dilemma can be driven downwards as far as they will go so that in the resulting proof no sentence occurrence standing as the conclusion of an application of dilemma stands as premiss for the application of any rule other than dilemma, $\forall I$ or $\exists E$. In summary we have the

Normalization theorem

Every proof can be converted into a proof in fully normal form.

We shall now turn our attention to the system of classical first order logic with identity but not functions, based on just the Sheffer strokes for connection and quantification. The rules of inference are as stated in Section 4.7; remember that the classical negation rule is reductio in the form

$$\begin{array}{c} \overline{\varphi|\varphi}^{\,(i)} \\ \vdots \\ \dfrac{\divideontimes}{\varphi}\,(i) \end{array}$$

The rules for identity are the axiom $\overline{a=a}$ (reflexivity) and the rule of substitutivity

$$\frac{\varphi \quad a=b}{\psi} \qquad \text{where } \varphi, \psi \text{ are atomic and } \varphi^a_b = \psi^a_b$$

We have reduction procedures by means of which we can remove from any Sheffer proof any sentence occurrence which stands simultaneously as the major premiss of an elimination, and as the conclusion either of a corresponding introduction or of the absurdity rule. By means of a further transformation:

$$\begin{array}{c} \overline{((\varphi\downarrow_x\psi)|(\varphi\downarrow_x\psi))}^{\,(i)} \\ \Delta \\ \begin{array}{ccc} \Gamma_1 & \Pi & \Gamma_2 \\ \Sigma_1 & \dfrac{\divideontimes}{\varphi\downarrow_x\psi}(i) & \Sigma_2 \\ \varphi^x_a & & \psi^x_a \end{array} \\ \hline \divideontimes \end{array} \quad \rightarrow \quad \begin{array}{c} \begin{array}{ccc} \Gamma_1 & & \Gamma_2 \\ \Sigma_1 & \overline{\varphi\downarrow_x\psi}^{\,(i)} & \Sigma_2 \\ \varphi^x_a & & \psi^x_a \end{array} \\ \hline \dfrac{\divideontimes}{((\varphi\downarrow_x\psi)|(\varphi\downarrow_x\psi))}\,(i) \\ \Delta \\ \Pi \\ \divideontimes \end{array}$$

(with or without the x's and a's) we can ensure that a proof in normal form can be converted into one in which no sentence occurrence stands simultaneously as the conclusion of reductio and as the major premiss of an elimination. A Sheffer proof of this kind is said to be in *fully normal form*. (Throughout this section 'proof' will mean 'Sheffer proof' in the appropriate contexts.)

A proof in fully normal form whose last step is an elimination must have the form

$$\begin{array}{ccc} \Gamma_1 & & \Gamma_2 \\ \Sigma_1 & & \Sigma_2 \\ \psi^x_a & \psi \mid_x \theta & \theta^x_a \\ \hline & \text{※} & \end{array} \qquad \text{(with or without the } x\text{'s and } a\text{'s)}$$

where the major premiss of the final elimination stands as an undischarged assumption. This is because it cannot stand as the conclusion of a corresponding introduction or of the absurdity rule (otherwise it would be maximal); nor, in virtue of the transformation above, as the conclusion of reductio; nor, since it is not atomic, as the conclusion of substitutivity.

Thus any proof in fully normal form containing more than one sentence occurrence satisfies just one of the following descriptions:

(i) Its last step is an application of the absurdity rule.
(ii) Its last step is an application of reductio.
(iii) Its last step is an application of substitutivity.
(iv) Its last step is an introduction.
(v) Its last step is an elimination whose major premiss stands as an undischarged assumption.

This classification will be useful in establishing the Interpolation Theorem below, for whose statement and proof we require a few more preliminary definitions.

Suppose $\Delta_1 \vdash \chi$ and $\Delta_2, \chi \vdash \varphi$. Then χ is called an interpolant from Δ_1 to φ via Δ_2. If proofs Π_1 and Π_2 justify the respective deducibility statements then the graphic representation of the interpolation of χ is

$$\begin{array}{c} \Delta_1 \\ \Pi_1 \\ \underbrace{\Delta_2, \chi} \\ \Pi_2 \\ \varphi \end{array}$$

The reader is advised to use this graphic aid when verifying subsequent interpolation claims for himself.

Suppose moreover that every name and predicate (other than

identity) which occurs in χ occurs in at least one member of Δ_1 and in at least one member of $\Delta_2 \cup \{\varphi\}$. Then we say that χ is a *well-behaved* interpolant from Δ_1 to φ via Δ_2.

In subsequent discussion $|\varphi|$ will be the formula in Sheffer notation obtained from φ in the obvious way by eliminating the usual operators in φ in favour of the strokes, in accordance with the definitions given in section 4.7.

$\forall\vec{x}\,\varphi^{\vec{a}}_{\vec{x}}$ $(\exists\vec{x}\,\varphi^{\vec{a}}_{\vec{x}})$ will be the universal (existential) closure of φ with respect to the names in the sequence $\vec{a}$, the variables in the sequence $\vec{x}$ being chosen in some sensible way.

Interpolation Theorem

Suppose Δ_1 and Δ_2 are disjoint with union Δ, and Π is a proof of φ depending on Δ. Then there is a well-behaved interpolant from Δ_1 to φ via Δ_2.

Proof. By induction on the complexity of Π. It suffices to consider only proofs Π in fully normal form (since every proof can be turned into one in fully normal form).

Basis

Case (i): $\Pi = \varphi \in \Delta_1$. Then φ is a well-behaved interpolant from Δ_1 to φ via Δ_2 (which is empty).

Case (ii): $\Pi = \varphi \in \Delta_2$. Then $|\forall x\, x = x|$ is a well-behaved interpolant from Δ_1 (which is empty) to φ via Δ_2.

Case (iii): $\Pi = (a = a)$. Then $(a = a)$ is a well-behaved interpolant from Δ_1 (which is empty) to $(a = a)$ via Δ_2 (which is empty).

Inductive step. By cases (i)–(v) of the classification above of proofs in fully normal form.

Case (i): Π is

$$\begin{array}{c}\Delta\\ \Sigma\\ \text{※}\\ \hline \varphi\end{array}$$

By IH applied to Σ there is some well-behaved interpolant χ from Δ_1 to ※ via Δ_2. But then χ is a well-behaved interpolant from Δ_1 to φ via Δ_2.

Case (ii): Π is

$$\begin{array}{c}\underbrace{\Delta,\ \overline{\varphi|\varphi}^{\,(\mathrm{i})}}\\ \Sigma\\ \text{※}\\ \hline \varphi\end{array}{\scriptstyle (\mathrm{i})} \qquad \text{where } \varphi|\varphi \notin \Delta.$$

By IH applied to Σ there is some well-behaved interpolant χ from Δ_1 to ※ via $\Delta_2 \cup \{\varphi|\varphi\}$. But then χ is a well-behaved interpolant from Δ_1 to φ via Δ_2.

Case (iii): Π is

$$\begin{array}{cc} \Gamma_1 & \Gamma_2 \\ \Sigma_1 & \Sigma_2 \\ \psi & a=b \\ \hline \multicolumn{2}{c}{\varphi} \end{array} \qquad \text{where } \Delta=\Gamma_1\cup\Gamma_2.$$

By IH applied to Σ_1 there is some well-behaved interpolant χ_1 from $\Delta_1\cap\Gamma_1$ to ψ via $\Delta_2\cap\Gamma_1$.
By IH applied to Σ_2 there is some well-behaved interpolant χ_2 from $\Delta_1\cap\Gamma_2$ to $a=b$ via $\Delta_2\cap\Gamma_2$.
But then $|\chi_1\,\&\,\chi_2|$ is a well-behaved interpolant from Δ_1 to φ via Δ_2.

Case (iv): Π is

$$\begin{array}{c} \underbrace{\Delta,\ \overline{\psi^x_a}^{\,(i)},\ \overline{\theta^x_a}^{\,(i)}} \\ \Sigma \\ ※ \\ \hline \psi\,{\mid}_x\,\theta \quad (i) \end{array} \qquad \text{where } \psi^x_a\notin\Delta,\ \theta^x_a\notin\Delta \text{ and } a \text{ does not occur in any member of } \Delta.$$

By IH applied to Σ there is some well-behaved interpolant χ from Δ_1 to ※ via $\Delta_2\cup\{\psi^x_a,\theta^x_a\}$. But then χ is a well-behaved interpolant from Δ_1 to $\psi\,{\mid}_x\,\theta$ via Δ_2. (For the propositional case, simply delete x and a in the foregoing.)

Case (v): Π is

$$\begin{array}{ccc} \Gamma_1 & & \Gamma_2 \\ \Sigma_1 & & \Sigma_2 \\ \psi^x_b & \psi\,{\mid}_x\,\theta & \theta^x_b \\ \hline \multicolumn{3}{c}{※} \end{array} \qquad \text{where } \Delta=\Gamma_1\cup\Gamma_2\cup\{\psi\,{\mid}_x\,\theta\} \text{ and } \varphi \text{ is ※}.$$

Subcase (a): $\psi\,{\mid}_x\,\theta\in\Delta_1$.
By IH applied to Σ_1 there is some well-behaved interpolant χ_1 from $\Gamma_1\cap\Delta_2$ to ψ^x_b via $\Gamma_1\cap\Delta_1$. By IH applied to Σ_2 there is some well-behaved interpolant χ_2 from $\Gamma_2\cap\Delta_2$ to θ^x_b via $\Gamma_2\cap\Delta_1$.

Let $\vec{a}$ contain just the names in χ_1 or χ_2 not occurring in any member of Δ_1. Then $|\forall\vec{x}(\chi_1|\chi_2)^{\vec{a}}_{\vec{x}}|$ is a well-behaved interpolant from Δ_1 to ※ via Δ_2. (Universal closure being necessary to ensure good behaviour with respect to names.)

Subcase (b): $\psi\,{\mid}_x\,\theta\in\Delta_2$.
By IH applied to Σ_1 there is some well-behaved interpolant χ_1 from $\Gamma_1\cap\Delta_1$ to ψ^x_b via $\Gamma_1\cap\Delta_2$. By IH applied to Σ_2 there is some well-behaved interpolant χ_2 from $\Gamma_2\cap\Delta_1$ to θ^x_b via $\Gamma_2\cap\Delta_2$. Let $\vec{a}$ contain just the names in χ_1 or χ_2 not occurring in any member of Δ_2 or in $\psi\,{\mid}_x\,\theta$. Then $|\exists\vec{x}(\chi_1\,\&\,\chi_2)^{\vec{a}}_{\vec{x}}|$ is a well-behaved interpolant from Δ_1 to ※ via Δ_2. (Existential closure being necessary to ensure good behaviour with respect to names.)

For the propositional case, simply delete x and a and mention of closure in the foregoing.

We have made this excursion into the Sheffer system in proving the Interpolation Theorem because the internal symmetry between the connective and quantifier rules and the neat characterization of proofs in fully normal form considerably reduces the overall case load in the inductive step. Since the strokes form an expressively complete basis for classical logic, we may consider the Interpolation Theorem proved for the usual system of classical logic involving the operators $\sim$, &, $\vee$, $\supset$, $\exists$ and $\forall$. To prove the theorem for intuitionistic logic (in which these operators are definitionally independent of one another) we have to resort to a much lengthier characterization of proofs in normal form (particularly in case (v)) and bear a much heavier case load in the inductive step.

Let us now return to the usual logical operators.

6.2 Joint consistency and definability theorems. We identify a language with the set of its predicates and distinguished names. Let Δ be a set of sentences of a language L. Then Δ is a *theory in L* if and only if Δ is closed under deducibility 'within L' in the following sense: every sentence of L which is deducible from Δ is in Δ. Δ is *consistent* if and only if ⋇ is not deducible from Δ.

Suppose L' includes L, Δ' includes Δ, Δ is a theory in L, Δ' is a theory in L', and every sentence in Δ' which is a sentence of L is in Δ. Then we say that Δ' *conservatively extends* Δ.

The following theorem, for whose proof we use the interpolation theorem, holds regardless of whether classical or intuitionistic deducibility is in question.

Joint Consistency Theorem

Suppose (I) $\Delta_0, \Delta_1, \Delta_2$ are consistent theories in L_0, L_1, L_2 respectively

(II) $L_1 \cap L_2 \subseteq L_0$

(III) Δ_1 and Δ_2 conservatively extend Δ_0.

Then $\Delta_1 \cup \Delta_2$ is consistent.

Proof. Suppose for reductio that $\Delta_1 \cup \Delta_2 \vdash$ ⋇. Then for some finite $\Gamma_1 \subseteq \Delta_1$, $\Gamma_2 \subseteq \Delta_2$ we have $\Gamma_1 \cup \Gamma_2 \vdash$ ⋇.

By the interpolation theorem there is some well-behaved interpolant χ from Γ_1 to ⋇ via $\Gamma_2 \setminus \Gamma_1$. By good behaviour and (II), χ is a sentence of L_0. By interpolation $\Gamma_1 \vdash \chi$ whence by (III) $\chi \in \Delta_0$; and $\Gamma_2, \chi \vdash$ ⋇ whence by (III) $(\sim\chi) \in \Delta_0$. But then Δ_0 is inconsistent, contradicting (I).

Thus $\Delta_1 \cup \Delta_2$ is consistent.

If Δ is a set of sentences and P and Q are n-place predicates then Δ^P_Q will be the set resulting from Δ by replacing every occurrence of P in every member of Δ by an occurrence of Q. Likewise if Π is a proof then Π^P_Q will be the result of replacing every occurrence of P in every sentence occurrence in Π by an occurrence of Q. We shall abbreviate $P(t_1,\ldots,t_n)$ to $P(\vec{t})$. Suppose some member of Δ contains the n-place predicate P. Consider the following condition for *implicit definition*:

> $\Delta,\Delta^P_Q \models \forall\vec{x}(P(\vec{x}) \equiv Q(\vec{x}))$, for any n-place predicate Q not occurring in Δ.

This may be understood as follows. If the extensions of names and predicates other than P occurring in Δ have been fixed, then there is at most one way of fixing the extension of P so as to satisfy Δ. We say that P is implicitly defined, relative to Δ, in terms of the other predicates and names occurring in Δ. Now consider the following condition for *explicit definability*:

> $\Delta \vdash \forall\vec{x}(P(\vec{x}) \equiv \psi(\vec{x}))$, for some formula $\psi(\vec{x})$ not involving P and involving only names and predicates (other than identity) occurring in Δ.

We say that P is explicitly definable, relative to Δ, in terms of the names and predicates (other than identity) occurring in Δ.

There is an intuitionistic logical consequence relation, to be defined below in 6.7, in terms of which the condition for implicit definition can be formulated for the intuitionistic system. For either the classical or intuitionistic readings of consequence and deducibility we have the following theorem, our second corollary to the interpolation theorem.

Definability Theorem

Suppose some member of Δ contains the predicate P, which is implicitly defined relative to Δ. Then P is explicitly definable relative to Δ.

Proof. Suppose P is n-place. Let Q be an n-place predicate not occurring in Δ. By implicit definability we have

$$\Delta, \Delta^P_Q \models \forall\vec{x}(P(\vec{x}) \equiv Q(\vec{x}))$$

By completeness of first order logic (classical or intuitionistic) to be proved in 6.5 and 6.7, we have

$$\Delta, \Delta^P_Q \vdash \forall\vec{x}(P(\vec{x}) \equiv Q(\vec{x}))$$

Let $a_1, \ldots, a_n$ be names not occurring in Δ. Then $\Delta, \Delta^P_Q, P(\vec{a}) \vdash Q(\vec{a})$. So for some finite $\Gamma \subseteq \Delta, \Theta \subseteq \Delta^P_Q$ we have $\Gamma, \Theta, P(\vec{a}) \vdash Q(\vec{a})$. Now by the interpolation theorem there is some well-behaved interpolant χ from $\Gamma \backslash \Theta, P(\vec{a})$ to $Q(\vec{a})$ via Θ, in virtue of proofs Π and Σ featuring thus:

$$\frac{\underbrace{\Gamma\backslash\Theta, P(\vec{a})}}{\begin{array}{c}\Pi\\ \underbrace{\Theta, \chi}\\ \Sigma\\ Q(\vec{a})\end{array}}$$

By good behaviour χ contains neither P nor Q, but only names and predicates (other than identity) occurring in Δ. The proof Π and the proof Σ^Q_P:

$$\begin{array}{c}\underbrace{\Theta^Q_P, \chi}\\ \Sigma^Q_P\\ P(\vec{a})\end{array}$$

show that χ and $P(\vec{a})$ are interdeducible relative to Δ, since both $\Gamma\backslash\Theta$ and Θ^Q_P are subsets of Δ. Hence $\Delta \vdash P(\vec{a}) \equiv \chi$. By choice of $a_1, \ldots, a_n$ we have $\Delta \vdash \forall\vec{x}(P(\vec{x}) \equiv \chi^{\vec{a}}_{\vec{x}})$. Thus P is explicitly defined relative to Δ.

6.3 Decidability of monadic logic. In our treatment of propositional logic we gave completeness proofs of an inductive character, which intrinsically provided methods of deciding whether a propositional argument was valid, and, if so, of finding a proof of it. As remarked then, this kind of completeness proof is not possible in the case of first order logic. This is because there is no method of deciding whether a first order argument is valid. This result – the *undecidability* of first order logic – is due to Church, and will be proved in due course.

There is, however, a decision method if the language is restricted so as to contain only *one-place* predicates and no function symbols. Such languages are called *monadic*. The reason why monadic logic is decidable is that any monadic sentence φ true in some model is true in a *finite* model the number of whose individuals is less than some finite number $n(\varphi)$ which can be determined by inspecting the sentence φ. Thus, given a monadic sentence φ we inspect the finitely many models based on domains with no more than $n(\varphi)$ individuals and involving the finitely many extra-logical expressions occurring in φ. If some such model satisfies φ, we shall eventually discover that this is so. On the other hand, of no such model satisfies φ, we shall also eventually discover that this is so; in which case we shall know that *no* model satisfies φ.

We can therefore decide, given φ, whether some or no model satisfies its negation $\sim\varphi$; that is, we can decide whether φ is falsifiable or logically true. Consequently we can decide, given any monadic argument involving only *finitely* many premisses, whether it is valid or invalid.

To prove the desired result let us consider first a monadic language *without* identity.

Finite Satisfiability Theorem for Monadic Languages without Identity

If a sentence φ of a monadic language without identity is satisfiable, then φ is satisfiable in a finite model.

Proof. Let $P_1, \ldots, P_k$ be the monadic predicates occurring in φ. Let M be any model for these predicates in which φ is true. Define an equivalence relation $\approx$ on the domain of M as follows:

$\alpha \approx \beta$ iff α and β satisfy the same predicates among $P_1, \ldots, P_k$ in M.

Let $|\alpha|$ be the equivalence class of α. There are at most 2^k such equivalence classes. Let $|M|$ be the model based on $\{|\alpha| \,\big|\, \alpha \in M\}$ with $|\alpha|$ satisfying P in $|M|$ just in case α satisfies P in M, and with any name a denoting $|\alpha|$ in $|M|$ just in case a denotes α in M. We now show by induction on φ that $|M| \models \varphi[|s|]$ iff $M \models \varphi[s]$, where $|s|$ assigns to any variable x the value $|s(x)|$. The basis step has been accomplished by definition of $|M|$. In the inductive step only quantified formulae need particular consideration, since the reasoning for connected formulae is trivial. So suppose $|M| \models \exists x\varphi[|s|]$. Then for some $|\alpha| \in |M|$, $|M| \models \varphi[|s|(x/|\alpha|)]$. Thus for some $|\alpha| \in |M|$, $|M| \models \varphi[|s(x/\alpha)|]$. By IH, for some $\alpha \in M$, $M \models \varphi[s(x/\alpha)]$. Hence $M \models \exists x\varphi[s]$. The converse is easy.

When identity is present, this construction of a finite model $|M|$ from M will not work. For, let φ be the sentence $\exists x \exists y(\sim x = y \,\&\, Px \,\&\, Py)$, and let M be the model consisting of two individuals α and β with both satisfying P. Then $|M|$ as defined above consists of only one individual, the equivalence class $\{\alpha, \beta\}$, satisfying P. φ is false in $|M|$.

Let $q(\varphi)$ be the least upper bound on the number of free variables in any subformula of φ. Could we define the required model $[M]$ so as to make it contain $q(\varphi)$ 'copies' of $|M|$? No. For, if φ is the sentence $\exists x \forall y(y = x \,\&\, Py)$ then $q(\varphi) = 2$; but any model satisfying φ contains exactly one individual, satisfying P.

How, then, should the required model $|M|$ be defined when identity is present? A model M for the predicates $P_1, \ldots, P_k$ occurring in φ which satisfies φ could have any number of members. If, however, we think of the *kind* of a member as determined by which of these predicates it satisfies in M, it is evident that there are fewer than 2^k *kinds* of member in M. M may therefore be represented by the following grid:

$$\alpha_1^1, \ldots, \alpha_1^{\mu 1}$$
$$\vdots$$
$$\alpha_m^1, \ldots, \alpha_m^{\mu m}$$

Each row corresponds to a kind. The ith row has μ_i members of the relevant kind. The number of rows, m, does not exceed 2^k, the maximum number of kinds exemplifiable in M. The equivalence class consisting of all the members of the ith row we shall call α_i.

Now let n_i be $\min(\mu_i, q(\varphi))$. The more complicated model $[M]$ that we require is obtained by allowing carefully controlled numbers of non-identicals of the same kind:

$$\alpha_1^1, \ldots, \alpha_1^{n1}$$
$$\vdots$$
$$\alpha_m^1, \ldots, \alpha_m^{nm}$$

with each row corresponding to the same kind as in the representation of M, and names co-referring in $[M]$ iff they co-refer in M.

Let s be an assignment to variables of members of M, and let $|s|$ be an assignment to the same variables of members of $[M]$. We define

$s \approx |s|$ iff for all variables x, y
(i) $s(x)$ is of the same kind as $|s|(x)$
(ii) $s(x) = s(y)$ iff $|s|(x) = |s|(y)$
(iii) for every name a, a denotes $s(x)$ in M iff a denotes $|s|(x)$ in $[M]$

Now let ψ be any subformula of φ and let s, $|s|$ be assignments to just the free variables of ψ of values in M, $[M]$ respectively, such that $s \approx |s|$. We show by induction on ψ that $M \models \psi[s]$ iff $[M] \models \psi[\,|s|\,]$.
Basis. The result obviously holds for atomic formulae $P(a)$, $P(x)$, $a=a$, $x=x$, $a=x$, $x=a$, $x=y$ by definition of $[M]$ and of $\approx$.
Inductive step. The reasoning is trivial when ψ has a connective dominant. So suppose ψ is $\exists x\theta$. Suppose $M \models \exists x\theta[s]$. Then for some α in M, $M \models \theta[s(x/\alpha)]$. Now choose β in $[M]$ as follows:

(1) if α is some $s(y)$, choose $|s|(y)$;
(2) otherwise, suppose α appears in α_i in our grid representation of M. By definition of n_i and $\approx$ we can choose some α_i^j in $[M]$ not in the range of values of $|s|$, which is named by a in $[M]$ iff α is named by a in M.

Clearly $s(x/\alpha) \approx |s|(x/\beta)$. Thus by IH $[M] \models \theta[\,|s|(x/\beta)\,]$. Hence $[M] \models \exists x\theta[\,|s|\,]$. The converse is similar.

As an obvious corollary, $M \models \varphi$ iff $[M] \models \varphi$. Moreover, $2^k.q(\varphi)$ is an upper bound on the size of $[M]$. We have thus established the Finite

Satisfiability Theorem for monadic languages *with* identity. As explained above, the decidability of monadic logic with identity follows.

6.4 Some major metatheorems via Henkin's method. So far in this chapter we have been considering classical first order logic. We have proved soundness in 4.11, normalization, interpolation, consistency and definability theorems, as well as the decidability of monadic logic. We turn now to the problem of proving completness.

We shall give an argument that is a suitable generalization of Henkin's method illustrated in the propositional case in the previous chapter. The argument establishes maximalization of consistent sets of sentences and satisfiability of maximal consistent sets, with some complications owing to the presence of quantifiers. The argument will be given without break in continuity, for the following reason. Certain material will be enclosed in braces, and the argument will be valid whether we read that material or delete it, provided that we do so uniformly in each case. These two options, combined with either intuitionistic or classical readings of ⊢, yield Theorems I, II and III, which are stated after the argument.

The Argument

Suppose $\Delta \nvdash ※$. Let $\varphi_0, \varphi_1, \ldots$ be a list of all sentences formed from expressions occurring in members of Δ and from the list $a_0, a_1, \ldots$ of all names occurring in members of Δ along with infinitely many names not so occurring. Let $\psi_0, \psi_1, \ldots$ be a list of all formulae with one free variable, constructed in the same way. $\exists x\psi$ and $\forall x\psi$ will be the results of binding the free variable in ψ by $\exists$ and $\forall$ respectively. ψt will be the result of substituting the term t for all free occurrences of that variable in ψ. In what follows a shall be the first name in our list above not to occur in the set of sentences next mentioned.

We define a sequence $\Delta = \Delta_0 \subseteq \ldots \subseteq \Delta_n \subseteq E_n \subseteq A_n \subseteq \Delta_{n+1} \subseteq \ldots$ of sets of sentences as follows:

E_n	$=$	$\Delta_n, \psi_n a$	if	$\Delta_n, \exists x\psi_n \nvdash ※$	. . . (1)
	$=$	Δ_n	if	$\Delta_n, \exists x\psi_n \vdash ※$	. . . (2)
A_n	$=$	$E_n, \forall x\{\sim\sim\}\psi_n$	if	$E_n, \forall x\{\sim\sim\}\psi_n \nvdash ※$	. . . (3)
	$=$	$E_n, \sim\psi_n a$	if	$E_n, \forall x\{\sim\sim\}\psi_n \vdash ※$	. . . (4)
Δ_{n+1}	$=$	A_n, φ_n	if	$A_n, \varphi_n \nvdash ※$	. . . (5)
	$=$	A_n	if	$A_n, \varphi_n \vdash ※$	. . . (6)

Let $\Delta = \cup_i \Delta_i$.

The informal picture of the construction is as follows:

Lists	$a_0, a_1, \ldots$	names
	$\varphi_0, \varphi_1, \ldots$	sentences
	$\psi_0, \psi_1, \ldots$	formulae with one free variable

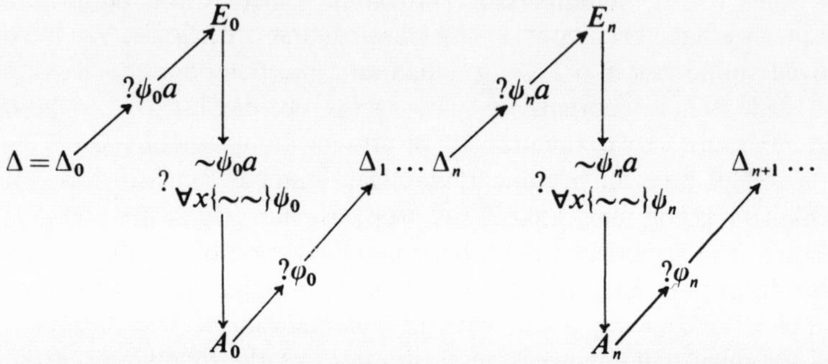

In forming E_n from Δ_n we look to the existential quantification of the nth formula ψ_n. If it is consistent with Δ_n, then we add a 'new instance' $\psi_n a$ as a 'witness' to the existential claim. Otherwise we add nothing. In forming A_n from E_n we look to the universal quantification of {the double negation of} the nth formula ψ_n. If it is consistent with E_n, we add it; otherwise we add a 'new counterinstance' $\sim\psi_n a$ as a 'witness' to the failure of the universal claim. In forming Δ_{n+1} from A_n we look to the nth sentence φ_n. If it is consistent with A_n we add it; otherwise we add nothing.

An important feature of this construction is that it preserves consistency: if Δ_n is consistent, then so is Δ_{n+1}. To prove this, we shall prove the contrapositive. We shall assume that Δ_{n+1} is inconsistent, and show that the inconsistency would be transmitted back via A_n and E_n to Δ_n.

So suppose $\Delta_{n+1} \vdash$ ※.

If $A_n, \varphi_n \nvdash$ ※ then by (5) $\Delta_{n+1} = A_n, \varphi_n$ and so $A_n, \varphi_n \vdash$ ※. Thus $A_n, \varphi_n \vdash$ ※. By (6) $\Delta_{n+1} = A_n$.

So $A_n \vdash$ ※.

If $E_n, \forall x\{\sim\sim\}\psi_n \nvdash$ ※ then by (3) $A_n = E_n, \forall x\{\sim\sim\}\psi_n$ and so $E_n, \forall x\{\sim\sim\}\psi_n \vdash$ ※. Thus $E_n, \forall x\{\sim\sim\}\psi_n \vdash$ ※ . . . (7). By (4) $A_n = E_n, \sim\psi_n a$ and so $E_n, \sim\psi_n a \vdash$ ※. Hence $E_n \vdash \{\sim\sim\}\psi_n a$, with a occurring parametrically for $\forall$-Introduction. (Note here that we need $\{\sim\sim\}$ when $\vdash$ is intuitionistic deducibility.) So $E_n \vdash \forall x\{\sim\sim\}\psi_n$. This, with (7), shows

$E_n \vdash$ ※.

If $\Delta_n, \exists x\psi_n \nvdash$ ※ then by (1) $E_n = \Delta_n, \psi_n a$ and so $\Delta_n, \psi_n a \vdash$ ※, with a occurring parametrically for $\exists$-Elimination. So $\Delta_n, \exists x\psi_n \vdash$ ※. Thus

$\Delta_n, \exists x\psi_n \vdash$ ※. By (2) $E_n = \Delta_n$.

Hence $\Delta_n \vdash$ ※.

Now we show that $\bar{\Delta}$ is consistent. Suppose for reductio that $\bar{\Delta} \vdash$ ※. Then ※ is deducible from finitely many premisses in $\bar{\Delta}$. All these premisses, by construction, will be in some Δ_k. So $\Delta_k \vdash$ ※. But then by the foregoing reasoning the inconsistency would be transmitted back to Δ_0, contrary to our main assumption. Thus $\bar{\Delta} \nvdash$ ※.

Next we show that $\bar{\Delta}$ is maximal. Suppose for reductio that neither φ nor $\sim\varphi$ is in Δ. Let φ occur in our list as φ_i and let $\sim\varphi$ occur as φ_j. Since φ_i is not in $\bar{\Delta}$ it is not in Δ_{i+1}, which therefore cannot be A_i, φ_i, whence the latter is inconsistent. Similarly A_j, φ_j is inconsistent. Let $m = \max(i, j)$. We have $A_i \subseteq A_m$ and $A_j \subseteq A_m$. Hence $A_m, \varphi \vdash$ ※ and $A_m, \sim\varphi \vdash$ ※. By the proof schema

$$\begin{array}{l}
\underbrace{A_m,\ \overline{\ \ }^{(1)}\!\!\!\!\!\!\!\varphi\ \ }\\
\quad\vdots\\
\quad ※\\
\overline{\qquad\quad}^{\,(1)}\\
\underbrace{A_m,\ \sim\varphi}\\
\quad\vdots\\
\quad ※
\end{array}$$

we have $A_m \vdash$ ※, contrary to our consistency result above. Thus for all φ, either φ is in $\bar{\Delta}$ or $\sim\varphi$ is in $\bar{\Delta}$.

Obviously also $\bar{\Delta}$ is closed, that is, for all φ if $\bar{\Delta} \vdash \varphi$ then $\varphi \in \bar{\Delta}$. Now we define a 'natural model' M and exploit the consistency, maximality and closure of $\bar{\Delta}$, as well as its provision of 'witnesses' as explained above, to show that $\bar{\Delta}$ is precisely the set of sentences true in M.

The 'natural model' M is defined as follows:

(i) Its domain is the set of all equivalence classes of terms under the equivalence relation $(t = u) \in \bar{\Delta}$.

(ii) Each name denotes its own equivalence class.

(iii) $M(f)$, the function assigned within M to the n-place function sign f, maps $|t_1|, \ldots, |t_n|$ to $|f(t_1, \ldots, t_n)|$.

(iv) $M(P)$, the extension assigned within M to the n-place primitive predicate P, contains $(|t_1|, \ldots, |t_n|)$ iff $P(t_1, \ldots, t_n) \in \bar{\Delta}$.

That $(t = u) \in \bar{\Delta}$ defines an equivalence relation between terms is evident from the deductive closure of $\bar{\Delta}$ under the rules

$$\frac{}{t=t}\ \text{(reflexivity)}$$

$$\frac{t=u}{u=t}\ \text{(symmetry)}$$

$$\frac{t=u \quad u=s}{t=s}\ \text{(transitivity)}$$

That (iii) is a sound definition can be seen from reflexivity and substitutivity of identicals. For, suppose t_i', t_i'' are distinct representatives of the equivalence class $|t_i|$ $(1 \leq i \leq n)$. Then the identities $t_i' = t_i''$ are in $\overline{\Delta}$. So also is the axiom $f(\overrightarrow{t'}) = f(\overrightarrow{t'})$. Thus by n applications of substitutivity the conclusion $f(\overrightarrow{t'}) = f(\overrightarrow{t''})$ is deducible from $\overline{\Delta}$. By closure it is in $\overline{\Delta}$, and so the terms $f(\overrightarrow{t'})$ and $f(\overrightarrow{t''})$ are in the same equivalence class.

That (iv) is a sound definition can be seen similarly. We can show that $P(\overrightarrow{t'})$ is in $\overline{\Delta}$ iff $P(\overrightarrow{t''})$ is in $\overline{\Delta}$ by n applications of substitutivity, and closure, in each direction.

Note that we have needed substitutivity of identicals only for *atomic* premisses in order to show that the natural model has been successfully defined.

It is immediate by induction that each term t denotes its equivalence class $|t|$ in M.

We now show by induction on sentences that for all φ {with $\sim\sim$ immediately after each universal quantifier prefix} we have $\varphi \in \overline{\Delta}$ iff $M \models \varphi$. The definition of M accomplishes the basis. In the inductive step the reasoning is as in the propositional case when φ has a connective dominant. It remains to consider the cases where φ is (i) $\exists x\psi$ or (ii) $\forall x\{\sim\sim\}\psi$.

(i) Suppose φ is $\exists x\psi$.

Suppose $\exists x\psi \in \overline{\Delta}$. By construction for some name a $\psi a \in \Delta$. By IH $M \models \psi a$. Thus $M \models \psi[|a|]$. Hence $M \models \exists x\psi$. Conversely suppose $M \models \exists x\psi$. Then for some $|t|$ in M, $M \models \psi[|t|]$. Since t denotes $|t|$, $M \models \psi t$. By IH $\psi t \in \Delta$. By $\exists$-Introduction $\overline{\Delta} \vdash \exists x\psi$. Hence by closure $\exists x\psi \in \overline{\Delta}$.

(ii) Finally suppose φ is $\forall x\{\sim\sim\}\psi$.

Suppose $\forall x\{\sim\sim\}\psi \in \overline{\Delta}$. By virtue of the proof schema

$$\cfrac{\cfrac{\forall x\{\sim\sim\}\psi}{\{\sim\sim\}\psi t} \qquad \sim\psi t}{※}$$

and consistency of $\overline{\Delta}$, we have for all t $\sim\psi t \notin \overline{\Delta}$, whence by IH $M \not\models \sim\psi t$, and so $M \models \{\sim\sim\}\psi t$. Since t denotes $|t|$, $M \models \{\sim\sim\}\psi[|t|]$. So for all $|t|$ in M, $M \models \{\sim\sim\}\psi[|t|]$. Thus $M \models \forall x\{\sim\sim\}\psi$. Conversely, suppose $M \models \forall x\{\sim\sim\}\psi$. Then for all $|t|$ in M, $M \models \{\sim\sim\}\psi[|t|]$. Since t denotes $|t|$, $M \models \{\sim\sim\}\psi t$. By IH $\{\sim\sim\}\psi t \in \overline{\Delta}$, whence $\sim\psi t \notin \overline{\Delta}$ since $\overline{\Delta}$ is consistent. So for all t $\sim\psi t \notin \Delta$. In particular this holds for all names. Thus by construction $\forall x\{\sim\sim\}\psi \in \bar{\Delta}$.

This concludes our argument.

From this argument, by deleting everything in braces and reading $\vdash$ as classical deducibility, we have

Theorem I

If $\Delta \nvdash_C ⁎$ then Δ has a model.

By reading everything in braces, and reading $\vdash$ as intuitionistic deducibility, we have

Theorem II

If $\Delta \nvdash_I ⁎$ then there is a model of all the members of Δ which have $\sim\sim$ immediately after every universal quantifier prefix.

By deleting everything in braces and reading $\vdash$ as intuitionistic deducibility in the system lacking $\forall$; and setting $A_n = E_n$, thereby omitting clauses (3) and (4) in the construction, we have

Theorem III

If Δ has no sentence involving $\forall$, and $\Delta \nvdash_I ⁎$ then Δ has a model.

We now come to our list of important corollaries.

Strong Completeness Theorem for Classical First Order Logic with Identity

If $\Delta \vDash \varphi$ then $\Delta \vdash \varphi$.

Proof. Suppose $\Delta \vDash \varphi$. Then $\Delta, \sim\varphi$ has no model. By Theorem I $\Delta, \sim\varphi \vdash ⁎$. Thus by classical reductio $\Delta \vdash \varphi$.

Compactness Theorem

If $\Delta \vDash \varphi$ then for some finite $\Gamma \subseteq \Delta, \Gamma \vDash \varphi$.

Proof. Suppose $\Delta \vDash \varphi$. By completeness there is a proof of φ from finitely many premisses in Δ. By soundness these premisses logically imply φ.

Countable Models Theorem

If Δ has a model then Δ has a countable model.

Proof. Suppose Δ has a model. By soundness $\Delta \nvdash ⁎$. By the proof of Theorem I Δ has a countable model whose individuals are sets (equivalence classes) of terms. Since there are only countably many terms, the model is countable.

Let $\forall\sim\sim[\varphi]$ be the result of inserting $\sim\sim$ immediately after every universal quantifier prefix in φ. Let $\approx\varphi$ be $\sim\sim(\forall\sim\sim[\varphi])$. Let $\vdash_{\forall\text{-}I}$ be the classical deducibility relation when $\forall$-*I* is not permitted. We have the following two generalizations of the Double Negation Theorem of propositional logic.

Double Negation Theorem I

If $\Delta \vdash_C \varphi$ then $\approx\Delta \vdash_I \approx\varphi$.

Proof. Suppose $\Delta \vdash_C \varphi$. Then $\Delta, \sim\varphi \vdash_C ⁎$. By soundness $\Delta, \sim\varphi$ has no model. Thus $\forall\sim\sim[\sim\sim\Delta], \forall\sim\sim[\sim\varphi]$ has no model. By Theorem II

$\forall{\sim}{\sim}[{\sim}{\sim}\Delta], \forall{\sim}{\sim}[{\sim}\varphi] \vdash_I \ast$; i.e. $\approx\Delta, {\sim}(\forall{\sim}{\sim}[\varphi]) \vdash_I \ast$.
So $\approx\Delta \vdash_I {\sim}{\sim}(\forall{\sim}{\sim}[\varphi])$, i.e. $\approx\Delta \vdash_I \approx\varphi$.
(Note also that the converse of this theorem is obvious.)

Double Negation Theorem II

If $\Delta \vdash_{\forall - I} \varphi$ then ${\sim}{\sim}\Delta \vdash_I {\sim}{\sim}\varphi$.

Proof. Suppose first that Δ and φ do not involve $\forall$. If φ is classically deducible from Δ then ${\sim}{\sim}\Delta, {\sim}\varphi$ has no model. Hence by Theorem III ${\sim}{\sim}\Delta, {\sim}\varphi \vdash_I \ast$, and so ${\sim}{\sim}\Delta \vdash_I {\sim}{\sim}\varphi$. We now proceed by induction on the number of applications of $\forall$-E in proofs. Indeed, since ${\sim}{\sim}\forall x\varphi \vdash_I {\sim}{\sim}\varphi^x_t$ the result is immediate.

Since the converse of the Double Negation Theorem I is obviously true, intuitionistic consequence is undecidable if classical consequence is. (We explain decidability and undecidability in Chapter 7.)

The cardinality of a language L is the cardinality of the set of expressions of L – names, function signs and primitive predicates. If the cardinality of L is infinite then it is the same as the cardinality of the set of all formulae of L. The construction in Henkin's argument given above can be generalized to languages of any infinite cardinality κ by ensuring that the list of names contains κ 'new' names not occurring in members of Δ. The cardinality of Δ will not exceed κ. The sequence $\{\Delta_\nu | \nu < \kappa\}$ will be defined as before; with the extra provision that at any limit ordinal $\lambda \leq \kappa$ Δ_λ will be $\cup_{\mu<\lambda}\Delta_\mu$. A natural model will be constructed from $\cup_{\nu<\kappa}\Delta_\nu$ as before; it will have at most κ members. Thus we shall have generalized the previous theorems for languages of cardinality κ. Most importantly, we shall have proved the following theorem.

Downward Löwenheim-Skolem Theorem

Any set of sentences in a language of an infinite cardinality κ which has a model has a model of cardinality $\leq \kappa$.

Now let Th(M) be the set of sentences (in a given language) true in M.

Upward Löwenheim-Skolem Theorem

Let M be a model of infinite cardinality ι for a language L of cardinality $\leq \iota$. Then Th(M) has a model of any cardinality $\kappa > \iota$.

Proof. Let $\alpha_0, \ldots, \alpha_\iota$ be all the members of M. Introduce new corresponding names $a_0, \ldots, a_\iota$ to form the model M of the augmented language L_ι. Let $L_{\iota+\kappa}$ result by augmenting L with further new names $b_0, \ldots, b_\kappa$. Let Δ be the set of all sentences of L_ι true in M_ι. Let Γ be the set of inequations $\{{\sim}b_\mu = b_\nu | \mu < \nu \leq \kappa\}$. To show each finite subset of $\Delta \cup \Gamma$ has a model it suffices to show that if Θ is a finite subset of Γ then $\Delta \cup \Theta$ has a model. Indeed, since Θ will involve only finitely many of the names $b_0, \ldots, b_\kappa$, these finitely many names can be made to name distinct members of M_ι, and the remaining ones can be made to name any members of M_1 we please. The result is obviously a model of $\Delta \cup \Theta$. Thus by compactness for languages of cardinality κ, $\Delta \cup \Gamma$ has a model which, given the membership of Γ, has at least κ members. By the Downward Löwenheim-Skolem Theorem for languages of cardinality κ, $\Delta \cup \Gamma$ has a model with exactly κ members. Since Th(M)$\subseteq \Delta$, our result follows.

Although stronger conclusions may be drawn from these results than those drawn below, we are presently interested only in extracting the full Löwenheim-Skolem Theorem for *countable* languages.

Löwenheim-Skolem Theorem for Countable Languages

Any set of sentences which has a model has a model of every infinite cardinality.

Proof. Immediate from the last two theorems.

6.5 Corollaries to compactness. We consider now some consequences of the compactness theorem. We consider only countable languages.

Compactness Corollary I

Any set of sentences with arbitrarily large finite models has an infinite model.

Proof. Suppose Δ has arbitrarily large finite models. Adjoin infinitely many new names $a_0, a_1, \ldots$ to the language of Δ. Every finite subset of $\Delta \cup \{\sim a_i = a_j \mid i < j\}$ has a model. For, if k is the largest index of new names occurring therein we can let $a_0, \ldots, a_k$ name distinct members within some model of at least $(k+1)$ members. Thus by compactness $\Delta \cup \{\sim a_i = a_j \mid i < j\}$ has a model, which must be infinite.

It follows that no set of sentences is true in all and only finite models. Another interesting result, which we cannot prove here, is Trakhtenbrot's Theorem: The set of sentences true in all finite models is not effectively enumerable. We explain effective enumerability in Chapter 7.

$$\text{Let } E_n \text{ be the sentence } \exists x_1 \ldots \exists x_n(\sim x_1 = x_2 \,\&\, \ldots \,\&\, \sim x_{n-1} = x_n).$$

E_n says 'There are at least n individuals'. The set $\{E_2, E_3, \ldots\}$ is satisfied in all and only infinite models. But no single sentence is. For, if φ were such a sentence, then $\sim\varphi$ would be true in all and only finite models, contrary to the result above.

Compactness Corollary II

No set of sentences (involving the two-place predicate R) is satisfied in all and only those models in which R represents a well-founded relation on the domain. (R represents a well-founded relation on the domain of M iff there is no infinite sequence $\alpha_0, \alpha_1, \ldots$ of members of M with $(\alpha_i, \alpha_j) \in M(R)$ for $i > j$.)

Proof. Suppose Γ is a set of sentences true in all and only those models in which R represents a well-founded relation. Consider the set Δ of axioms for a strict total ordering by R with a terminal element, in which every non-initial element has an immediate predecessor:

$$\forall y \forall x(Rxy \supset \sim Ryx)$$
$$\forall x \forall y(x=y \vee Rxy \vee Ryx)$$
$$\forall x \forall y \forall z((Rxy \,\&\, Ryz) \supset Rxz)$$
$$\exists x \forall y(Rxy \supset x=y)$$
$$\forall x(\exists y Ryx \supset \exists y(Ryx \,\&\, \sim\exists z(Ryz \,\&\, Rzx))).$$

Since every finite model of Δ would satisfy Γ and since there are arbitrarily large finite models of Δ, there would be arbitrarily large finite models of $\Delta \cup \Gamma$. Thus $\Delta \cup \Gamma$ would have an infinite model. But in every infinite model of Δ R cannot represent a well-founded relation. For, in such a model an infinite descending R-chain is constructible from the terminal element of the ordering by taking immediate predecessors. Thus no such set as Γ exists.

6.6 Kripke semantics for first order intuitionistic logic. We recall the discussion in 5.8 of the philosophical motivation for Kripke's semantics for propositional logic. The discussion extends to first order logic with the following extra observations.

A canonical proof of $\forall x\psi$ consists in a method that, applied to any term t known to denote an object, would yield a proof of ψt. A canonical proof of $\exists x\psi$ consists in a proof of ψt for some term t known to denote an object.

The evolution of my present position i into some future position j might involve the 'construction' of new objects by way of coming to know of certain terms that they do denote. (In some intuitionists' view mathematical objects *are* the very terms that denote them – concrete arrangements of marks on a piece of paper.) New atomic axioms and rules that hold at i can involve only such terms as are known by i to denote. Once an object has been 'constructed', it exists for ever after.

Thus in the characterization of first order Kripke models each index $i \in I$ is assigned a set of atomic sentences of the form $Pt_1 \ldots t_n$. Only the terms involved in atomic sentences in $\underline{i}$ are to be taken as denoting at i. If at i we know only that t denotes, and know nothing else at all about its denotation, then the identity $t=t$ will be the only atomic sentence involving t in $\underline{i}$. $/i/$ will be the set of terms involved in the atomic sentences comprising $\underline{i}$. Obviously $/i/$ can be determined from $\underline{i}$. If $i \leq j$ then $/i/ \subseteq /j/$ and $\underline{i} \subseteq \underline{j}$. For each t in $/i/$, $(t=t)$ is in $\underline{i}$.

In the definition of forcing we have two new clauses for quantified sentences:

(5) $i \Vdash \forall x\psi$ iff for all $j \geqslant i$, for all $t \in /j/, j \Vdash \psi t$.
(6) $i \Vdash \exists x\psi$ iff for some $t \in /i/, i \Vdash \psi t$.

Each of these clauses is intended to capture the explanation above of canonical proofs of the respective quantified sentences. Clause (5) tells us that $\forall x\psi$ is true at i iff 'as soon as' we construct an object t, ψt becomes true. This is what one would expect as the result of having an effective method that, applied to any term t known to denote, would yield a proof of ψt. Similar remarks apply to clause (6).

In the definition of (R-) intuitionistic sets of sentences we add a fourth clause in the first order case:

(4) If $\exists x\psi \in \Delta$ then for some term t involved in the atomic closure of Δ, $\psi t \in \Delta$. (Δ is *existential*.)

The reader will easily supply the extra cases for quantified sentences in the inductive steps of the proofs of the Eternity Lemma and the Soundness Theorem. We shall prove here in the necessary detail the maximalization theorem.

First Order Intuitionistic Maximalization Theorem

If $\Delta \nvdash_R \varphi$ then Δ is included in an R-intuitionistic set not containing φ.

Proof. By a Henkin construction. Let $a_0, a_1, \ldots$ be a list of names containing all those occurring in Δ, φ along with infinitely many others. Let $\varphi_0, \varphi_1, \ldots$ and $\psi_0, \psi_1, \ldots$ respectively be lists of all sentences, and of all formulae with one free variable, of the language of Δ, φ augmented by those names. Set

$$
\begin{array}{lcll}
\Delta_0 & = & \Delta & \\
\Psi_n & = & \Delta_n, \psi_n a & \text{if} \quad \Delta_n, \exists x\psi_n \nvdash_R \varphi \\
 & & \multicolumn{2}{l}{\text{where } a \text{ is the first name on our list}} \\
 & & \multicolumn{2}{l}{\text{not to occur in } \Delta_n, \exists x\psi_n;} \\
 & & \Delta_n, \exists x\psi_n \supset \varphi & \text{if} \quad \Delta_n, \exists x\psi_n \vdash_R \varphi \\
\Delta_{n+1} & = & \Psi_n, \varphi_n & \text{if} \quad \Psi_n, \varphi_n \nvdash_R \varphi \\
 & & \Psi_n, \varphi_n \supset \varphi & \text{if} \quad \Psi_n, \varphi_n \vdash_R \varphi \\
\bar{\Delta} & = & \cup_i \Delta_i &
\end{array}
$$

To show $\bar{\Delta} \nvdash_R \varphi$ it suffices, for by now familiar reasons, to show that if $\Delta_{n+1} \vdash_R \varphi$ then $\Delta_n \vdash_R \varphi$.

So suppose $\Delta_{n+1} \vdash_R \varphi$. Suppose $\Psi_n, \varphi_n \nvdash_R \varphi$. Then $\Delta_{n+1} = \Psi_n, \varphi_n$ and so $\Psi_n, \varphi_n \vdash_R \varphi$. Thus $\Psi_n, \varphi_n \vdash_R \varphi$. Hence $\Delta_{n+1} = \Psi_n, \varphi_n \supset \varphi$ by construction, and $\Psi_n \vdash_R \varphi_n \supset \varphi$ by $\supset$-*I*. But now $\Psi_n, \varphi_n \supset \varphi \vdash_R \varphi$. Hence by transitivity $\Psi_n \vdash_R \varphi$.

Now suppose $\Delta_n, \exists x\psi_n \nvdash_R \varphi$. Then $\Psi_n = \Delta_n, \psi_n a$ whence $\Delta_n, \psi_n a \vdash_R \varphi$

with a occurring parametrically for $\exists$-E, and so $\Delta_n, \exists x\psi_n \vdash_R \varphi$. Thus $\Delta_n, \exists x\psi_n \vdash_R \varphi$. Hence $\Psi_n = \Delta_n, \exists x\psi_n \supset \varphi$ by construction and $\Delta_n \vdash_R \exists x\psi_n \supset \varphi$ by $\supset$-I. But now $\Delta_n, \exists x\psi_n \supset \varphi \vdash_R \varphi$. Hence by transitivity $\Delta_n \vdash_R \varphi$.

Therefore $\overline{\Delta} \nvdash_R \varphi$, whence $\varphi \notin \overline{\Delta}$ and $\overline{\Delta} \nvdash_R *$. The same argument as in the propositional case shows that $\overline{\Delta}$ is R-closed and disjunctive. It remains to show that $\overline{\Delta}$ is existential. So suppose $\exists x\psi \in \overline{\Delta}$. Then $\exists x\psi \supset \varphi \notin \overline{\Delta}$. Hence by construction $\psi a \in \overline{\Delta}$ for some a. Moreover since $(a=a) \in \overline{\Delta}$, a is involved in the atomic closure of $\overline{\Delta}$.

The proof of the Intuitionistic Satisfiability Theorem now requires only two extra clauses in the inductive step, to deal with quantified sentences:

Suppose $\exists x\psi \in \Delta$. Since Δ is R-intuitionistic, $\psi t \in \Delta$ for some term t in the atomic closure of Δ. By IH $\Delta \Vdash \psi t$. So (by Corollary 2 to the Soundness Theorem) $\Delta \Vdash \exists x\psi$. The converse is direct.

Finally suppose $\forall x\psi \in \Delta$. Take any $\Gamma \geqslant \Delta$. So $\Delta \subseteq \Gamma$ and $\underline{\Delta} \subseteq \underline{\Gamma}$. Suppose t is involved in $\underline{\Gamma}$. Since $\forall x\psi \in \Delta \subseteq \Gamma$, $\Gamma \vdash_R \psi t$. Thus $\psi t \in \Gamma$ since Γ is R-closed. By IH $\Gamma \Vdash \psi t$. So by defn. of $\Vdash$, $\Delta \Vdash \forall x\psi$. Conversely suppose that $\forall x\psi \notin \Delta$. So $\Delta \nvdash_R \forall x\psi$. Take some name a not involved in Δ. We cannot have $\Delta \vdash_R \psi a$, since a would be parametrical for $\forall$-I; so $\Delta \nvdash_R \psi a$. Now by the maximalization theorem let $\Gamma \geqslant \Delta$ be an R-intuitionistic set not containing ψa, and involving a in its atomic closure. By IH $\Gamma \nVdash \psi a$. Hence by definition of $\Vdash$, $\Delta \nVdash \forall x\psi$.

CHAPTER 7

First order theories

7.1
Computable and recursive functions; Church's thesis *p.136*
7.2
Undecidability of first order functional logic *p.140*
7.3
Properties of theories *p.141*
7.4
General results *p.142*
7.5
The theory of dense strict unbounded orderings *p.144*
7.6
Non-categoricity of arithmetic *p.145*
7.7
Second order arithmetic and logic *p.146*
7.8
Completeness and decidability of successor arithmetic *p.146*
7.9
Representability in Q; limitative theorems for logic and arithmetic *p.152*
7.10
Universally free logic for descriptions and set theory *p.163*

7.1 Computable and recursive functions; Church's thesis. Several results in this chapter call for a preliminary discussion of the notion of 'effective method' and 'computable function'; and the formal notion of 'recursive function' proposed as a precise explication of the latter. Proofs of the many results of recursive function theory are, however, beyond the scope of this book. Our aim here is simply to state and prove one required result, namely the Representability Theorem, and then to concentrate on its application in the so-called 'diagonal method' in proofs of the undecidability of logic and arithmetical theories. For a full development of recursive function theory the reader is referred to the excellent sources listed in the bibliography.

An *effective* method or operation is one which applies to objects of a given class in a mechanical or algorithmic way to produce as value some object (in, perhaps, some other class). In principle an effective method is one that can be carried out (or performed, or applied) by a suitably designed and programmed machine governed by deterministic laws and not subject to any limitations of size or malfunction. In other words, in applying an effective method there is no need for creativity, ingenuity, insight, random choice, divination or divine intervention. An effective method should consist in a recipe or programme for computation that unequivocally determines, at any stage of computation, how the computation shall proceed and terminate.

Examples of effective operations are those represented by the following arrows.

(1) Natural numbers m, n → the sum of m and n
(2) Sequence of symbols ψ → the answer 'yes' or 'no' to the question 'Is ψ a sentence?'
(3) Natural number n → the answer 'yes' or 'no' to the question 'Is n prime?'
(4) Array of sentences Π → the answer 'yes' or 'no' to the question 'Is Π a proof?'

(1) and (3) are numerical examples, while (2) and (4) involve objects such as sequences of symbols and arrays of sentences. However, all finite syntactical objects – expressions, sequences of expressions, tree-like arrays of sequences of expressions – can be *coded* as natural numbers. This coding is known for historical reasons as Gödel numbering, after its inventor. For each type Φ of syntactic objects we have a coding function #. Given any $\varphi \in \Phi$ we can effectively determine $\#(\varphi)$, the code number of φ. No two distinct objects have the same code number. Given a natural number and a type one can

effectively determine whether the number codes an object of that type, and, if so, which object. There is a variety of coding functions in the literature. We shall be interested only in their general properties, and not in any of their details.

Codings are presently defined so that not all numbers need be code numbers (for a given class Φ with its coding #). That is, # need not map Φ *onto* $\mathbb{N}$. This can in general be remedied as follows. First define $\gamma(n)$, the number of objects in Φ whose code numbers are less than or equal to n:

$$\begin{aligned} \gamma(0) &= 1 \quad \text{if } \#\varphi = 0 \text{ for some } \varphi \in \Phi \\ &\ 0 \quad \text{otherwise} \\ \gamma(n+1) &= 1 + \gamma(n) \quad \text{if } \#\varphi = n+1 \text{ for some } \varphi \in \Phi \\ &\ \gamma(n) \quad \text{otherwise} \end{aligned}$$

Then define $\divideontimes$ as a coding from Φ *onto* $\mathbb{N}$ as follows:

$$\divideontimes(\varphi) = \gamma(\#(\varphi) - 1).$$

$\divideontimes$ is obviously a one-one mapping from Φ onto $\mathbb{N}$ effective in both directions.

Henceforth we shall assume codings of Φ to be onto $\mathbb{N}$, without loss of generality. The inverse $\#^{-1}$ of a coding # may therefore be regarded as an effective enumeration $\#^{-1}(0)$, $\#^{-1}(1), \ldots$ of all the members of Φ. Trivially, $\mathbb{N}$ is coded by the identity map.

We shall be interested only in effective operations on such objects as can be coded as natural numbers. Therefore we confine our attention to effective operations from numbers to numbers, which are called *computable functions*. For the sake of simplicity we shall assume that computable functions are everywhere defined. That is, for each sequence $\vec{n}$ of natural numbers, the value $f(\vec{n})$ of any computable function f exists (and can be computed). We shall also deal with only one-place functions wherever the discussion extends in an obvious way to functions of more than one argument.

Suppose P is a property of objects of type Φ. Then we define c_P, the characteristic function of P, as follows:

$$\begin{aligned} c_P(\#\varphi) &= 0 \quad \text{if} \quad P(\varphi) \\ c_P(\#\varphi) &= 1 \quad \text{if} \quad \text{not-}P(\varphi). \end{aligned}$$

P is said to be *decidable* just in case c_P is computable.

No explanation of effectiveness can serve precisely to define the class of computable functions, for it is a strictly informal notion. The remedy is to give a precise mathematical definition of some class of functions maintained to coincide exactly with the class of computable functions. These precisely defined functions are called *recursive* functions. The thesis that a function is computable if *and only if* it is recursive is called Church's Thesis (with emphasis on the bolder half).

Various definitions of *recursive* have been given by different authors. They have arrived at their definitions from different directions, yet all extant definitions have been shown to define the same class of functions. Thus it appears that the notion of computable function is highly natural and invariant with respect to different attempts formally to characterize it. It is highly unlikely that several radically different but provably coincident explications of the notion should all fall short in exactly the same way. The co-extensiveness of all definitions of *recursive* endows Church's Thesis with considerable plausibility. There are three main kinds of definition of *recursive*.

(I) Definitions in terms of computing machines.

These were arrived at as a result of analysing the essential features of deterministic computation. A function is said to be recursive if and only if some machine of a well-defined kind will compute as output its value for any given arguments as input. It is this kind of definition that makes Church's Thesis *prima facie* most plausible.

(II) Inductive definitions.

Certain basic functions (identity, constant functions, projection functions, succession, addition, etc.) are defined to be recursive, and certain operations (composition, etc.) are specified that form recursive functions from recursive functions. A function is defined to be recursive if and only if it can be built up from the basic functions by means of these operations. It is this kind of definition that is mathematically most readily understood and tractable, and that is exploited for the proof of the Representability Theorem below.

(III) Definitions in terms of equational systems.

We shall give this definition in detail, since we shall exploit it below in our first proof of the undecidability of first order logic.

Consider a language with 0, $s(\ )$, $=$ and infinitely many n-place function signs for each n. We shall call it a language of *first order functional* logic. 0, $s(0)$, $s(s(0))$, ... are the *numerals* respectively for the natural numbers 0, 1, 2, ... We shall write $\underline{n}$ for the numeral for the natural number n. An *equation* will be either a sentence of the form $t=u$ or the universal closure of a formula of the form $t=u$. A *recursion* is a finite set R of equations such that

(1) if $R \vdash \underline{m}=\underline{n}$ then $m=n$, and

(2) for any k-place function sign f involved in R, and any numbers $n_1, \ldots, n_k$ there is a unique number m such that $R \vdash f(\underline{n}_1, \ldots, \underline{n}_k)=\underline{m}$.

By (2) we may naturally associate a function f^R with f:

$$f^R(n_1, \ldots, n_k)=m \quad \text{iff} \quad R \vdash f(\underline{n}_1, \ldots, \underline{n}_k)=\underline{m}$$

A *recursive* function is one of the form f^R for some recursion R involving f.

Example. Consider the recursion R on the left, with its members re-written on the right in a more familiar way:

$\forall x\, f(x,0)=x$	$\forall x\, x+0=x$
$\forall x \forall y\, f(x,s(y))=s(f(x,y))$	$\forall x \forall y\, x+s(y)=s(x+y)$
$\forall x\, g(x,0)=0$	$\forall x\, x.0=0$
$\forall x \forall y\, g(x,s(y))=f(g(x,y),x)$	$\forall x \forall y\, x.s(y)=(x.y)+x$
$\forall x\, h(x,0)=s(0)$	$\forall x\, x^0=s(0)$
$\forall x \forall y\, h(x,s(y))=g(x,h(x,y))$	$\forall x \forall y\, x^{s(y)}=x.x^y$

f^R is addition, g^R is multiplication and h^R is exponentiation.

That a recursive function in sense (III) is computable is seen as follows. Suppose the function is f^R. To compute $f^R(\vec{n})$ for any $\vec{n}$ enumerate all proofs whose undischarged assumptions are in R. After a finite time (by (2)) we shall find one with conclusion $f(\vec{\underline{n}})=\underline{m}$, for some unique natural number m; which is therefore $f^R(\vec{n})$, by (1).

As can be expected, the converse is more difficult to make plausible. All one can point to in the case of recursive functions in sense (III) is the fact that in general a proof (in normal form) of $f(\vec{\underline{n}})=\underline{m}$ from R will consist of $\forall$-eliminations followed by substitution of identicals in equations involving terms built up from 0, s and function letters involved in R. Effecting these substitutions is tantamount to 'operating on' the results of 'prior computations' (corresponding to the appropriate sub-proofs) so as to compute overall the value m for $f^R(\vec{n})$. Since the proof is finite, only finitely many prior computations will be involved. That this very general feature of computation can always be enshrined in proofs from an appropriate recursion is the gist of the claim that every computable function is recursive.

As an example, the following proof in the more familiar notation (with parentheses omitted wherever possible) establishes that $1^1=1$:

$$\dfrac{\dfrac{\forall x\, x+0=x}{0+0=0} \qquad \dfrac{\dfrac{\dfrac{\dfrac{\dfrac{\dfrac{\forall x \forall y\, x^{sy}=x.x^y}{\forall y\, s0^{sy}=s0.s0^y}}{s0^{s0}=s0.s0^0} \quad \dfrac{\forall x\, x^0=s0}{s0^0=s0}}{s0^{s0}=s0.s0} \quad \dfrac{\dfrac{\forall x \forall y\, x.sy=(x.y)+x}{\forall y\, s0.sy=(s0.y)+s0}}{s0.s0=(s0.0)+s0}}{s0^{s0}=(s0.0)+s0} \quad \dfrac{\forall x\, x.0=0}{s0.0=0}}{s0^{s0}=0+s0} \quad \dfrac{\dfrac{\forall x \forall y\, x+sy=s(x+y)}{\forall y\, 0+sy=s(0+y)}}{0+s0=s(0+0)}}{s0^{s0}=s(0+0)}}{s0^{s0}=s0}$$

7.2 Undecidability of first order functional logic. The natural model $\mathbb{N}$ consists of the natural numbers with 0 (the number) named by 0 (the name), and with successor, addition and multiplication respectively represented by s, $+$ and $.$. The first order language whose only (distinguished) extra-logical expressions are 0, s, $+$ and $.$ will be known as the *language of arithmetic*. Given a recursion R we may extend the natural model $\mathbb{N}$ to $\mathbb{N}_R$ by assigning to each function sign f involved in R the function f_R.

Lemma 1. Any equation deducible from R is true in $\mathbb{N}_R$.

Proof. By induction on the number of occurrences of universal quantifiers plus the number of occurrences of function signs other than s occurring in an equation.

Basis. If $R \vdash \underline{m}=\underline{n}$ then by (1) $\mathbb{N}_R \models \underline{m}=\underline{n}$.

Inductive step. Case (i): $R \vdash t=u$ where $t=u$ involves a term $h(\underline{\vec{n}})$. By (2) there is a unique m such that $R \vdash h(\underline{\vec{n}})=\underline{m}$. So $h(\underline{\vec{n}})$ and $\underline{m}$ denote the same member of $\mathbb{N}_R$; and by substitutivity $R \vdash (t=u)^{h(\underline{\vec{n}})}_{\underline{m}}$. By IH $(t=u)^{h(\underline{\vec{n}})}_{\underline{m}}$ is true in $\mathbb{N}_R$; so $t=u$ is also.

Case (ii): $R \vdash \forall x\psi$. For all n $R \vdash \psi\underline{n}$ whence by IH $\mathbb{N}_R \models \psi\underline{n}$. Thus $\mathbb{N}_R \models \forall x\psi$.

We are presently dealing with a language of first order functional logic, to which we now add just one one-place predicate P. Call the resulting language L.

Lemma 2. For any decidable set D of natural numbers there is a sentence φ of L such that for all n $n \in D$ iff $\varphi \vdash P\underline{n}$.

Proof. By Church's Thesis, for some recursion R involving f, f^R is the characteristic function of D. Extend $\mathbb{N}_R$ to M by assigning P the extension D. Obviously $M \models \forall x(fx=0 \supset Px)$. By Lemma 1, $\&R$, the conjunction of all the members of R, is true in M. Let φ be the sentence $\&R \,\&\, \forall x(fx=0 \supset Px)$. Then φ is true in M. Now suppose $n \in D$. Then $f^R(n)=0$. So $R \vdash f\underline{n}=0$. By $\&$-, $\forall$- and $\supset$-eliminations $\varphi \vdash P\underline{n}$. Conversely suppose $\varphi \vdash P\underline{n}$. Since φ is true in M, so is $P\underline{n}$. Thus $n \in D$.

Theorem. Theoremhood in L is undecidable.

Proof. By a diagonal construction. Suppose for reductio that theoremhood in L is decidable. Let $\varphi_0, \varphi_1, \ldots$ be an effective enumeration of sentences of L. Then $\{n \mid \nvdash \varphi_n \supset P\underline{n}\}$ is a decidable set of natural numbers. By Lemma 2 for some k $\nvdash \varphi_n \supset P\underline{n}$ iff $\varphi_k \vdash P\underline{n}$ (for all n). In particular $\varphi_k \nvdash P\underline{k}$ iff $\varphi_k \vdash P\underline{k}$, a contradiction.

In later sections we shall obtain further undecidability results for languages with a more restricted vocabulary than the language L above. Inspection of our proof above reveals that we have proved undecidability when the deductive system contains only the rules for identity and the elimination rules for $\&$, $\supset$ and $\forall$. Thus both classical and intuitionistic theoremhood in L is undecidable.

7.3 Properties of theories. Henceforth, unless otherwise indicated, we shall be concerned with first order languages with identity with a classical underlying logic. Theories will be deductively closed sets of sentences (in a given language). In this section we shall define several interesting properties of theories and indicate their general interrelationships.

(1) Completeness.

This property was called *maximality* in the previous chapter, so as not to confuse it with completeness of the underlying logic that was being discussed there. Now we define: a theory Δ is *complete* iff for all φ (in the language of Δ) either $\varphi \in \Delta$ or $(\sim\varphi) \in \Delta$.

(2) Categoricity (in power).

Δ is *categorical* iff any two models of Δ are isomorphic. By the Löwenheim-Skolem Theorem, however, no theory with an infinite model is categorical. Thus we define a narrower notion:

> Δ is *categorical in power* κ (Δ is κ-*categorical*) iff any two models of Δ with exactly κ members are isomorphic.

A definitive way of showing that a theory (usually presented axiomatically) is consistent is to exhibit a *finite* model of the theory. Thus we shall be interested in the property

(3) Δ has a finite model.

How does one know when one 'has' a theory? A theory may be presented in a very abstract way, for example

> the set of sentences of the language of arithmetic which are true in the natural model $\mathbb{N}$

or it may be presented axiomatically, either by listing its axioms or providing a general method for recognizing when a sentence is an axiom. The theory would then be understood as the deductive closure of those axioms. A third way, which will provide our definition of axiomatizability, is simply to give a method for listing all theorems of the theory. The method must be effective:

(4) Δ is *axiomatizable* iff there is an effective enumeration of all the members of Δ.

A stronger condition than axiomatizability is that of decidability:

(5) Δ is *decidable* iff there is an effective method for deciding, given any sentence of the language of Δ, whether it is in Δ.

The next properties to be formulated are of special interest in arithmetical theories, but can be defined reasonably abstractly. We suppose that the language of Δ contains an effectively enumerable sequence $\underline{0}, \underline{1}, \underline{2}, \ldots$ of distinct terms. We say that

(6) Δ is *representing* iff for any decidable property P of natural

numbers there is a formula ψx of the language of Δ such that for any n $P(n)$ iff $\Delta \vdash \psi \underline{n}$.

Note that any representing theory is consistent.

(7) Δ is *strongly representing* iff for any decidable property P of natural numbers there is a wff ψx in the language of Δ such that for any natural number n if $P(n)$ then $\Delta \vdash \psi \underline{n}$ and if not-$P(n)$ then $\Delta \vdash \sim\psi \underline{n}$.

Note that any consistent strongly representing theory is representing, and any consistent extension of a strongly representing theory is strongly representing.

Let $\varphi \rightarrow \overline{\varphi}$ be a mapping of sentences to closed terms (in the language of Δ). Given a formula $\psi(x)$ with one free variable we shall say

(8) Δ is *self-representing* (via ψ) iff for every sentence φ $\psi(\overline{\varphi}) \in \Delta$ iff $\varphi \in \Delta$.

Let $\theta \rightarrow \overline{\overline{\theta}}$ be a mapping of formula with one free variable to closed terms (in the language of Δ). Given a formula $\delta(x,y)$ we shall say

(9) δ is a diagonal for Δ iff for every formula θ with one free variable, $\delta(\overline{\overline{\theta}},a) \dashv\vdash^{\Delta} a = \overline{\theta(\overline{\overline{\theta}})}$, with a parametrical.

Thus a diagonal δ 'represents' a mapping that assigns to each formula θ with one free variable the sentence $\theta(\overline{\overline{\theta}})$, which results from substituting the associated term $\overline{\overline{\theta}}$ for the free variable in θ. We do not concern ourselves here with the nature of the mappings $^{-}$, $^{=}$. In actual applications below $\overline{\varphi}$ will be $\underline{\natural\varphi}$ (the numeral for the code number of φ, for some fixed coding $\natural$ of sentences) and $\overline{\overline{\theta}}$ will likewise be $\underline{\#\theta}$ (for some fixed coding # of formulae with one free variable).

7.4 General results. We now have the following general results.

(I) Every decidable theory is axiomatizable.

Proof. Go down an effective enumeration of sentences in the language of the theory, deciding which are theorems of the theory, thereby forming an effective enumeration of the latter.

(II) Axiomatizability is deducibility from a decidable set.

Proof. Suppose Δ is given by an effective enumeration $\varphi_0, \varphi_1, \ldots$. Let $\varphi_n{}^*$ be the n-fold conjunction of φ_n with itself. Obviously Δ^* is decidable and logically implies just the members of Δ. Conversely, suppose Δ is the set of all conclusions deducible from a decidable set. We can effectively enumerate all proofs in the language (augmented by infinitely many new names for proof-theoretical purposes). We can effectively determine of each proof whether its undischarged assumptions are in the given decidable set. Finally we can effectively determine of each proof what its conclusion is. Thus we can form an effective enumeration of all the members of Δ.

(III) Every complete axiomatizable theory is decidable.

Proof. Suppose the complete theory Δ is effectively enumerated by $\varphi_0, \varphi_1, \ldots$. Given any sentence φ we know that either φ will occur as some φ_n or that $(\sim\varphi)$ will so occur. Thus we can effectively determine whether φ or $(\sim\varphi)$ is in Δ.

(IV) Every theory categorical in some infinite power, with no finite models, is complete.

Proof. Suppose Δ is categorical in the infinite power κ and has no finite models. Suppose $\varphi \notin \Delta$. Then $\Delta, \sim\varphi \nvdash$ ※. Thus $\Delta, \sim\varphi$ has a model, which must be infinite. By the Löwenheim-Skolem Theorem, $\Delta, \sim\varphi$ has a model of power κ. Similarly, if $(\sim\varphi) \notin \Delta$ then Δ, φ has a model of power κ. But these models would be non-isomorphic, contrary to κ-categoricity. So either $\varphi \in \Delta$ or $(\sim\varphi) \in \Delta$.

(V) Every representing theory is undecidable.

Proof. Suppose Δ is representing and, for reductio, decidable. Then the property $\psi_n \underline{n} \notin \Delta$ of natural numbers would be decidable, where $\psi_0, \psi_1, \ldots$ is an effective enumeration of all formulae with one free variable. Since Δ is representing there would be some such formula ψ_k such that for all n $\psi_n \underline{n} \notin \Delta$ iff $\psi_k \underline{n} \in \Delta$. In particular we would have $\psi_k \underline{k} \notin \Delta$ iff $\psi_k \underline{k} \in \Delta$, a contradiction.

This argument also establishes that any consistent extension of a strongly representing theory is undecidable.

(VI) Every consistent self-representing theory with a diagonal is incomplete.

Proof. Suppose (1) for every sentence φ $\psi(\bar\varphi) \in \Delta$ iff $\varphi \in \Delta$; and
(2) for every formula θ with one free variable
$$\delta(\bar{\bar\theta}, a) \dashv^{\Delta}\vdash a = \overline{\theta(\bar{\bar\theta})}.$$

Let $\varepsilon(y)$ be the formula $\forall x\, \delta(y, x) \supset \sim\psi(x)$ and let γ be the sentence $\varepsilon(\bar{\bar\varepsilon})$. The following two proofs show (3) $\gamma \dashv^{\Delta}\vdash \sim\psi(\bar\gamma)$:

$$\dfrac{\dfrac{\dfrac{}{\Delta, \bar\gamma = \overline{\varepsilon(\bar{\bar\varepsilon})}}\text{ by defn. of } \gamma}{\delta(\bar{\bar\varepsilon}, \bar\gamma)}\text{ by (2)} \qquad \dfrac{\forall x\, \delta(\bar{\bar\varepsilon}, x) \supset \sim\psi(x)}{\delta(\bar{\bar\varepsilon}, \bar\gamma) \supset \sim\psi(\bar\gamma)}}{\sim\psi(\bar\gamma)}$$

$$\dfrac{\dfrac{\dfrac{\dfrac{\dfrac{\Delta, \overline{\delta(\bar{\bar\varepsilon}, a)}^{\,(1)}}{a = \overline{\varepsilon(\bar{\bar\varepsilon})}}\text{ by (2)} \qquad \dfrac{}{\bar\gamma = \overline{\varepsilon(\bar{\bar\varepsilon})}}\text{ by defn. of } \gamma}{a = \bar\gamma} \qquad \sim\psi(\bar\gamma)}{\sim\psi(a)}}{\delta(\bar{\bar\varepsilon}, a) \supset \sim\psi(a)}{}^{(1)}}{\forall x\, \delta(\bar{\bar\varepsilon}, x) \supset \sim\psi(x),\ \text{i.e. } \gamma.}$$

Intuitively, given the diagonal δ, the sentence γ 'says of itself' (via the mappings $^{-}$, $^{=}$) that it lacks ψ. Notice that the interdeducibility result just given does not depend on any condition on ψ. If, however, we assume (1) – that ψ is a representing predicate for Δ – then we can show that neither γ nor $(\sim\gamma)$ is in Δ.

For, suppose $\gamma \in \Delta$. By (1) $\psi(\overline{\gamma}) \in \Delta$, and by (3) $\sim\psi(\overline{\gamma}) \in \Delta$, thereby rendering Δ inconsistent.

Next, suppose $(\sim\gamma) \in \Delta$. By (3) $\psi(\overline{\gamma}) \in \Delta$, whence by (1) $\gamma \in \Delta$, again rendering Δ inconsistent.

This establishes our result.

7.5 The theory of dense strict unbounded orderings. In this section we investigate the properties of the theory of dense strict unbounded orderings, given by the following axioms.

$$\forall x \forall y (x < y \supset \sim y < x)$$
$$\forall x \forall y \forall z ((x < y \,\&\, y < z) \supset x < z)$$
$$\forall x \forall y (x = y \vee x < y \vee y < x)$$
$$\forall x \forall y (x < y \supset \exists z (x < z \,\&\, z < y))$$
$$\forall x (\exists y\, y < x \,\&\, \exists y\, x < y).$$

Theorem. The theory given by the axioms above is $\aleph_0$-categorical.

Proof. Suppose A and B are countably infinite domains endowed with orderings satisfying the axioms above. By countability there is a mapping f of $\mathbb{N}$ onto A and a mapping g of $\mathbb{N}$ onto B. Now define two mappings f', g' of $\mathbb{N}$ onto A, B respectively by means of the following interlocking clauses:

For $n = 2k$ (i) let $g'(n) = g(k)$
(ii) choose $f'(n)$ to correspond to $g(k)$;
for $n = 2k+1$ (i) let $f'(n) = f(k)$
(ii) choose $g'(n)$ to correspond to $f(k)$,

where the 'correspondence' in question ensures that the induced map given by $f'(j) \to g'(j)$, for $j \leq n$, is an order isomorphism between $\{f'(0), \ldots, f'(n)\}$ and $\{g'(0), \ldots, g'(n)\}$.

Choices (ii) are always possible because of the density and unboundedness of each ordering. Since f and g are onto A and B respectively, so are f' and g' by (i). Thus the induced map given by $f'(j) \to g'(j)$, for all j, is an order isomorphism between A and B.

The theory in question obviously has no finite models. Therefore by (IV) it is complete. It is axiomatized. Therefore by (III) it is decidable.

7.6 Non-categoricity of arithmetic. Another non-trivial theory with no finite models is the theory of successor arithmetic, given by the following axioms.

(1) $\forall x \sim 0 = s(x)$
(2) $\forall x \forall y\, s(x) = s(y) \supset x = y$
(3) all instances of the induction schema
$(\psi(0)\,\&\,\forall x(\psi(x)\supset\psi(s(x)))) \supset \forall x\psi(x).$

It is a background assumption of our formal semantics that all names denote and all function signs represent functions everywhere defined on the domain. With an arrow to represent succession we know by (1) that we cannot have

$$\overset{\curvearrowleft}{\underset{0}{\cdot}}$$

Thus we have $\underset{0}{\cdot} \longrightarrow \underset{s(0)}{\cdot}$. By (2) we cannot have $\underset{0}{\cdot} \longrightarrow \overset{\curvearrowleft}{\underset{s(0)}{\cdot}}$ and by (1) we cannot have $\underset{0}{\cdot} \longleftrightarrow \underset{s(0)}{\cdot}$; so, since the successor function is everywhere defined, we have $\underset{0}{\cdot} \longrightarrow \underset{s(0)}{\cdot} \longrightarrow \underset{s(s(0))}{\cdot}$. Repeating these considerations we know we must have an infinite progression starting with 0 within any model of our axioms. Since the successor function is single valued, there will be only one such progression in any such model. Its members will be called the *natural numbers* of that model. The property of being a natural number is that of 'being finitely many steps of succession away from 0'. Thus 0 is a natural number, and if n is a natural number then so is $s(n)$. Thus if we could take the property of being a natural number as a substitution instance of ψ in the induction schema (3) we would have that every individual in any model of the axioms is a natural number (within that model). Thus all models of the theory would be isomorphic to the infinite progression above. We would have ruled out the possibility of 'non-natural' members; in other words, we would have ensured that the natural numbers are the *only* individuals in any model.

The problem, however, is that we may substitute for ψ in (3) only such predicates as are expressible in the language. It turns out, indeed, that '... is a natural number' is not one of these. This is the upshot of the following theorem.

Theorem. Th($\mathbb{N}$) is not $\aleph_0$-categorical.

Proof. Let a be a name governed by the inequations $\sim a = 0$, $\sim a = s(0)$, ... Call the set of these inequations Δ. If $\sim a = s^k(0)$ is the last of them to occur in a finite subset of Th($\mathbb{N}$)$\cup\Delta$ then by letting a denote the same number as $s^{k+1}(0)$ we have in the model $\mathbb{N}$ thus extended a model of the finite subset in question. Thus by compact-

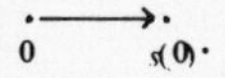

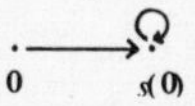

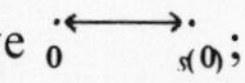

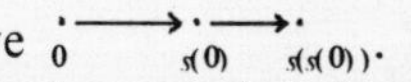

ness $Th(\mathbb{N}) \cup \Delta$ has a model. By the Löwenheim-Skolem theorem $Th(\mathbb{N}) \cup \Delta$ has a model of cardinality $\aleph_0$. Such a model must contain a member named by *a* which is not a natural number of that model.

Thus not even all first order truths about the natural number sequence ensure that a countable model of those truths consists only of the natural number sequence.

7.7 Second order arithmetic and logic. In a *second order* language of arithmetic, which allowed quantification over predicates, we could express the principle of induction by the single sentence

$$\forall\psi((\psi(0) \,\&\, \forall x(\psi(x) \supset \psi(s(x)))) \supset \forall x\psi(x)).$$

If we interpret second order quantification, when giving our formal semantics, as over all subsets of the domain then in our arithmetical example the numbers would form such a subset and would therefore, by the principle of induction, exhaust the domain. Thus the set Σ of second order axioms for successor arithmetic:

$$\forall x \sim 0 = s(x)$$
$$\forall x \forall y\ s(x) = s(y) \supset x = y$$
$$\forall\psi((\psi(0) \,\&\, \forall x(\psi(x) \supset \psi(s(x)))) \supset \forall x\psi(x))$$

would have only one model (up to isomorphism) in the natural number sequence. So, in contrast to the first order case, second order successor arithmetic is $\aleph_0$-categorical.

With the set Δ of inequations as above, and by the same argument as given there, every finite subset of $\Sigma \cup \Delta$ has a model. Since, however, no model of $\Sigma \cup \Delta$ is isomorphic to the natural number sequence it follows that $\Sigma \cup \Delta$ has no model.

Thus second order logical consequence is not compact. In the case of second order logic, therefore, we cannot have the general completeness result that any logical consequence of a set of premisses is deducible therefrom. The possibility remains, however, that for *finite* sets of premisses this result would still hold. But we shall see below that the set of all second order logical truths is not axiomatizable.

Thus the increase in *expressive* power that is obtained by allowing second order quantification and that is reflected by the categoricity of second order successor arithmetic, is offset by a crucial loss of deductive power.

7.8 Completeness and decidability of successor arithmetic. In 7.5 we proved the theory of strict dense unbounded orderings to be complete, hence decidable, by showing that it was $\aleph_0$-categorical. This method is not available in the case of first order successor arithmetic, which we have shown not to be $\aleph_0$-categorical.

There is, however, another method for proving completeness and decidability of the theory of successor arithmetic. This is known as the method of quantifier elimination for reasons which will become apparent by Lemma 8 below. The method tells us how to find, for any sentence of the language, a provably equivalent quantifier-free sentence which, because it is quantifier-free, is readily decidable. In applying the method we need some intimacy with the internal workings of the theory, which it is the purpose of subsequent lemmata to impart. We shall also require the following preliminaries.

$s^n t$ will be the term $s(s(\ldots(t)\ldots))$ with n occurrences of s to the left of t. Thus $\underline{n}$ is $s^n 0$. We shall write $\&_i^n \varphi_i$ for the conjunction of $\varphi_0, \ldots \varphi_n$ (where the ordering of bracketing does not matter). From now on I shall omit brackets whenever possible.

For ease in writing out proofs we shall turn the axioms of successor arithmetic into rules of inference:

(1) $\dfrac{0 = st}{\divideontimes}$

(2) $\dfrac{st = su}{t = u}$

(3) $$\dfrac{\varphi(0) \quad \begin{matrix} \overline{\varphi(a)}^{(i)} \\ \vdots \\ \varphi(s(a)) \end{matrix}_{(i)}}{\varphi(t)}$$

where a does not occur in any assumption other than $\varphi(a)$ on which $\varphi(s(a))$ depends.

Obviously any consequence of the axioms can be proved (from no assumptions) by using these rules, and only such consequences can be so proved. We shall use $\vdash$ in the new, extended sense arising out of the incorporation of the rules above.

Lemma 1. If $m \neq n$ then $\vdash \sim s^m t = s^n t$.

Proof. By repeated application of Rule (2) followed by an application of rule (1) prove $\divideontimes$ from the assumption $s^m t = s^n t$, and then apply $\sim$-introduction.

Obviously if $m = n$ then $\vdash s^m t = s^n t$ (reflexivity of identity).

Lemma 2. $\&_i^n \sim b = \underline{i} \dashv\vdash \exists x\, b = s^{n+1} x$.

(Example: $\sim b = 0 \,\&\, \sim b = s0 \,\&\, \sim b = ss0 \dashv\vdash \exists x\, b = sssx$.)

Proof. By induction on n.

Basis. We establish $\sim b = 0 \dashv\vdash \exists x\, b = sx$ by means of the following two proofs:

$$\dfrac{\sim b=0 \qquad \dfrac{\dfrac{\dfrac{\dfrac{\overline{0=0} \quad \overline{\sim 0=0}^{(1)}}{\text{※}}}{\exists x\, 0=sx}}{\sim 0=0 \supset \exists x\, 0=sx}{\scriptstyle (1)} \qquad \dfrac{\dfrac{\overline{sa=sa}}{\exists x\, sa=sx}}{\sim sa=0 \supset \exists x\, sa=sx}}{\sim b=0 \supset \exists x\, b=sx}\text{Rule (3)}}{\exists x\, b=sx}$$

and

$$\dfrac{\exists x\, b=sx \qquad \dfrac{\dfrac{\dfrac{{}^{(2)}\overline{b=sa} \quad \overline{b=0}^{(1)}}{0=sa}}{\text{※}}}{\sim b=0}{\scriptstyle (1)}}{\sim b=0}{\scriptstyle (2)}$$

Inductive hypothesis. $\&_i^{n-1}\sim b=\underline{i} \dashv\vdash \exists x\, b=s^n x$

Inductive step. We establish $\sim b=\underline{n}\,\&\,(\&_i^{n-1}\sim b=\underline{i}) \dashv\vdash \exists x\, b=s^{n+1}x$ by means of the following two proofs:

$$\dfrac{\dfrac{\sim b=\underline{n}\,\&\,(\&_i^{n-1}\sim b=\underline{i})}{\&_i^{n-1}\sim b=\underline{i}} \atop {\text{IH}\ \vdots \atop \exists x\, b=s^n x} \qquad \dfrac{\dfrac{\dfrac{\dfrac{{}^{(3)}\overline{b=s^n a} \quad \overline{a=0}^{(1)}}{b=\underline{n}} \quad \dfrac{\sim b=\underline{n}\,\&\,(\&_i^{n-1}\sim b=\underline{i})}{\sim b=\underline{n}}}{\text{※}}}{\sim a=0}{\scriptstyle (1)} \atop {\text{Basis}\ \vdots \atop \exists x\, a=sx} \qquad \dfrac{\dfrac{{}^{(2)}\overline{a=sc} \quad \overline{b=s^n a}^{(3)}}{b=s^{n+1}c}}{\exists x\, b=s^{n+1}x}}{\exists x\, b=s^{n+1}x}{\scriptstyle (2)}}{\exists x\, b=s^{n+1}x}{\scriptstyle (3)}$$

and

$$\dfrac{\exists x\, b=s^{n+1}x \qquad \dfrac{\dfrac{\dfrac{\dfrac{{}^{(2)}\overline{b=s^{n+1}a} \quad \overline{b=\underline{n}}^{(1)}}{\underline{n}=s^{n+1}a} \atop {\text{n applications of Rule (2)}\ \vdots \atop 0=sa}}{\text{※}}}{\sim b=\underline{n}}{\scriptstyle (1)} \qquad \dfrac{\dfrac{\overline{b=s^{n+1}a}^{(2)}}{\text{i.e. } b=s^n sa}}{\exists x\, b=s^n x} \atop {\text{IH}\ \vdots \atop \&_i^{n-1}\sim b=\underline{i}}}{\sim b=\underline{n}\,\&\,(\&_i^{n-1}\sim b=\underline{i})}}{\sim b=\underline{n}\,\&\,(\&_i^{n-1}\sim b=\underline{i})}{\scriptstyle (2)}$$

Lemma 3. $\vdash \forall x_1 \ldots \forall x_n \exists y\, \&_i^n \sim y=x_i$

Proof. By induction on *n*.

Basis. We have the proof

$$
\dfrac{
\dfrac{\dfrac{\dfrac{\overline{0=s0}^{\,(3)}}{\text{※}}}{\sim s0=0}{\scriptstyle(3)}}{\exists y{\sim}y=0}
\qquad
\dfrac{\overset{(4)}{\overline{\exists y{\sim}y=k}}\qquad \dfrac{\dfrac{\dfrac{\dfrac{\overline{sa=sk}^{\,(1)}}{a=k}\quad \overline{\sim a=k}^{\,(2)}}{\text{※}}}{\sim sa=sk}{\scriptstyle(1)}}{\exists y{\sim}y=sk}}{\exists y{\sim}y=sk}{\scriptstyle(2)}
}{
\dfrac{\exists y{\sim}y=b}{\forall x\exists y{\sim}y=x}
}{\scriptstyle(4)}
$$

Inductive step. We have the proof schema

$$
\dfrac{
\dfrac{\dfrac{\text{By IH}}{\forall x^{1}\dots\forall x_n\exists y\,\&_i^n{\sim}y=x_i}}{\exists y\,\&_i^n{\sim}y=a_i}
\qquad
\dfrac{
\dfrac{\dfrac{\dfrac{\overset{(2)}{\overline{\&_i^n{\sim}b=a_i}}\quad \overline{\sim b=c}^{\,(1)}}{\&_i^n{\sim}b=a_i\,\&{\sim}b=c}}{\exists y\,\&_i^n{\sim}y=a_i\,\&{\sim}y=c}
\qquad
\begin{matrix}\overset{(2)}{\overline{\&_i^n{\sim}b=a_i}}\quad \overline{b=c}^{\,(1)}\\ \underbrace{\hphantom{\&_i^n{\sim}b=a_i\quad b=c}}_{\Pi}\\ \exists y\,\&_i^n{\sim}y=a_i\,\&{\sim}y=c\end{matrix}}{\exists y\,\&_i^n{\sim}y=a_i\,\&{\sim}y=c}{\scriptstyle(1)}
}{\exists y\,\&_i^n{\sim}y=a_i\,\&{\sim}y=c}{\scriptstyle(2)}
}{
\forall x_1\dots\forall x_{n+1}\exists y\,\&_i^{n+1}{\sim}y=x_i
}
$$

where Π will contain many applications of dilemma rounding off a consideration of all possible cases of immediate succession between the $(n+1)$ objects $a_1, \dots, a_n, c$ under consideration. In each case at least one of $a_1, \dots, a_n, c$ will not be the immediate predecessor of any of the others. Its successor will then yield to $\exists y$ in the conclusion of that case. By the applications of dilemma mentioned, this conclusion common to each case will be brought down as the displayed conclusion of Π above. The details are straightforward but too lengthy to display exhaustively on the page. Lemma 3 generalizes easily to

Lemma 4. $\vdash \forall x_1 \dots \forall x_n \exists y\, \&_i^n {\sim} s^n y = x_i$

Lemma 5. Let φ be a conjunction of equations of the form $t=u$ and inequations of the form ${\sim}t=u$, at least one of which involves the name a. Then there is a quantifier-free sentence ψ not involving a, such that $\exists x\varphi_x^a \dashv\vdash \psi$. Moreover any name other than 0 which occurs in ψ occurs in φ.

Proof. Each conjunct of φ involving a has one of the forms

(1) $s^n a = t$

(2) ${\sim}s^n a = t$

(where t does not involve a – that is, t is a numeral or is of the form $s^m b$ for some name b distinct from a)

(3) $s^n a = s^m a$

(4) ${\sim}s^n a = s^m a$

where without loss of generality we consider only the given orderings of terms within the equations and inequations.

Suppose there is a conjunct of form (1) in φ. Choose such a conjunct with n least: suppose it is $s^n a = t$. Consider the sentence

$$\psi =_{df} \varphi_t^{s^n a} \,\&\, (\&_i^n \sim t = \underline{i})$$

Note that ψ does not involve a, and involves only such names other than 0 as occur in φ. The following two proofs show $\exists x \varphi_x^a \dashv\vdash \psi$:

$$\dfrac{\exists x \varphi_x^a \qquad \dfrac{\dfrac{\overset{(1)}{\overline{\varphi}} \qquad \dfrac{\overset{(1)}{\overline{\varphi}}}{s^n a = t}(\&\text{-E's})}{\varphi_t^{s^n a}} \qquad \left.\begin{array}{c}\dfrac{\dfrac{\overset{(1)}{\overline{\varphi}}}{s^n a = t}(\text{by } \&\text{-E's})}{\exists x\, t = s^n x} \\ \&_i^n \sim t = \underline{i}\end{array}\right\} \text{by Lemma 2}}{\varphi_t^{s^n a} \,\&\, (\&_i^n \sim t = \underline{i})}}{\varphi_t^{s^n a} \,\&\, (\&_i^n \sim t = \underline{i})}\,(1)$$

and

$$\dfrac{\text{by Lemma 2}\left\{\begin{array}{c}\dfrac{\varphi_t^{s^n a} \,\&\, (\&_i^n \sim t = \underline{i})}{\&_i^n \sim t = \underline{i}} \\ \exists x\, t = s^n x\end{array}\right. \qquad \dfrac{\dfrac{\overset{(1)}{\overline{t = s^n a}} \qquad \dfrac{\varphi_t^{s^n a} \,\&\, (\&_i^n \sim t = \underline{i})}{\varphi_t^{s^n a}}}{\dfrac{\varphi}{\exists x \varphi_x^a}}}{}}{\exists x \varphi_x^a}\,(1)$$

Now suppose there is no conjunct of form (1) in φ. Replace any conjunct of form (3) by $0=0$ if $m=n$, and by $\sim 0=0$ if $m \neq n$. Replace any conjunct of form (4) by $\sim 0=0$ if $m=n$, and by $0=0$ if $m \neq n$. Call the sentence which results from φ by these replacements χ. By Lemma 1 we have $\varphi \dashv\vdash \chi$. If there are any occurrences of a in χ they are all in conjuncts of form (2). Suppose these are

$$\sim s^{n_1} a = t_1, \ldots, \sim s^{n_k} a = t_k$$

Let n be the maximum of $n_1, \ldots, n_k$. Replace each inequation

$$\sim s^{n_i} a = t_i$$

in χ by the inequation

$$\sim s^n a = s^{(n-n_i)} t_i \qquad (1 \leq i \leq k)$$

Call the sentence which results from χ by these replacements χ^n. By Rule (2) we have $\chi \dashv\vdash \chi^n$. Let ψ be the conjunction of all conjuncts of χ^n that do not involve a. Then $\exists x \chi_x^{na}$ is interdeducible with

$$\psi \,\&\, \exists x(\sim s^n x = s^{(n-n_1)} t_1 \,\&\ldots\&\, \sim s^n x = s^{(n-n_k)} t_k)$$

But by Lemma 4 the right hand conjunct of the last sentence is provable. Thus $\exists x \chi_x^{na} \dashv\vdash \psi$. Hence $\exists x \varphi_x^a \dashv\vdash \psi$, where ψ involves only such names other than 0 as occur in φ.

Lemma 6. Let $\exists x\varphi$ have φ quantifier-free. Then there is a quantifier-free sentence ψ such that $\exists x\varphi \dashv\vdash \psi$. Moreover any name other than 0 that occurs in ψ occurs in φ.

Proof. Choose a name a not occurring in φ. φ^x_a is interdeducible with a disjunctive normal form $\varphi_1 \vee \ldots \vee \varphi_n$, where each disjunct φ_i involving a satisfies the hypotheses of Lemma 5. Now let

$$\exists x\varphi_{1}{}^{a}_{x} \vee \ldots \vee \exists x\varphi_{n}{}^{a}_{x}$$

be obtained by prefixing existential quantifiers to just those disjuncts that involve a. By Lemma 5 there are quantifier-free sentences $\psi_1, \ldots, \psi_n$ not involving a, and involving only such names other than 0 as occur in $\varphi_1, \ldots, \varphi_n$ respectively, such that

$$\psi_i \dashv\vdash \exists x\varphi_{i}{}^{a}_{x} \; (1 \leq i \leq n)$$

Hence we have

$$\psi_1 \vee \ldots \vee \psi_n \dashv\vdash \exists x\varphi_{1}{}^{a}_{x} \vee \ldots \vee \exists x\varphi_{n}{}^{a}_{x}$$

Furthermore by easy proofs we have

$$\exists x\varphi_{1}{}^{a}_{x} \vee \ldots \vee \exists x\varphi_{n}{}^{a}_{x} \dashv\vdash \exists x(\varphi_1 \vee \ldots \vee \varphi_n)^a_x$$

Finally we have

$$\exists x(\varphi_1 \vee \ldots \vee \varphi_n)^a_x \dashv\vdash \exists x\varphi.$$

Thus $\psi =_{df} \psi_1 \vee \ldots \vee \psi_n$ is as required.

Lemma 7. Any sentence φ is interdeducible with a sentence ψ that has no quantifiers and no names other than 0 that do not occur in φ.

Proof. Replace every quantifier prefix $\forall x$ in φ by $\sim\exists x\sim$. Call the sentence that results from φ by these replacements θ. Obviously $\varphi \dashv\vdash \theta$. We now show Lemma 7 holds for θ, by induction on the complexity of sentences not involving the universal quantifier.

Basis. For θ atomic, we can take θ as the desired sentence ψ.

Inductive step. For θ with a connective dominant the result is immediate from the inductive hypothesis.

For $\theta = \exists x\chi$: choose a name a not occurring in θ. Consider χ^x_a. By IH there is a sentence η which has no quantifiers and no names other than 0 not occurring in χ^x_a, such that $\chi^x_a \dashv\vdash \eta$. If η does not involve a, take η as the desired sentence ψ. If η does involve a, apply Lemma 6 to $\exists x\eta^a_x$ to obtain the desired sentence ψ.

Lemma 8. Let φ be a sentence of successor arithmetic involving no names other than 0. Then φ is interdeducible with a truthfunctional compound of equations and inequations involving only numerals.

Proof. Immediate from Lemma 7.

Lemma 9. Let φ be a truthfunctional compound of equations and inequations involving only numerals. Then either $\vdash \varphi$ or $\vdash \sim\varphi$.

Proof. Let τ assign T to provable equations involving only numerals and assign F to disprovable ones. By Lemma 1 τ assigns a value to every equation. Moreover every member of the truth set τ_φ is a theorem of successor arithmetic. By the Truth Set Theorem, if $\tau(\varphi)=T$ then $\tau_\varphi \vdash \varphi$, and if $\tau(\varphi)=F$ then $\tau_\varphi \vdash \sim\varphi$. Therefore either $\vdash \varphi$ or $\vdash \sim\varphi$.

Theorem on Completeness of Successor Arithmetic

Let φ be a sentence of successor arithmetic containing no names other than 0. Then either $\vdash \varphi$ or $\vdash \sim\varphi$.

Proof. By Lemma 8 and Lemma 9.

By (III) the axiomatic theory of successor arithmetic is also decidable. Notice, however, that in all the inductive proofs of results culminating in the last theorem there is implicit a method for finding either a proof or a disproof, from the axioms of successor arithmetic, of any sentence containing *s*( ) and 0 as its only non-logical expressions.

7.9 Representability in Q; limitative theorems for logic and arithmetic. By a more complicated application of the method of quantifier elimination we can establish the decidability and completeness of the axiomatic theory of successor and additive arithmetic. This theory is obtained by adding to the axioms for successor arithmetic the recursion for addition:

$$\forall x\, x+0=x$$
$$\forall x \forall y\, x+sy=s(x+y).$$

When multiplication is introduced, however, the situation is altered. There is a single sentence, which we shall call Q, formulated in the language of full arithmetic, whose deductive closure is undecidable. Q is the conjunction of the following sentences:

$$\forall x \sim sx=0$$
$$\forall x \forall y\, sx=sy \supset x=y$$
$$\forall x(x=0 \vee \exists y\, x=sy)$$
$$\forall x \forall y\, x+y=0 \supset x=0$$
$$\forall x \forall y(\forall z(\sim x+sz=y \,\&\, \sim y+sz=x) \supset x=y)$$
$$\forall x \forall y\, sx+y=s(x+y)$$
$$\forall x\, x+0=x$$
$$\forall x \forall y\, x+sy=s(x+y)$$
$$\forall x\, x.0=0$$
$$\forall x \forall y\, x.sy=(x.y)+x$$

Q is obviously true in the natural model $\mathbb{N}$. By 'Q' we shall sometimes mean the deductive closure of the sentence Q. In this sense we shall also refer to the sentences above as the axioms of Q.

By deducibility in (a theory) Δ we shall mean deducibility relative to Δ. In subsequent discussion of deducibility in Q we shall find it convenient to consider the following rules of inference respectively equivalent to the axioms just given:

$$\frac{st=0}{\divideontimes}$$

$$\frac{st=su}{t=u}$$

$$\begin{array}{ccc} {}^{(i)}\overline{} & & \overline{}^{(i)} \\ t=0 & & t=sa \\ \vdots & & \vdots \\ \varphi & & \varphi \\ \hline & \varphi & \end{array}{}_{(i)}$$

where a does not occur in t, φ or any assumption other than $t=sa$ on which the conclusion φ in the right hand subproof depends

$$\frac{t+u=0}{t=0}$$

$$\frac{\forall z(\sim t+sz=u\ \&\ \sim u+sz=t)}{t=u}$$

Any intersubstitutions of

$st+u$	with	$s(t+u)$
$t+0$	with	t
$t+su$	with	$s(t+u)$
$t.0$	with	0
$t.su$	with	$(t.u)+t$

Q is arithmetically rich enough, as we shall show below, to enable us to prove the following theorem.

Representability Theorem

For every recursive function f there is a formula $\varphi(\vec{x},y)$ of the language of arithmetic such that for all $\vec{n}$

$$\varphi(\underline{\vec{n}},a)\ \dashv_{Q}\vdash\ a=\underline{f(\vec{n})},$$

with a not occurring in $\varphi(\vec{x},y)$. (Recall that $\underline{n}$ is the numeral for the natural number n.)

Example. The formula $x+y=z$ represents addition in Q, since (as we shall see below) for all m,n $\underline{m}+\underline{n}=a\ \dashv_{Q}\vdash\ a=\underline{m+n}$. Note here that $\underline{m}+\underline{n}$ is the additive term formed from the numeral for m and the numeral for n, whereas $\underline{m+n}$ is the numeral for the sum of m and n.

We shall often use a function symbol like + both to denote the corresponding sign of the object language and to represent the usual arithmetical operation in the metalanguage. Context will easily settle which use is intended.

The proof of the Representability Theorem will exploit the *inductive* kind of definition of recursive function explained above. As in the example just given, it is easy to provide representing formulae for the basic recursive functions listed in such a definition. One then proceeds by induction on the length of 'pedigree' of recursive functions, showing how to obtain a representing formula for a freshly constructed recursive function from the previous representing formulae assumed, by inductive hypothesis, to exist for the functions involved at the last stage of construction. We shall use the following inductive definition of recursive function.

The *basic* recursive functions will be

$+$ (addition)
$\cdot$ (multiplication)
$c_=$ (if $m=n$ then $c_=(m,n)=1$, and if $m \neq n$ then $c_=(m,n)=0$)
id_k^m (for $k \leq m$; where $id_k^m(n_1, \ldots, n_m)=n_k$)

The means for constructing new recursive functions from old ones will be

> *Composition*: If f is n-place and $g_1, \ldots, g_n$ are m-place then $f(g_1, \ldots, g_n)$ will be m-place

and

> *Minimization of regular functions*: Suppose f is an $(n+1)$-place function such that for all $\vec{m}$ there is some p such that $f(\vec{m},p)=0$. Then f is said to be *regular*; and the n-place function g is obtained by *minimization of* f iff for all $\vec{m}$ $g(\vec{m})$ is the *least* number p such $f(\vec{m},p)=0$.

Before giving our proof of the Representability Theorem exploiting this inductive definition of recursive function some preliminary remarks and lemmata are in order. Q is not claimed to be the *weakest* theory (in any interesting sense) for which the Representability Theorem holds. Our choice of Q is determined by ease in proving representability and by the fact that Q is finitely axiomatized. (The importance of the latter consideration will emerge below.) Indeed, in our proof of representability we shall appeal only to the following facts about deducibility in Q:

(1) For all m,n $\quad \vdash \underline{m}+\underline{n}=\underline{m+n}$

(2) For all m,n $\quad \vdash \underline{m}.\underline{n}=\underline{m.n}$

(3) For all m,n $\quad$ if $m \neq n$ then $\underline{m}=\underline{n} \vdash \text{※}$

(4) For all $n>0$ $\quad \{\varphi(\underline{k}) \mid k<n\},\ a+sb=\underline{n} \vdash \varphi(a)$

(5) For all n $\quad \forall z(\sim \underline{n}+sz=a \,\&\, \sim a+sz=\underline{n}) \vdash a=\underline{n}$.

So any theory within which (1)–(5) held would do in place of Q for the proof of representability. Let us, however, proceed to establish (1)–(5) in the case of Q.

Proof of fact (*1*). By induction on n.

Basis. $\vdash \underline{m}+0=\underline{m}$, i.e. $\underline{m+0}$.

Inductive step. $\vdash \underline{m}+s\underline{n}=s(\underline{m}+\underline{n})$. By IH $\vdash \underline{m}+\underline{n}=\underline{m+n}$. So, substituting, $\vdash \underline{m}+s\underline{n}=s(\underline{m+n})$. That is, $\vdash \underline{m}+\underline{sn}=\underline{m+sn}$.

Proof of fact (*2*). By induction on n.

Basis. $\vdash \underline{m}.0=0$, i.e. $\underline{m.0}$.

Inductive step. By IH and Fact 1 we have a proof

$$\dfrac{\dfrac{\dfrac{}{\underline{m}.s\underline{n}=(\underline{m}.\underline{n})+\underline{m}} \qquad \dfrac{\vdots\,\text{IH}}{\underline{m}.\underline{n}=\underline{m.n}}}{\underline{m}.s\underline{n}=\underline{m.n}+\underline{m}} \qquad \dfrac{\vdots\,\text{Fact 1}}{\underline{m.n}+\underline{m}=\underline{(m.n)+m}}}{\underline{m}.s\underline{n}=\underline{(m.n)+m}}$$

i.e. $\underline{m}.\underline{sn}=\underline{m.sn}$

Proof of fact (*3*). Use $|m\text{-}n|$ applications of the rule $\dfrac{st=su}{t=u}$ followed by an application of the rule $\dfrac{st=0}{\text{※}}$.

Proof of fact (*4*). By induction on n.

Basis. For $n=1$ we have the proof

$$\dfrac{\varphi(0) \qquad \dfrac{\overset{(1)}{\dfrac{}{a=0}} \qquad \dfrac{\dfrac{\dfrac{\dfrac{\dfrac{\dfrac{a+sb=s0}{s(a+b)=s0}}{a+b=0}}{a=0} \qquad \overset{(1)}{\dfrac{}{a=sc}}}{sc=0}}{\text{※}}}{a=0}_{(1)}}{a=0}}{\varphi(a)}$$

Inductive step. By IH we have a proof

by reflexivity of identity and $\vee$-introductions:

$$\underbrace{\overline{\{(\vee_{i=0}^{n-1}x=\underline{i})^x_j \mid j<n\}}, \qquad \dfrac{\dfrac{\dfrac{a+sb=\underline{sn} \quad \overline{a=sc}^{\,(2)}}{sc+sb=\underline{sn}}}{s(c+sb)=\underline{sn}}}{c+sb=\underline{n}}}$$

$$\dfrac{\dfrac{\overline{a=0}^{\,(2)} \quad \varphi(0)}{\varphi(a)} \qquad \dfrac{\vee_{i=0}^{n-1}c=\underline{i} \quad \left\{\dfrac{\dfrac{\overset{(1)}{\overline{c=\underline{i}}}}{\varphi(s\underline{i})}\text{ by IH }\vdots \quad \dfrac{\overset{(1)}{\overline{c=\underline{i}}} \quad \overset{(2)}{\overline{a=sc}}}{a=s\underline{i}}}{\varphi(a)}\right\}_{i<(n-1)} \quad \dfrac{\dfrac{\overset{(1)}{\overline{c=\underline{n-1}}}}{\varphi(\underline{n})} \quad \dfrac{\overset{(1)}{\overline{c=\underline{n-1}}} \quad \overset{(2)}{\overline{a=sc}}}{a=\underline{n}}}{\varphi(a)}}{\varphi(a)}\,{}_{(1)}}{\varphi(a)}\,{}_{(2)}$$

Proof of fact (5). Obvious from the Q-rule given above corresponding to the fifth axiom.

We are now in a position to prove the Representability Theorem. It follows from the following lemmata.

Lemma 1. $x+y=z$ represents addition. This is obvious from fact (1).

Lemma 2. $x.y=z$ represents multiplication. This is obvious from fact (2).

Lemma 3. $x_1=x_1\,\&\,\ldots\,\&\,x_m=x_m\,\&\,y=x_k$ represents id^m_k. This is obvious by &-*I*, &-*E* and reflexivity of identity.

Lemma 4. $(x=y\,\&\,z=\underline{1})\vee(\sim x=y\,\&\,z=0)$ represents $c_=$.

Proof. By cases, according as $m=n$ or $m\neq n$.

Suppose $m=n$. Then we have the proofs

$$\dfrac{(\underline{m}=\underline{n}\,\&\,a=\underline{1})\vee(\sim\underline{m}=\underline{n}\,\&\,a=0) \qquad \dfrac{\overset{(1)}{\overline{\underline{m}=\underline{n}\,\&\,a=\underline{1}}}}{a=\underline{1}} \qquad \dfrac{\dfrac{\dfrac{\overline{\sim\underline{m}=\underline{n}\,\&\,a=0}^{\,(1)}}{\sim\underline{m}=\underline{n}} \quad \overline{\underline{m}=\underline{n}}}{※}}{a=\underline{1}}\,{}_{(1)}}{a=\underline{1}}$$

i.e. $a=\underline{c_=(m,n)}$

and

$$\dfrac{\dfrac{\overline{\underline{m}=\underline{n}} \quad \overline{a=\underline{1}}}{\underline{m}=\underline{n}\,\&\,a=\underline{1}}}{(\underline{m}=\underline{n}\,\&\,a=\underline{1})\vee(\sim\underline{m}=\underline{n}\,\&\,a=0)}.$$

Now suppose $m \neq n$. Then we have the proofs

$$\dfrac{(\underline{m}=\underline{n}\,\&\,a=\underline{1})\vee(\sim\underline{m}=\underline{n}\,\&\,a=0) \qquad \dfrac{\begin{array}{c}\dfrac{\dfrac{}{\underline{m}=\underline{n}\,\&\,a=\underline{1}}{}^{(1)}}{\underline{m}=\underline{n}}\\ \vdots \text{ by fact (3)}\\ ※\end{array}}{a=0} \qquad \dfrac{\dfrac{}{\sim\underline{m}=\underline{n}\,\&\,a=0}{}^{(1)}}{a=0}}{a=0}{}^{(1)}$$

$$\text{i.e. } a=\underline{c_{=}(m,n)}$$

and

$$\dfrac{\dfrac{\dfrac{\begin{array}{c}\dfrac{}{\underline{m}=\underline{n}}{}^{(1)}\\ \vdots \text{ by fact (3)}\\ ※\end{array}}{\sim\underline{m}=\underline{n}}{}^{(1)} \qquad a=0}{\sim\underline{m}=\underline{n}\,\&\,a=0}}{(\underline{m}=\underline{n}\,\&\,a=\underline{1})\vee(\sim\underline{m}=\underline{n}\,\&\,a=0)}\,.$$

Thus we have shown that our basic recursive functions are representable. We continue with two lemmata on representability of derived recursive functions – functions obtained by composition or minimization.

Lemma 5. Suppose f is m-place, represented by φ, and $g_1, \ldots, g_m$ are k-place, respectively represented by $\psi_1, \ldots, \psi_m$. Then $f(g_1, \ldots, g_m)$ is represented by the formula

$$\exists y_1 \ldots \exists y_m(\mathop{\&}_{i=1}^{m}\psi_i(\vec{x},y_i)\,\&\,\varphi(y_1, \ldots, y_m, y)).$$

Proof. Suppressing parentheses wherever possible, we have the proof

$$\dfrac{\exists y_1 \ldots \exists y_m \mathop{\&}_{i=1}^{m}\psi_i\underline{\vec{n}}y_i\,\&\,\varphi y_1 \ldots y_m a \qquad \begin{array}{c}\dfrac{\dfrac{{}^{(1)}\dfrac{}{\mathop{\&}_{i=1}^{m}\psi_i\underline{\vec{n}}b_i\,\&\,\varphi b_1 \ldots b_m a}}{\varphi b_1 \ldots b_m a} \qquad j=1,\ldots,m\left\{\begin{array}{c}\dfrac{\dfrac{}{\mathop{\&}_{i=1}^{m}\psi_i\underline{\vec{n}}b_i\,\&\,\varphi b_1 \ldots b_m a}{}^{(1)}}{\psi_j\underline{\vec{n}}b_j}\\ \vdots\\ (\text{since } \psi_j\\ \text{represents } g_j)\\ \vdots\\ b_j=\underline{g_j\vec{n}}\end{array}\right\}}{\varphi\underline{g_1\vec{n}} \ldots \underline{g_m\vec{n}}a}\\ \vdots\\ (\text{since } \varphi \text{ represents } f)\\ \vdots\\ a=\underline{fg_1\vec{n} \ldots g_m\vec{n}}\end{array}}{a=\underline{fg_1\vec{n} \ldots g_m\vec{n}}}{}^{(1)}$$

and the proof

$$
\dfrac{\dfrac{\text{since } \psi_i \text{ represents } g_i\text{:}\quad \overline{\psi_1\underline{\vec{n}}\,\underline{g_1\vec{n}}}\ \ldots\ \overline{\psi_m\underline{\vec{n}}\,\underline{g_m\vec{n}}} \qquad \begin{array}{c} a=\underline{fg_1\vec{n}\ldots g_m\vec{n}} \\ \vdots \\ (\text{since } \varphi \text{ represents } f) \\ \vdots \\ \varphi\underline{g_1\vec{n}}\ldots\underline{g_m\vec{n}}a \end{array}}{\mathop{\&}\limits_{i=1}^{m}\psi_i\underline{\vec{n}}\underline{g_i\vec{n}}\,\&\,\varphi\underline{g_1\vec{n}}\ldots\underline{g_m\vec{n}}a}}{\exists y_1\ldots\exists y_m \mathop{\&}\limits_{i=1}^{m}\psi_i\underline{\vec{n}}y_i\,\&\,\varphi y_1\ldots y_m a}
$$

Lemma 6. Suppose f is a regular $(n+1)$-place function represented by $\varphi(\vec{x},y,z)$; that is for all $\vec{m},p$ $\varphi(\underline{\vec{m}},\underline{p},a) \dashv\vdash a=\underline{f(\vec{m},p)}$. Let g be obtained by minimization of f; i.e. for all $\vec{m}$ $g(\vec{m})$ is the least number p such that $f(\vec{m},p)=0$. Then g is represented by the formula

$$\varphi(\vec{x},y,0)\,\&\,\forall z\forall w(z+sw=y\supset\sim\varphi(\vec{x},z,0));$$

i.e. for all $\vec{m}$ $\quad\varphi(\underline{\vec{m}},a,0)\,\&\,\forall z\,\forall w(z+sw=a\supset\sim\varphi(\underline{\vec{m}},z,0)) \dashv\vdash a=\underline{g(\vec{m})}$.

Proof. Since $f(\vec{m},g(\vec{m}))=0$ we have by representability

$$\vdash \varphi(\underline{\vec{m}},\underline{g(\vec{m})},0).$$

For all $i<g(\vec{m}), f(\vec{m},i)\neq 0$; whence again by representability

$$\vdash \sim\varphi(\underline{\vec{m}},\underline{i},0).$$

Hence by fact (4) about deducibility in Q we have

$$a+sb=\underline{g(\vec{m})} \vdash \sim\varphi(\underline{\vec{m}},a,0) \qquad \ldots\ (*)$$

We now have the proof

$$
\dfrac{\dfrac{\overline{\varphi\underline{\vec{m}}\,\underline{g\vec{m}}\,0} \qquad \dfrac{\dfrac{\begin{array}{c}\overline{a+sb=\underline{g\vec{m}}}^{\,(1)} \\ \vdots\ \text{by } (*) \\ \sim\varphi(\underline{\vec{m}},a,0)\end{array}}{a+sb=\underline{g\vec{m}}\supset\sim\varphi\underline{\vec{m}}a0}\,(1)}{\forall z\forall w(z+sw=\underline{g\vec{m}}\supset\sim\varphi\underline{\vec{m}}z0)}}{\varphi\underline{\vec{m}}\,\underline{g\vec{m}}\,0\,\&\,\forall z\forall w(z+sw=\underline{g\vec{m}}\supset\sim\varphi\underline{\vec{m}}z0) \qquad a=\underline{g\vec{m}}}}{\varphi\underline{\vec{m}}a0\,\&\,\forall z\forall w(z+sw=a\supset\sim\varphi\underline{\vec{m}}z0)}
$$

and the proof opposite:

$$\dfrac{\dfrac{\dfrac{\varphi\underline{\vec{m}}\,\underline{g\vec{m}}\,0}{} \quad \dfrac{\dfrac{(1)}{\underline{g\vec{m}}+sb=a} \quad \dfrac{\dfrac{\varphi\underline{\vec{m}}a0\ \&\ \forall z\forall w(z+sw=a\supset\sim\varphi\underline{\vec{m}}z0)}{\forall z\forall w(z+sw=a\supset\sim\varphi\underline{\vec{m}}z0)}}{\underline{g\vec{m}}+sb=a\supset\sim\varphi\underline{\vec{m}}\,\underline{g\vec{m}}\,0}}{\sim\varphi\underline{\vec{m}}\,\underline{g\vec{m}}\,0}}{※}}{\sim\underline{g\vec{m}}+sb=a}\,(1)$$

$$\dfrac{\dfrac{\dfrac{\varphi\underline{\vec{m}}a0\ \&\ \forall z\forall w(z+sw=a\supset\sim\varphi\underline{\vec{m}}z0)}{\varphi\underline{\vec{m}}a0} \quad \dfrac{\dfrac{2)}{a+sb=\underline{g\vec{m}}}\ \vdots\ (*)}{\sim\varphi\underline{\vec{m}}a0}}{※}}{\sim a+sb=\underline{g\vec{m}}}\,(2)$$

$$\dfrac{\dfrac{\sim\underline{g\vec{m}}+sb=a \qquad \sim a+sb=\underline{g\vec{m}}}{\sim\underline{g\vec{m}}+sb=a\ \&\sim a+sb=\underline{g\vec{m}}}}{\forall z(\sim\underline{g\vec{m}}+sz=a\ \&\sim a+sz=\underline{g\vec{m}})}$$

$$\vdots \quad \text{by fact (5)}$$

$$a=\underline{g\vec{m}}$$

The Representability Theorem is an immediate consequence of Lemmata (1)–(6) concerning representability of basic and derived recursive functions.

Corollary 1. Q is strongly representing.

Proof. Suppose P is a decidable property of natural numbers. By Church's Thesis its characteristic function c_P is recursive. By the Representability Theorem there is a formula $\psi(x,y)$ such that for all n $\psi(\underline{n},a)\ \dashv^{Q}\vdash\ a=\underline{c_P(n)}$. We show that the predicate $\psi(x,0)$ strongly represents P:

(i) Suppose $P(n)$. Then $c_P(n)=0$. Thus $Q\vdash\psi(\underline{n},0)$.

(ii) Suppose not-$P(n)$. Then $c_P(n)=1$. Thus $Q,\psi(\underline{n},0)\vdash 0=\underline{1}$, whence $Q\vdash\sim\psi(\underline{n},0)$.

Corollary 2. Q has a diagonal.

Proof. Suppose $\#$ is a coding of formulae with one free variable and $\natural$ is a coding of sentences. The mapping

$$n\rightarrow\natural(\#^{-1}(n)(\underline{n}))$$

is effective. By Church's Thesis it is recursive. Hence by the Representability Theorem there is a formula $\delta(x,y)$ such that for all n

$$\delta(\underline{n},a)\ \dashv^{Q}\vdash\ a=\underline{\natural(\#^{-1}(n)(\underline{n}))}$$

If θ is a formula with one free variable let $\overline{\overline{\theta}}=\underline{\#\theta}$, and if θ is a sentence let $\overline{\theta}=\underline{\natural\theta}$. Then for all ψ $\delta(\underline{\#\psi},a)\ \dashv^{Q}\vdash\ a=\underline{\natural(\#^{-1}(\#\psi)(\underline{\#\psi}))}$, that is, $\delta(\overline{\overline{\psi}},a)\ \dashv^{Q}\vdash\ a=\overline{\psi(\overline{\overline{\psi}})}$.

Corollary 3. Any axiomatizable subtheory of Th($\mathbb{N}$) containing Q is self-representing. (Hence, by (vi) and Corollary 2, is incomplete.)

Proof. Suppose Δ is an axiomatisable subtheory of Th($\mathbb{N}$) containing Q. Let Δ be given by the effective enumeration $\theta_0, \theta_1, \ldots$ and let $\varphi_0, \varphi_1, \ldots$ be an effective enumeration of all sentences. Consider the decidable relation R of natural numbers defined by

$$\varphi_m = \theta_n$$

that is, the m'th sentence is the n'th theorem of Δ. By Church's Thesis the characteristic function c_R is recursive. By the Representability Theorem there is a formula $\psi(x,y,z)$ such that for all m,n $\psi(\underline{m},\underline{n},a) \dashv^{Q}\vdash a = \underline{c_R(m,\dot{n})}$. Hence $\varphi_m = \theta_n$ iff $Q \vdash \psi(\underline{m},\underline{n},0)$. We now show that $\varphi_m \in \Delta$ iff $\exists x\psi(\underline{m},x,0) \in \Delta$.

(i) Suppose $\varphi_m \in \Delta$. Then for some n $\varphi_m = \theta_n$, whence $c_R(m,n) = 0$. Thus $Q \vdash \psi(\underline{m},\underline{n},0)$. By $\exists$-I, $Q \vdash \exists x\psi(\underline{m},x,0)$ and so $\exists x\psi(\underline{m},x,0) \in \Delta$.

(ii) Conversely suppose $\exists x\psi(\underline{m},x,0) \in \Delta$. Since $\Delta \subseteq \mathrm{Th}(\mathbb{N})$, $\mathbb{N} \models \exists x\psi(\underline{m},x,0)$. So for some n $\mathbb{N} \models \psi(\underline{m},\underline{n},0)$. Now if $c_R(m,n) = 1$ then $Q \vdash \sim\psi(\underline{m},\underline{n},0)$, whence $\mathbb{N} \models \sim\psi(\underline{m},\underline{n},0)$. Thus $c_R(m,n) = 0$, i.e. $\varphi_m = \theta_n$. Thus $\varphi_m \in \Delta$.

Since $\underline{m} = \overline{\varphi_m}$, we have for all φ, $\varphi \in \Delta$ iff $\exists x\psi(\bar{\varphi},x,0) \in \Delta$. So Δ is self-representing via the predicate $\exists x\psi(y,x,0)$.

We are assuming that all theories and subtheories mentioned are in the language of arithmetic. From the Corollaries above there now follow certain very important results.

(VII) Any theory consistent with Q is undecidable.

Proof. Suppose Δ is a theory consistent with Q. Since Q is strongly representing, Δ, Q is representing; hence, by (V), is undecidable. Now if Δ were decidable, then by testing whether $Q \supset \varphi$ was in Δ we could decide whether φ was in Δ, Q. Thus Δ is undecidable.

In particular, we have

(VII) The set of logical truths in the language of arithmetic is undecidable,

an improvement on our earlier undecidability result for first order functional logic; and

(IX) Any subtheory of $\mathrm{Th}(\mathbb{N})$ is undecidable.

Thus from (III) we have

(X) Any axiomatizable subtheory of $\mathrm{Th}(\mathbb{N})$ is incomplete

and

(XI) $\mathrm{Th}(\mathbb{N})$ is unaxiomatizable.

The diagonal for Q serves as a diagonal for any theory containing Q; in particular, $\mathrm{Th}(\mathbb{N})$. Since the latter is complete we have by (VI)

(XII) Th($\mathbb{N}$) is not self-representing.

That is, for no predicate ψ do we have for all φ $\psi(\overline{\varphi}) \in \mathrm{Th}(\mathbb{N})$ iff $\varphi \in \mathrm{Th}(\mathbb{N})$.

A fortiori we have

(XIII) Th($\mathbb{N}$) has no 'truth predicate' ψ such that for all φ

$$(\varphi \equiv \psi(\overline{\varphi})) \in \mathrm{Th}(\mathbb{N}).$$

The force of the last two results may be brought out as follows, to make them clearly independent of the mapping $\varphi \to \overline{\varphi}$.

Any representing predicate or truth predicate for Th($\mathbb{N}$) is useless unless we can tell *which* sentence is represented as true by a given predication. The only referring terms available in the language of Th($\mathbb{N}$) are the numerals. Therefore a minimal requirement on any system of reference to sentences is that it consist in an effective mapping $\varphi \to \overline{\varphi}$ of sentences to numerals. Let $\natural$ be a coding of formulae with one free variable and define $^{=}$ so that for any such formula θ, $\overline{\overline{\theta}} = \underline{\natural\theta}$. Now define the computable function d by

$$d(n) = \nu(\overline{\natural^{-1}(n)(\underline{n})}) \qquad (\text{where } \nu(\underline{m}) = m).$$

By Church's Thesis d is recursive. Hence by representability there is some δ such that for all n $\delta(\underline{n}, a) \dashv^{Q}\vdash a = \underline{d(n)}$. Hence for all formulae θ with one free variable,

$$\delta(\natural\theta, a) \dashv^{Q}\vdash a = \underline{d(\natural\theta)}$$
$$\text{i.e.} \quad \delta(\overline{\overline{\theta}}, a) \dashv^{Q}\vdash a = \underline{\nu(\overline{\natural^{-1}(\natural\theta)(\underline{\natural\theta})})},$$
$$\text{i.e.} \quad \delta(\overline{\overline{\theta}}, a) \dashv^{Q}\vdash a = \theta(\overline{\overline{\theta}}).$$

So δ is a diagonal for Q and by the same reasoning as before, Th($\mathbb{N}$) is not self-representing.

From Corollary 3 and (VI) it follows that

(XIV) Any axiomatizable subtheory Δ of Th($\mathbb{N}$) containing Q is incomplete. Moreover Δ is incomplete by virtue of an independent sentence γ *which can be shown to be true in* $\mathbb{N}$.

Proof. We need only prove the last claim. The independent sentence γ provided by the proof of (VI) is constructed from the diagonal γ of Corollary 2 and the representing predicate $\exists z\psi(x, z, 0)$ of Corollary 3 as follows:

Let $\varepsilon(y)$ be $\forall x\delta(y, x) \supset \sim\exists z\psi(x, z, 0)$ and let γ be $\varepsilon(\overline{\varepsilon})$, that is, $\forall x\delta(\overline{\varepsilon}, x) \supset \sim\exists z\psi(x, z, 0)$. We show γ is true in $\mathbb{N}$:

We know γ is not in Δ. So with Δ given by the effective enumeration $\theta_0, \theta_1, \ldots$ we have for all n γ is not θ_n. Suppose γ appears as

φ_k in our list of all sentences. Then for all n φ_k is not θ_n, whence not-$R(k,n)$, whence $c_R(k,n)=1$. Hence by representation of c_R by ψ, for all n $\sim\psi(\underline{k},\underline{n},0)\in\Delta$. Since $\Delta\subseteq\text{Th}(\mathbb{N})$ we have for all n $\psi(\overline{\gamma},\underline{n},0)$ is false in $\mathbb{N}$.

Now we know $\mathbb{N}$ *contains only the numbers 0, 1, 2,....*; thus $\sim\exists z\psi(\overline{\gamma},z,0)$ is true in $\mathbb{N}$. Since $\overline{\gamma}$ is the only numeral for which $\delta(\overline{\overline{\varepsilon}},\overline{\gamma})$ is true in $\mathbb{N}$, we have $\forall x(\delta(\overline{\overline{\varepsilon}},x)\supset\sim\exists z\psi(x,z,0))$ is true in $\mathbb{N}$.

This argument, known as the 'semantical argument' for the truth of the independent sentence γ, turns essentially on concluding that $\forall x\varphi(x)$ is true in $\mathbb{N}$ from the premiss that for every n, $\varphi(\underline{n})$ is true in $\mathbb{N}$ – or from the infinitely many premisses

$\varphi(0)$ is true in $\mathbb{N}$, $\varphi(\underline{1})$ is true in $\mathbb{N}$, $\varphi(\underline{2})$ is true in $\mathbb{N}$, ...

The reasoning here is carried out in the *metalanguage*, not in the formal system of proof in the object language. It suggests that we might regain completeness for Δ by incorporating into such a system an infinitary rule of inference:

$$\frac{\varphi(0) \quad \varphi(\underline{1}) \quad \varphi(\underline{2}) \quad \ldots}{\forall x\varphi(x)}$$

This is known as the ω-rule. It is an attempt to capture, within the formal system, our semantical conception of $\mathbb{N}$ as consisting *only* of the natural numbers $0,1,2,\ldots$. The ω-rule, however, allows the formation of infinitely large 'proofs' (which we shall call ω-proofs), which are interesting mathematical objects but which do not satisfy the requirement of effective checkability that we placed on proofs when first analyzing them. The notion of ω-proof is captured precisely by adding to our earlier inductive definition of proof the inductive clause corresponding to the ω-rule. Thus an ω-proof may be infinitely 'wide' as a result of applications of the ω-rule, but it will be only finitely 'deep', since it will contain only finitely many applications of rules of inference.

Let Δ^ω be the theory in the language of arithmetic arising from Δ by means of ω-proofs.

(xv) $Q^\omega = Th(\mathbb{N})$

Proof. Q and Th($\mathbb{N}$) contain exactly the same atomic sentences. The result then follows by induction on the complexity of sentences, appealing to the ω-rule when considering quantified sentences.

Thus Q^ω is unaxiomatizable, which is not surprising given the infinitary nature of the ω-rule. It is interesting to note that finite proofs using the axioms for successor, addition and multiplication and the principle of induction cannot, by (x), generate as conclusions all truths about $\mathbb{N}$. Yet if we replace the principle of induction by its infinitary version, the ω-rule, the infinite 'proofs' then constructible do generate as conclusions all truths about **N**.

Another way to regain completeness is to consider Q^2, obtained from Q by replacing $\forall x{\sim}x=0\supset\exists y\, x=s(y)$ by the second order induction axiom $\forall\psi((\psi(0)\,\&\,\forall x(\psi(x)\supset\psi(s(x))))\supset\forall x\psi(x))$. Q^2 is categorical – all its models are isomorphic to **N**. This is because the second order induction axiom ensures that the natural number sequence guaranteed by the successor axioms exhausts the domain, while the axioms for successor, addition and multiplication uniquely determine those operations on this sequence. Those first order sentences that are second order logical consequences of Q^2 therefore comprise exactly Th(**N**), which is unaxiomatizable. Since there is an effective method for telling whether a sentence is a first order sentence, the second order logical consequences of Q^2 must form an unaxiomatizable set. Moreover any effective enumeration of all second order logical truths would, by checking for enumerated sentences of the form $Q^2\supset\varphi$, yield an effective enumeration of all second order logical consequences of Q^2, which as we have seen is impossible. Thus we may conclude

(XVI) Second order logical truth is unaxiomatizable.

7.10 Universally free logic for descriptions and set theory. The system of first order logic developed above dealt with names and functional terms, on the semantical assumptions that every name denotes and every function is everywhere defined in the domain – and, therefore, that every term denotes. Another semantical assumption was that the domain was non-empty.

Let us now consider another two kinds of expressions, which one's grammatical intuitions at first incline one to categorize as terms: *descriptive terms* and *class terms*.

First, in a sentence of the form 'The φ is ψ' one is inclined to regard the descriptive term 'The φ' as completing the predicate '_ is ψ'. The descriptive term is itself complex, apparently built up from the term-forming operator 'The __' and the predicate '_ is φ'. Thus categorially we appear to have

$$\psi(\text{The}(\varphi(\ )))$$

which in logical notation would be

$$\psi(\iota x\varphi(x))$$

where the inverted iota, binding the variable x, represents 'The'.

Secondly, in a sentence of the form 'The set of φ's is ψ' one is inclined to regard the class term 'The set of φ's' as completing the predicate '_ is ψ'. By similar considerations as above we would advance to a logical translation such as

$$\psi(\{x \mid \varphi(x)\})$$

with $\{x \mid \varphi(x)\}$ representing 'The set of φ's'.

ι and $\{\mid(\ )\}$ are called variable binding term forming operators. They form terms from formulae by binding hitherto free variables in an obvious fashion. Their presence in the formal language is incompatible with the semantical assumptions mentioned above.

For, firstly, we may form the descriptive term $\iota x(\psi x \,\&\, {\sim}\psi x)$, which obviously denotes nothing. Secondly, the class operator is to be used along with a membership predicate $\in$, whose relationship thereto is strictly governed by the *conversion schema*:

> An object is a member of the set of all ψ's
> iff
> it has property ψ.

Formally this is expressed by the axiom schema $\forall x(x \in \{y \mid \psi y\} \equiv \psi x)$. Given this schema, Russell's famous paradox ensues. We take ${\sim}x \in x$ as an instance of ψx:

$$\forall x(x \in \{y \mid {\sim}y \in y\} \equiv {\sim}x \in x).$$

Instantiating with the supposedly denoting class term $\{y \mid {\sim}y \in y\}$ we obtain

$$\{y \mid {\sim}y \in y\} \in \{y \mid {\sim}y \in y\} \equiv {\sim}\{y \mid {\sim}y \in y\} \in \{y \mid {\sim}y \in y\}$$

which is inconsistent, by virtue of the proof

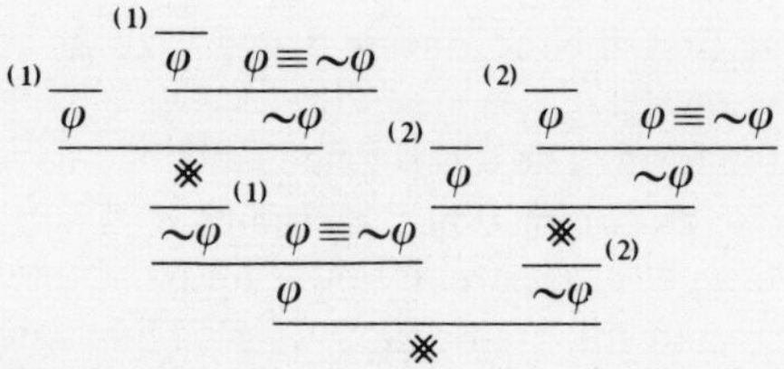

Thus if we wish to include descriptive and class terms in our formal language we must abandon the semantical assumption that every term denotes. This conclusion is compelling in the case of descriptive terms. In the case of class terms it is compelling insofar as we are not prepared to place any restrictions (whether *ad hoc* or with philosophical motivation) on the predicates to which the class-forming operator may sensibly be applied or on the terms that may sensibly flank the membership sign.

Perhaps the most widely adopted solutions to the problem of non-denoting terms involve the method of so-called contextual elimination (or definition) of occurrences of the 'terms' in question. One may decide, for example, that 'descriptive terms' are not genuine terms, and should not be represented as such in logical notation. This is the main tenet of Russell's theory of descriptions. According to this theory the truth conditions of

The φ is ψ

are just those of the sentence

There is exactly one φ and it is ψ,

which has the logical translation

$$\exists x(\forall y(y=x \equiv \varphi y) \,\&\, \psi x).$$

The latter is then proposed as the proper logical translation of the original sentence 'The φ is ψ'. The 'descriptive term' is thus analyzed away, and is seen to have meaning only within the context of the whole sentence in which it occurs. There is consequently no need for a descriptive operator in the formal language. It is to be introduced, if at all, only by way of convenient abbreviation. $\psi(\iota x \varphi x)$ will be an *abbreviation* of the sentence $\exists x(\forall y(y=x \equiv \varphi y) \,\&\, \psi x)$, and will not be a sentence of the formal language proper. These abbreviations are sometimes more troublesome than the original sentences, since in complicated cases 'scope markers' for the descriptive terms have to be supplied in order to avoid ambiguous abbreviation. For example, without some further notational device we cannot tell whether $\sim\psi(\iota x \varphi x)$ is an abbreviation of $\exists x(\forall y(y=x \equiv \varphi y) \,\&\, {\sim}\psi x)$ or of $\sim\exists x(\forall y (y=x \equiv \varphi y) \,\&\, \psi x)$.

Quine has applied Russell's theory even to names. Names are construed as naming-predicates; a sentence $\psi(a)$ is interpreted as ψ(the a-er), and Russell's theory is invoked to deal with the descriptive term. But this would appear to forfeit the original Fregean justification for our categorization of predicates and quantifiers. By withdrawing the name a from the sentence $\psi(a)$ we obtain the predicate ψ__. According to Quine's method, however, the residue would be $\exists x(\forall y(y=x \equiv \_\_) \,\&\, \psi x)$, depriving us of a clear grasp of the simplest cases upon which to base the Fregean hierarchy of syntactic categories.

The strategy of contextual elimination is available also for class terms. One modern treatment of class terms in Zermelo-Fraenkel set theory is the following:

$x \in \{y \mid \psi y\}$	becomes	ψx (tantamount to the conversion schema)
$\{z \mid \psi z\} \in x$	becomes	$\exists y(\forall z(z \in y \equiv \psi z) \,\&\, y \in x)$
$\{z \mid \psi z\} \in \{x \mid \varphi x\}$	becomes	$\exists y(\forall z(z \in y \equiv \psi z) \,\&\, y \in \{x \mid \varphi x\}$.

The interesting feature of this contextual definition of class terms is that it is far more contextual than that of descriptive terms. In atomic predications all occurrences of descriptive terms carry denotational commitment, whereas on the present treatment of class terms only those occurrences of class terms to the left of the membership sign carry such commitment. For example, $(\imath z \psi z) \in (\imath y \varphi y)$ becomes $\exists x(\forall z(z = x \equiv \psi z) \,\&\, \exists w(\forall y(y = w \equiv \varphi y) \,\&\, x \in w)$, whereas $\{z \mid \psi z\} \in \{y \mid \varphi y\}$ becomes $\exists x(\forall z(z \in x \equiv \psi z) \,\&\, \varphi x)$. This raises problems about the term-like status of class terms even when the class operator is taken as primitive, and not contextually defined. We are obliged to consider the question whether an expression is a term only if it must denote in order that an atomic predication involving it be true. If the answer is affirmative then the method above for eliminating class terms must be modified. We might instead adopt a 'tandem' method, construing $\{x \mid \psi x\}$ as $\imath z \forall x(x \in z \equiv \psi x)$, and then treating the latter according to Russell's method. Alternatively we might take the class operator as primitive in the formal language, and lay down such rules of inference as secure its equivalence with the descriptive complex $\imath z \forall x(x \in z \equiv \_(x))$.

Whichever of the methods mentioned above for dealing with class terms is adopted, the argument for Russell's paradox now serves simply to show that there is no such thing as the set of all non-self-membered things. The statement $\exists x \forall y(y \in x \equiv \sim y \in y)$ leads to absurdity in just the same way as does the statement that some man shaves all and only those men who do not shave themselves.

It is beyond the scope of this chapter to review the many treatments of names, descriptive terms and class terms besides those already mentioned. The literature is well supplied with competing theories variously involving presupposition, truth-value gaps, third truth values, and arbitrary or outlandish denotations for otherwise non-denoting terms. There are also set theories that distinguish between sets and proper classes. Some theories are favoured for their formal elegance, paucity of primitives or sparseness of ontology; others because they allegedly do fuller justice to our intuitions about logical or grammatical form, or to ordinary usage.

The major difficulty, from our point of view, is to combine (i) an analysis of the logical form of predications according to which terms are genuine expressions of the language, with (ii) the semantical assumption that a term's failure to denote renders any atomic predication involving it false. Russell, at philosophical pains to show that 'the φ' was not a term in a genuine logical sense, abbreviated his analysis in a way which retained surface pretences in the face of this logical conviction. For there is no doubt that we manipulate descriptive terms as terms rather than as quantifying phrases in mathematical and everyday reasoning. We shall provide an account on which logical invention respects grammatical convention. We shall be in agreement with Russell about the truth conditions of sentences involving descriptive terms, but the latter will be treated as genuine expressions of the formal language, and not introduced only by way of abbreviation.

We must therefore develop a logic free of the semantical assumption that every term denotes. Such logics are called free logics. If in addition we drop the assumption that the domain is non-empty, we shall have a *universally free* logic. Universal freedom calls for certain constraints on the quantifier rules, as will emerge below.

In the new model-theoretic semantics a model M for a set of extra-logical expressions need not have a non-empty domain. Even when the domain is non-empty, not every name need denote. Moreover functions need not be everywhere defined. An assignment of individuals to variables will satisfy an atomic formula if and only if all its terms denote (relative to that assignment) and the relation in question holds between those denotations. In particular, if any of the terms fails to denote (relative to that assignment) then the assignment will not satisfy the atomic formula. A functional term $f(t_1 \ldots t_n)$ may fail to denote in M either because one of $t_1, \ldots, t_n$ fails to denote or because the mapping $M(f)$ is not defined for their denotations as arguments.

If φ is a formula with x free, then $\imath x\varphi$ will be a descriptive term in which x is bound by the initial occurrence of $\imath x$. If there is exactly one individual α such that $s(x/\alpha)$ satisfies φ then $\imath x\varphi$ denotes that individual relative to s; otherwise it denotes nothing. Obviously if the descriptive term is closed (i.e. has no free variables) then it denotes the same individual (if it denotes at all) relative to every assignment.

We abbreviate $\exists x\, x = t$ ('t exists') as $\exists!t$.

The modified quantifier rules are as follows:

$$\exists\text{-}I: \quad \frac{\exists!t \quad \varphi^x_t}{\exists x\varphi}$$

∃-*E*:

$$\dfrac{\exists x\varphi \qquad \begin{array}{c}\underbrace{\overset{(i)}{\overline{\varphi^x_a}}\ ,\ \overset{(i)}{\overline{\exists! a}}}\\ \vdots \\ \psi\end{array}}{\psi}\,(i)$$

where a does not occur in $\exists x\varphi$, ψ or any assumption other than φ^x_a and $\exists! a$ on which the upper occurrence of ψ depends

∀-*I*:

$$\dfrac{\begin{array}{c}\overset{(i)}{\overline{\exists! a}}\\ \vdots \\ \varphi\end{array}}{\forall x \varphi^a_x}\,(i)$$

where a does not occur in any assumption other than $\exists! a$ on which φ depends

∀-*E*:

$$\dfrac{\exists! t \qquad \forall x\varphi}{\varphi^x_t}$$

Reduction procedures are obvious for ∃ and ∀ governed by these rules. Reflexivity of identity is now expressed by the rule

$$\dfrac{\exists! t}{t=t}$$

Substitutivity of identicals and the rules for absurdity and the connectives are as before.

We add a *denotation rule* for atomic sentences φ (including identities) which involve a term t not within the scope of any occurence of $\imath$:

$$\dfrac{\varphi}{\exists! t}$$

Finally we come to the question of introduction and elimination rules for the descriptive operator. It is different from other logical operators insofar as it has dominant occurrences in *terms* rather than in *sentences*. The easiest way to display a dominant occurrence of the descriptive operator is by way of an identity involving a descriptive term. Thus our introduction rule for $\imath$ will tell us the conditions under which we may infer a conclusion of the form $t = \imath x\varphi$, and the elimination rules will tell us what we may infer from a premiss of that form (along with certain other premisses):

ι-*I*:

$$\begin{array}{c} \begin{array}{ccc} \overline{a=t}^{\,(i)} & & \underbrace{\overline{\exists! a}^{\,(i)} \;,\; \overline{\varphi^x_a}^{\,(i)}} \\ \vdots & & \vdots \end{array} \\ \dfrac{\varphi^x_a \quad \exists! t \quad a=t}{t=\iota x\varphi}\,{\scriptstyle (i)} \end{array}$$

ι-*E*:

$$\frac{t=\iota x\varphi \quad u=t}{\varphi^x_u} \qquad \frac{t=\iota x\varphi \quad \varphi^x_u \quad \exists! u}{u=t}$$

The reduction procedures for ι are as follows:

$$\begin{array}{c} \begin{array}{cc} (a=t) & (\exists! a),(\varphi^x_a) \\ \Pi_1 & \Pi_2 \end{array} \\ \dfrac{\dfrac{\varphi^x_a \quad \exists! t \quad a=t}{t=\iota x\varphi} \qquad u=t}{\varphi^x_u} \end{array} \quad \rightarrow \quad \begin{array}{c} u=t \\ \Pi_1 u^a_u \\ \varphi^x_u \end{array}$$

$$\begin{array}{c} \begin{array}{cc} (a=t) & (\exists! a),(\varphi^x_a) \\ \Pi_1 & \Pi_2 \end{array} \\ \dfrac{\dfrac{\varphi^x_a \quad \exists! t \quad a=t}{t=\iota x\varphi} \qquad \varphi^x_u \quad \exists! u}{u=t} \end{array} \quad \rightarrow \quad \begin{array}{c} \underbrace{\exists! u, \varphi^x_u} \\ \Pi_2 u^a_u \\ u=t \end{array}$$

Our new rules of inference are obviously truth preserving according to the new semantics. Their role in the completeness proof will become clear below. We shall now derive certain deducibility statements using the rules stated above.

Let $\exists_1 x\psi$ be the uniqueness claim $\exists x\forall y(y=x\equiv\psi^x_y)$.

(A) $$\frac{t=\iota x\psi}{\psi^x_t}$$

Proof:

$$\dfrac{t=\iota x\psi \qquad \dfrac{\dfrac{t=\iota x\psi}{\exists! t}}{t=t}}{\psi^x_t}\,(\iota\text{-}E)$$

(B) $$\frac{\forall x(x=t\equiv\psi) \quad \exists! t}{t=\iota x\psi}$$

Proof:

$$\dfrac{\dfrac{\overline{a=t}^{\,(1)} \qquad \dfrac{\dfrac{\overline{a=t}^{\,(1)}}{\exists! a} \quad \forall x(x=t\equiv\psi)}{a=t\equiv\psi^x_a}}{\psi^x_a} \qquad \exists! t \qquad \dfrac{\overline{\psi^x_a}^{\,(1)} \qquad \dfrac{\overline{\exists! a}^{\,(1)} \quad \forall x(x=t\equiv\psi)}{a=t\equiv\psi^x_a}}{a=t}}{t=\iota x\psi}\,{\scriptstyle (1)}\;(\iota\text{-}I)$$

(C) $\dfrac{\exists_1 x\psi}{\exists!\iota x\psi}$

Proof:

$$\dfrac{\exists_1 x\psi \qquad \dfrac{\overset{(1)}{\overline{\exists! a}} \qquad \dfrac{\overset{(1)}{\overline{\exists! a}} \qquad \overline{\forall x(x=a\equiv\psi)}^{(1)}}{a=\iota x\psi}\,(\mathrm{B})}{\exists!\iota x\psi}\,(1)}{\exists!\iota x\psi}$$

(D) $\dfrac{\exists!\iota x\psi}{\exists_1 x\psi}$

Proof:

$$\dfrac{\exists!\iota x\psi \qquad \dfrac{\overset{(3)}{\overline{\exists! a}} \qquad \dfrac{\dfrac{\dfrac{\overset{(3)}{\overline{a=\iota x\psi}} \quad \overset{(2)}{\overline{\exists! b}} \quad \overline{\psi^x_b}^{(1)}}{b=a}\,(\iota\text{-}E) \qquad \dfrac{\overset{(3)}{\overline{a=\iota x\psi}} \quad \overline{b=a}^{(1)}}{\psi^x_b}\,(\iota\text{-}E)\,(1)}{b=a\equiv\psi^x_b}}{\forall y(y=a\equiv\psi^x_y)}\,(2)}{\exists_1 x\psi}\,(3)}{\exists_1 x\psi}$$

The inferences (A), (C) and (D) suffice for the completeness proof and could therefore be taken as primitive, if so desired, instead of the introduction and elimination rules for ι given above.

The completeness proof proceeds as usual, with certain modifications. The Henkin expansion of a consistent set Δ is as follows, with the notational conventions of the argument in section 6.4.

$$\begin{array}{lll}
\Delta_0 & =\Delta & \\
E_n & =\Delta_n, \psi_n a, \exists! a & \text{if} \quad \Delta_n, \exists x\psi_n \nvdash \text{※} \\
 & \quad \Delta_n & \text{if} \quad \Delta_n, \exists x\psi_n \vdash \text{※} \\
A_n & = E_n, \forall x\{\sim\sim\}\psi_n & \text{if} \quad E_n, \forall x\{\sim\sim\}\psi_n \nvdash \text{※} \\
 & \quad E_n, \sim\psi_n a, \exists! a & \text{if} \quad E_n, \forall x\{\sim\sim\}\psi_n \vdash \text{※} \\
I_n & = A_n, \exists!\iota x\psi_n & \text{if} \quad A_n, \exists_1 x\psi_n \nvdash \text{※} \\
 & \quad A_n & \text{if} \quad A_n, \exists_1 x\psi_n \vdash \text{※} \\
\Delta_{n+1} & = I_n, \varphi_n & \text{if} \quad I_n, \varphi_n \nvdash \text{※} \\
 & \quad I_n & \text{if} \quad I_n, \varphi_n \vdash \text{※} \\
\overline{\Delta} & =\cup_i \Delta_i &
\end{array}$$

To show $\overline{\Delta}$ is consistent it suffices, for familiar reasons, to show that if $\Delta_{n+1} \vdash \text{※}$ then $\Delta_n \vdash \text{※}$. The only step missing from our earlier demonstration in section 6.4 is the following: if $I_n \vdash \text{※}$ then $A_n \vdash \text{※}$. So suppose $I_n \vdash \text{※}$. Suppose $A_n, \exists_1 x\psi_n \nvdash \text{※}$. Since $\exists_1 x\psi_n \vdash \exists!\iota x\psi_n$ we have $A_n, \exists!\iota x\psi_n \nvdash \text{※}$, whence $I_n \nvdash \text{※}$. But $I_n \vdash \text{※}$. Thus $A_n, \exists_1 x\psi_n \vdash \text{※}$. Hence $I_n = A_n$, and $A_n \vdash \text{※}$.

Therefore as in our earlier completeness proof $\overline{\Delta}$ is consistent, maximal, deductively closed and replete with 'witnesses'.

The natural model for $\bar{\Delta}$ is defined as follows.

(i) Its domain is the set of all equivalence classes of terms t such that $\exists! t \in \bar{\Delta}$, under the equivalence relation $(t = u) \in \bar{\Delta}$.
(ii) Each name names its own equivalence class.
(iii) $M(f)$ maps $|t_1|, \ldots, |t_n|$ to $|f(t_1, \ldots, t_n)|$ if $\exists! f(t_1, \ldots, t_n) \in \bar{\Delta}$; otherwise $M(f)$ is not defined for those arguments.
(iv) $\langle |t_1|, \ldots, |t_n| \rangle \in M(P)$ if and only if $P(t_1, \ldots, t_n) \in \bar{\Delta}$.

That this is a sound definition is seen easily as before.
Simplification Lemma. For every term t such that $\exists! t \in \bar{\Delta}$ there is a term u not involving $\imath$ such that $\exists! u \in \bar{\Delta}$ and $|t| = |u|$.
Proof. Suppose $\exists! \imath x \psi \in \bar{\Delta}$. By construction for some name a $\exists! a \in \bar{\Delta}$ and $(a = \imath x \psi) \in \bar{\Delta}$. Hence $|\imath x \psi| = |a|$. The lemma now follows by induction on the number of occurrences of $\imath$ in t.

Now define the *depth* of terms and formulae as follows:

$$d(x) = d(a) = 0$$
$$d(f(t_1, \ldots, t_n)) = d(P(t_1, \ldots, t_n)) = max\{d(t_i) | 1 \leqslant i \leqslant n\}$$
$$d(\sim\psi) = d(\forall x \psi) = d(\exists x \psi) = 1 + d(\psi)$$
$$d(\varphi \vee \psi) = d(\varphi \,\&\, \psi) = d(\varphi \supset \psi) = 1 + max\{d(\varphi), d(\psi)\}$$
$$d(\imath x \psi) = 3 + d(\psi)$$

We now show by a simultaneous induction on the depth of the terms and formulae metioned that

(I) If $\exists! t \in \bar{\Delta}$ then t denotes $|t|$ in M
(II) $\varphi \in \bar{\Delta}$ if and only if φ is true in M

Note that for the purposes of our induction the sentence $\exists_1 x \psi$ is less complex than the sentence $\exists! \imath x \psi$.

The basis for (I) and (II) is obvious.

Inductive step for (I)
Case (i): t is $f(t_1, \ldots, t_n)$.
Suppose $\exists! f(t_1, \ldots, t_n) \in \bar{\Delta}$. By virtue of the proofs

$$\dfrac{\exists x\, x = f(t_1, \ldots, t_n) \qquad \dfrac{\dfrac{}{a = f(t_1, \ldots, t_n)}{\scriptstyle (1)}}{\exists! t_i}{\scriptstyle (1)}}{\exists! t_i}$$

for $1 \leqslant i \leqslant n$, and closure of $\bar{\Delta}$, we have $\exists! t_i \in \bar{\Delta}$. By IH(I) t_i denotes $|t_i|$ in M. So $f(t_1, \ldots, t_n)$ denotes $M(f)(|t_1|, \ldots, |t_n|)$, which is precisely $|f(t_1, \ldots, t_n)|$.
Case (ii): t is $\imath x \psi$.
Suppose $\exists! \imath x \psi \in \bar{\Delta}$. By construction for some name a $(a = \imath x \psi) \in \bar{\Delta}$, whence $|a| = |\imath x \psi|$. Since $a = \imath x \psi \vdash \psi^x_a$ and $\bar{\Delta}$ is closed, we have $\psi^x_a \in \bar{\Delta}$.

By IH(II) ψ^x_a is true in M. Since a denotes $|a|$ in M, $M \vDash \psi[|a|]$. Moreover since $\exists!\imath x\psi \vdash \exists_1 x\psi$ and $\bar{\Delta}$ is closed, we have $\exists_1 x\psi \in \bar{\Delta}$. By IH(II) again, $\exists_1 x\psi$ is true in M. So $|a|$ is the unique satisfier of ψ in M, and is therefore the denotation of $\imath x\psi$ in M; that is, $|\imath x\psi|$ is the denotation of $\imath x\psi$ in M.

Inductive step for (II)

When φ has a connective dominant the reasoning is as before. We shall simply consider the case where φ is $\exists x\psi$. Suppose $\exists x\psi \in \bar{\Delta}$. By construction for some name a $\exists!a \in \bar{\Delta}$ and $\psi a \in \bar{\Delta}$. By IH(II) ψa is true in M. Since a denotes $|a|$ in M, $\exists x\psi$ is true in M. Conversely suppose $\exists x\psi$ is true in M. Then for some $|t|$ in M, $M \vDash \psi[|t|]$. By simplification, for some $|u|$ in M, where u does not involve $\imath$, $M \vDash \psi[|u|]$. Since u denotes $|u|$ in M (by IH(I)), ψu is true in M. By choice of u, ψu is less complex than $\exists x\psi$, so by IH(II) we have $\psi u \in \bar{\Delta}$. Moreover $\exists!u \in \bar{\Delta}$. By $\exists$-I and closure of $\bar{\Delta}$, $\exists x\psi \in \bar{\Delta}$.

All the metatheorems of Chapter 6 now extend to our system of universally free logic for functional and descriptive terms.

We can incorporate class terms by means of the following introduction and elimination rules for $\{\ \}$, similar to those for $\imath$:

$$\{\ \}\text{-}I:\quad \begin{array}{ccc} \overline{a \in t}^{\,(i)} & & {}^{(i)}\overline{\varphi^x_a}\ ,\ \overline{\exists!a}^{\,(i)} \\ \vdots & & \vdots \\ \varphi^x_a \quad \exists!t & & a \in t_{(i)} \\ \hline & t = \{x|\varphi\} & \end{array}$$

where a does not occur in $t = \{x|\varphi\}$ nor in any undischarged assumptions of the subordinate proofs other than those of the form displayed

$$\{\ \}\text{-}E:\quad \frac{t = \{x|\varphi\} \quad u \in t}{\varphi^x_u} \qquad \frac{t = \{x|\varphi\} \quad \varphi^x_u \quad \exists!u}{u \in t}$$

Reduction procedures are obvious. By means of these rules we can construct proofs similar to the ones above, for the following deducibility statements.

(A)$_\varepsilon$ $\quad t = \{x|\psi\} \vdash \forall x(x \in t \equiv \psi)$
(B)$_\varepsilon$ $\quad \forall x(x \in t \equiv \psi), \exists!t \vdash t = \{x|\psi\}$
(C)$_\varepsilon$ $\quad \exists_1 x\forall y(y \in x \equiv \psi^x_y) \vdash \exists!\{x|\psi\}$
(D)$_\varepsilon$ $\quad \exists!\{x|\psi\} \vdash \exists_1 x\forall y(y \in x \equiv \psi^x_y)$

The Henkin expansion is as before, except that somewhere during the n'th stage we add $\exists!\{x|\psi_n\}$ if we could add $\exists_1 x\forall y(y \in x \equiv \psi_n{}^y_x)$ consistently. By (C)$_\varepsilon$ this addition would preserve consistency.

The natural model is defined as before, and the simplification lemma holds. The depth of $\{x|\psi\}$ is defined as $7+d(\psi)$, so that the sentence $\exists_1 x\forall y(y\in x\equiv\psi^x_y)$ is less complex for inductive purposes than the sentence $\exists!\{x|\psi\}$. (I) and (II) are proved as before by a joint induction. Case (ii) in the inductive step for (I) is easily re-worked with $\{x|\psi\}$ in place of $\imath x\psi$; for, in any model M of our formal language with the membership predicate $\in$, the denotation of $\{x|\psi\}$ relative to an assignment s is the unique α (should there be one) in M such that for all β in M $\langle\beta,\alpha\rangle$ is in the extension $M(\in)$ iff $M\vDash\psi[s(x/\beta)]$. In other respects the completeness proof is unchanged.

Universally free logic for identity, functions, descriptions, class abstractions and membership is an adequate logical foundation for classical mathematics. The introduction and elimination rules for $\{\ \}$ specify the logical interrelationship between class abstraction and membership. The introduction rule quickly yields the so-called principle of extensionality for sets:

$$\frac{\forall x(x\in t\equiv x\in u)\quad \exists!t\quad \exists!u}{t=u}$$

while the two elimination rules are tantamount to the conversion schema. The rules are truth preserving in models containing at most one individual with no members (as can readily be seen from extensionality).

The step from logic to mathematics is taken when we assert the existence of certain sets, either outright or conditionally upon the existence of others. Other axioms of set theory may lay down global constraints on the membership relation. The axioms of any set theory will be motivated by a particular conception of the universe of sets that the axioms are intended adequately to convey.

The set theory most widely adopted at present is that of Zermelo and Fraenkel. The motivating conception is of a cumulative hierarchy of 'pure' sets, starting with the empty set and generating more sets of 'higher rank' in an iterative fashion. Its axioms are as follows:

Existence of the empty set

$$\exists!\{x|\sim x=x\}$$

Axiom of Unions

$$\forall x\exists!\{y|\exists z(y\in z\,\&\,z\in x)\}$$

(The set consisting of all members of any given set's members exists.)

Axiom of Powers

$$\forall x\exists!\{y|\forall z(z\in y\supset z\in x)\}$$

(The set of all subsets of any given set exists.)

Axiom Schema of Replacement

$$\forall x(\forall y \forall z \forall w(\psi yz \,\&\, \psi yw \supset z = w) \supset \exists!\{y \mid \exists z(z \in x \,\&\, \psi zy)\})$$

(The image of any set projected by a many-one relation is a set.)

Axiom of Foundation

$$\forall x(\exists y\, y \in x \supset \exists z(z \in x \,\&\, \sim \exists y(y \in z \,\&\, y \in x)))$$

(Any non-empty set has a member with no members in common with it. Thus there are no self-membered sets or membership 'loops'.)

These axioms are all satisfiable in a model in which each set has only finitely many members. In order to secure the existence of infinite sets some such set must be said to exist. The set chosen for this purpose is the set of all finite ordinals, defined as follows.

First, an ordinal is a set closed under and connected by the membership relation:

$$0x =_{df} \forall y(y \in x \supset \forall z((z \in y \supset z \in x) \,\&\, (z \in x \supset (z = y \vee z \in y \vee y \in z))))$$

$s(x)$, the successor of x, is defined as $\{y \mid y = x \vee y \in x\}$, and $\emptyset$ is by definition $\{x \mid \sim x = x\}$. Finally, we define ω as the set of all ordinals that, along with each of their members, are either $\emptyset$ or the successor of some ordinal:

$$\omega =_{df} \{x \mid 0x \,\&\, \forall y(y = x \vee y \in x \supset (y = \emptyset \vee \exists z(0z \,\&\, y = s(z))))\}$$

The *Axiom of Infinity* is $\exists!\omega$.

Within any model of our axioms the denotation of ω must have infinitely many members. A set is defined to be *countable* just in case there is a 1-1 correspondence (in a suitably defined set-theoretic sense) between its members and all those of ω or of some member of ω. Provably there is no such correspondence between the members of any set and all its subsets. Thus the set of all subsets of ω is uncountable.

We are now faced with Skolem's paradox: if set theory is consistent then by the Countable Models Theorem it has a countable model, within which the set of all subsets of ω will have *only countably many* members. Absolute uncountability would appear to elude formal characterization at first order. Note that the 'uncountability' of the power set of ω is due to the absence from the countable model, as indeed from *any* model, of a member which, within that model, constitutes a 1-1 correspondence between members of (the denotation of) ω and all members of (the denotation of) $\{x \mid \forall y\, y \in x \supset y \in \omega\}$. Nevertheless, from outside the countable model, we deem such a set to exist. Such is the gulf between fugitive and captive ontology.

Within set theory one can develop a theory of recursive definition that allows one to assert the existence (as sets of an appropriate kind) of operations defined on ordinals by certain recursion schemes. Thus, using the scheme

$$\alpha + \emptyset = \alpha$$
$$\alpha + s(\beta) = s(\alpha + \beta)$$
$$\alpha . \emptyset = \emptyset$$
$$\alpha . s(\beta) = (\alpha . \beta) + \alpha$$

we may assert the existence of addition and multiplication as operations on finite ordinals, and introduce + and . as defined function signs. With $\emptyset$ in place of 0, s defined as above, + and . introduced by recursive definition and all quantifications relativized to the set of finite ordinals, the axioms of the 'arithmetical' theory Q translate into *theorems* of set theory. Thus $\exists!0$ becomes the set-theoretical theorem $\emptyset \in \omega$, $\forall x\, x + 0 = x$ becomes the theorem $\forall x(x \in \omega \supset x + \emptyset = x)$, and so on. Set theory thereby inherits the undecidability and incompleteness of Q.

Zermelo-Fraenkel set theory is incomplete in other respects. The Axiom of Choice (any set X of non-empty mutually disjoint sets has in common with some set exactly one member from each of its (i.e. X's) members) is independent of Zermelo-Fraenkel set theory. So is the Continuum Hypothesis, which states that the infinity of subsets of ω is the least uncountable infinity. The foundations of classical mathematics, if not shaky, are generously supplied with expansion cracks. A complete picture of what Mostowski has called the 'crashing incompleteness' of set theory calls for a detailed development of the theory itself, which is beyond the scope of this book.

Notes *p.178*

References *p.181*

Exercises *p.185*

Glossary *p.191*

Index *p.193*

NOTES

Chapter 1

The problem of truth bearers is central in philosophical analysis. See Cartwright 1966, Kneale 1972, Lemmon 1966, Quine 1970 and Thomson 1969.

The definition of logical consequence, the single most important concept in logic, is due to Bolzano and Tarski. See Tarski's paper 'On the concept of logical consequence' in Tarski 1956.

The atomistic ontology of logical semantics has excellent philosophical credentials. Definitive modern discussions are Quine 1960, Strawson 1959 and Wittgenstein 1961. See also Quine 1960 for a discussion on the ontological commitments of theories.

Frege's seminal contribution to the study of first order languages is *Begriffschrift* (1879). Other relevant papers of his are translated in Geach and Black 1960. See also Dummett's highly influential book on Frege's philosophy of language (1973).

Gentzen's work in proof theory is collected in ed. Szabo 1969.

For introductions to the various philosophical logics, see Hughes and Cresswell 1968, Hintikka 1962 and McArthur 1976.

Chapter 2

T. Potts invented the categorial notation used here. Several attempts to provide formal semantics for natural language have been based on a categorial approach. See Lewis 1972 and Montague 1974.

The use of 'linkages' in explaining quantification is to be found in Jeffrey 1967.

Chapter 3

An introduction to the problem of universals, with a useful reading list, is Staniland 1973. On non-denoting terms the reader can do no better than consult the *loci classici*: Frege's 'On sense and reference' in ed. Geach and Black 1960, Russell's 'On denoting' (1905) and Strawson's 'On referring' (1950).

Whether the truth functional connective $\supset$ is an adequate logical translation of the English 'If ... then ...' is discussed by numerous authors in the journal *Analysis*. The problem of entailment is to provide an analysis and logical systematization of that elusive relation between premisses and conclusion of 'genuinely' valid arguments. See Anderson and Belnap 1975, Bennett 1969, Geach 1958, Smiley 1959 and von Wright 1957.

Tarski's paper 'The concept of truth in formalized languages' in *Logic, Semantics, Metamathematics* (1956) is the source of our semantical treatment. An interesting discussion of the possibility of any other kind of approach is Wallace 1970. Davidson's oeuvre on a theory of truth as a theory of meaning for natural language has given rise to a current paradigm, consolidated and assessed in Evans and MacDowell 1976.

For further reading in mathematical model theory see Bell and Slomson 1971, and Chang and Keisler 1973.

Chapter 4

The system of proof developed in this chapter is adapted from Prawitz 1965. We use dilemma as our preferred classical rule of negation.

Heyting's original formalization of intuitionistic logic (3rd ed. 1971) has been superseded by the more natural one due to Gentzen 1969. More recently Martin-Löf 1975 has developed an intuitionistic theory of types in which logical and mathematical operations are treated in a single system.

Sheffer's stroke has long been regarded as a mere quirk, probably because of Nicod's system based on the axiom

$$(A|(B|C))|((D|(D|D))|((E|B)|((A|E)|(E|A)))).$$

The quantifier stroke is due to Schönfinkel 1924. Our introduction and elimination rules are intended to make the stroke more of a quark.

The connective $\times$ of section 12 is 'tonk', Prior's runabout inference ticket (1967). Our discussion owes a great deal to Prawitz. See also Belnap.

Contexts which do not permit substitutions as required by the principle of extensionality are called ***intensional***; and, in the case of contexts for singular terms, ***referentially opaque***. Paradigmatic cases are contexts within the scope of a modal operator such as 'It is necessarily the case that ...' or a verb of propositional attitude such as 'He believes that ...'. A useful collection of papers on the problems of opacity and intensionality is Linsky 1971.

Chapter 5

Our proof of compactness is from Bell and Slomson 1971, where it is attributed to Rado.

The proof of completeness via truth sets is due to Kalmár 1934–5. The normalization theorem, for a system with classical reductio in place of dilemma and without disjunction, is due to Prawitz 1965. The dual proof of completeness via *conjunctive* normal forms is due to Post 1921. The maximalization method is due to Henkin 1949.

The double negation theorem was first proved by Glivenko 1929.

The 'possible worlds' semantics for intuitionistic logic is due to Kripke 1965. Our proof of maximalization is adapted from Aczel 1968.

Chapter 6

Our proof of interpolation is adapted from Prawitz 1965. The theorem on interpolation is due to Craig 1957 and Lyndon 1959; on joint consistency to Robinson; definability – Beth; completeness – Gödel 1930; countable models – Skolem 1920; double negation – Glivenko 1929, Gödel 1933 and Gentzen 1933.

Chapter 7

Excellent texts on computability and recursive functions are Rogers 1967 and Minsky 1967. The monograph Tarski, Mostowski and Robinson 1968 contains a short proof of representability of recursive functions in a subtheory of Q based on infinitely many axioms, exploiting an inductive definition of recursive function due to Julia Robinson. Shoenfield 1967 proves representability in a finitely axiomatized theory slightly different from Q, using a different inductive definition of recursive function. Boolos and Jeffrey prove representability, using yet another definition, in a finitely axiomatized subtheory of our theory Q.

Our proof of undecidability of first order functional logic is taken from Schwartz 1969. The equational definition of recursive function is due to Herbrand and Gödel (see Kleene 1952). The compressed treatment of self-representing theories with diagonals is taken from Tait 1976.

Results (II)–(VI) are due respectively to Craig 1953, Janiczak 1950, Vaught 1954, Shoenfield 1960–1 and Tait 1976. The diagonal method originates with Gödel 1931. The order isomorphism in section 5 was first proved by Cantor (1895).

Our proof of decidability of successor arithmetic amplifies a sketch in Smiley 1970. (XIII) is due to Tarski 1956.

Our semantics for universally free logic with descriptions is due to Smiley 1970; our introduction and elimination rules for ɿ unpack his single axiom.

For further reading on sets, see Gödel 1964, Boolos 1971, Drake 1974, and Takeuti and Zaring 1971. For philosophical implications of results in mathematical logic see Benacerraf 1965, Dummett 1963, Myhill 1952, Mostowski 1972, Anderson 1964, and Wang 1975.

REFERENCES

Aczel, P. (1968) 'Saturated intuitionistic theories' in Schmidt, Schütte and Thiele (eds.) *Contributions to Mathematical Logic* (Amsterdam).

Anderson, A. R. (ed.) (1964) *Minds and Machines* (Englewood Cliffs).

Anderson, A. R. and Belnap, N. D. (1975) *Entailment* Vol. I (Princeton).

Bell, M. and Slomson, A. (1971) *Models and Ultraproducts* (Amsterdam).

Belnap, N. D. 'Tonk, plonk and plink' in Strawson 1967.

Benacerraf, P. (1965) 'What numbers could not be' *Philosophical Review*, 74, 47-73.

Benacerraf, P. and Putnam, H. (eds.) (1964) *Philosophy of Mathematics, Selected Readings* (Englewood Cliffs).

Bennett, J. (1969) 'Entailment', *Philosophical Review* 68, 197-236.

Beth, E. (1953) 'On Padoa's method in the theory of definition', *Konink. Ned. Akad. Wetensch. Proc.* Ser. A 56 (= Indag. Math. 15) 330-9.

Boolos, G. (1971) 'The iterative conception of set', *Journal of Philosophy* 68 215-31.

Boolos, G. and Jeffrey, R. C. (1974) *Computability and Logic* (Cambridge).

Cantor, G. (1895) 'Beiträge zur Begründung der Transfiniten Mengenlehre', *Mathematische Annalen* 96, 481-512.

Cartwright, R. (1966) 'Propositions', in R. J. Butler (ed.), *Analytical Philosophy 1st Series* (Oxford).

Chang, C. C. and Keisler, H. J. (1973) *Model Theory* (Amsterdam).

Craig, W. (1953) 'On axiomatisability within a system', *Journal of Symbolic Logic* 18, 30-2.

— (1957) 'Linear reasoning', ibid. 22, 250-68.

Davidson, D. (1965) 'Theories of meaning and learnable languages', in Y. Bar-Hillel (ed.), *Logic, Methodology and Philosophy of Science* (Amsterdam) 384-94.

— (1967) 'Truth and meaning', *Synthese* 17, 304-23.

— (1969) 'True to the facts', *Journal of Philosophy* 66, 748-64.

— (1970) 'Semantics for natural languages', in B. Visentini et al. (eds.) *Linguaggi – nella società et nella tecnica* (Milan) 177-89.

— (1973) 'In defense of Convention *T*' in H. Leblanc (ed.) *Truth, Syntax and Modality* (Amsterdam) 76-86.

Drake, F. (1974) *Set Theory: An Introduction to Large Cardinals* (Amsterdam).

Dummett, M. A. E. (1963) 'The philosophical implications of Gödel's incompleteness theorem', *Ratio* 5, 140-55.

— (1973) *Frege: Philosophy of Language* (London).

— (1973) 'The justification of deduction', *Proc. of the British Academy* 59, 1-34.

— (1975) 'The philosophical basis of intuitionistic logic', in Rose and Shepperdson 1975.

Evans, G. and MacDowell, J. (eds.) (1976) *Truth and Meaning* (Oxford).

Frege, G. (1879) *Begriffschrift*, tr. in van Heijenoort.

— (1960) *Philosophical Writings*, tr. and ed. by P. Geach and M. Black (2nd ed., Oxford).

Geach, P. (1958) 'Entailment', *Proc. of the Aristotelian Society*, Supp. Vol. 32, 157-72.

Gentzen, G. (1933) 'On the relation between intuitionist and classical arithmetic', in *The Collected Papers of Gerhard Gentzen,* tr. and ed. by M. E. Szabo, 53-67 (Amsterdam, 1969).

— (1969) *The Collected Papers of Gerhard Gentzen*, tr. and ed. by M. E. Szabo (Amsterdam).

Glivenko, V. (1929) 'Sur quelques points de la logique de M. Brouwer', *Académie Royale de Belgique, Bulletins de la classe des sciences*, sér. 5, vol. 15, 183-8.

Gödel, K. (1930) 'Die Vollständigkeit der Axiome des logischen Funktionenkalküls', *Monatshefte für Mathematik und Physik* 37, 349-60. Tr. in van Heijenoort.

— (1931) 'Über formal unentscheidbare Sätze der Principia Mathematica und verwandter Systeme I', ibid. 38, 173-98. Tr. in van Heijenoort.

— (1933) 'Zur intuitionistischen Arithmetik und Zahlentheorie', *Ergebnisse eines Mathematischen Kolloquiums* no. 4, 34-8.

— (1964) 'What is Cantor's continuum problem?', in Benacerraf and Putnam 1964.

Haack, S. (1976) 'The justification of deduction', *Mind* 85, 112-19.

Henkin, L. (1949) 'The completeness of the first order functional calculus', *Journal of Symbolic Logic* 14, 159-66.

Heyting, A. (1971) *Intuitionism: An Introduction* (3rd ed., Amsterdam).

Hintikka, K. J. J. (1962) *Knowledge and Belief: An Introduction to the Logic of the Two Notions* (Ithaca).

Hughes, G. E. and Cresswell, M. J. (1968) *An Introduction to Modal Logic* (London).

Janiczak, A. (1950) 'A remark concerning the decidability of complete theories', *Journal of Symbolic Logic* 15, 277-9.

Jeffrey, R. C. (1967) *Formal Logic: Its Scope and Limits* (New York).

Kalmár, L. (1934-5) 'Über die Axiomatisierbarkeit des Aussagenkalküls', *Acta Sci. Math.* (Szeged) 7, 222-43.

Kleene, S. C. (1952) *Introduction to metamathematics* (Amsterdam).

Kneale, W. (1972) 'Propositions and truth in natural languages', *Mind* 81, 225-43.

Kripke, S. (1965) 'Semantical analysis of intuitionistic logic I', in J. N. Crossley and M. A. E. Dummett (eds.) *Formal Systems and Recursive Functions* (Amsterdam) 92-130.

Lemmon, E. J. (1966) 'Sentence, statement and proposition', in B. Williams and A. Montefiore (eds.) *British Analytical Philosophy* (London).

Lewis, D. (1972) 'General semantics', in G. Harman and D. Davidson (eds.) *Semantics for Natural Language* (Dordrecht).

Linsky, L. (ed.) (1971) *Reference and Modality* (London).

Lyndon, R. (1959) 'An interpolation theorem in the predicate calculus', *Pacific Journal of Mathematics* 9, 129-42.

Martin-Löf, P. (1975) 'An intuitionistic theory of types: predicative part', in Rose and Shepperdson 1975.

McArthur, R. P. (1976) *Tense Logic* (Dordrecht).

Minsky, M. L. (1967) *Computation: Finite and Infinite Machines* (Englewood Cliffs).

Montague, R. M. (1974) *Formal Philosophy*, ed. by R. H. Thomason (New Haven).

Mostowski, A. (1972) 'Philosophical implications of recent results in set theory' in I. Lakatos (ed.) *Problems in the Philosophy of Mathematics* (2nd pr., Amsterdam).

Myhill, J. (1952) 'Some philosophical implications of mathematical logic', *Review of Metaphysics* 5.

Nicod (1917–20) *Proc. Camb. Philos. Soc.* 19, 32-41.

Post, E. J. (1921) 'Introduction to a general theory of elementary propositions', *American Journal of Mathematics* 43, 163-85. Also in van Heijenoort.

Prior, A. N. (1967) 'The runabout inference ticket', in Strawson 1967.

Prawitz, D. (1965) *Natural Deduction: A Proof Theoretical Study* (Stockholm).

— (1974) 'On the idea of a general proof theory', *Synthese* 27, 63-77.

Quine, W. V. O. (1934) 'Ontological remarks on the propositional calculus', *Mind* 43, 472-6.

— (1960) 'On what there is', in *From a Logical Point of View* (Cambridge, Mass.).

— (1960a) *Word and Object* (Cambridge, Mass.).

— (1970) *Philosophy of Logic* (Englewood Cliffs).

Robinson, A. (1956) 'A result on consistency and its application to the theory of definition', *Konink. Ned. Akad. Wetensch. Proc.* Ser. A 59 (=Indag. Math. 18) 47-58.

Rogers, H. (1967) *Theory of Recursive Functions and Effective Computability* (New York).

Rose, H. E. and Shepperdson, J. (eds.) (1975) *Logic Colloquium '73* (Amsterdam).

Russell, B. (1905) 'On denoting', *Mind* 14, 479-93.

Schönfinkel, M. (1924) 'Über die Bausteine der mathematischen Logik', *Mathematische Annalen* 92, 305-16. Tr. in van Heijenoort.

Schwartz, T. (1969) 'A simple treatment of Church's theorem on the decision problem', *Logique et Analyse* 12, 153-6.

Shoenfield, J. R. (1960–1) 'Undecidable and creative theories', *Fundamenta Mathematicae* 49, 171-9.

— (1967) *Mathematical Logic* (Reading, Mass.).

Skolem, T. (1920) 'Logisch-kombinatorische Untersuchungen über die Erfüllbarkeit oder Beweisbarkeit mathematischer Sätze nebst einem Theorem über dichte Mengen', *Skrifter utgit av Videnskapsselskapet i Kristiana, I. Matematisk-naturvidenskabelig Klasse 1920* no. 4. Tr. in van Heijenoort.

Smiley, T. J. (1959) 'Entailment and deducibility', *Proc. of the Aristotelian Society* 59, 233-54.

— (1970) Lecture Notes in Mathematical Logic (University of Cambridge).

Staniland, H. (1973) *Universals* (London).

Strawson, P. F. (1950) 'On referring', *Mind* 59, 320-44.

— (1959) *Individuals: an essay in descriptive metaphysics* (London).

— (1967) (ed.) *Philosophical Logic* (London).

Tait, W. (1976) Lecture on Tarski's Theorem (University of Chicago). Notes by J. W. Snapper.

Takeuti, G. and Zaring, W. (1971) *Introduction to Axiomatic Set Theory* (New York).

Tarski, A. (1956) *Logic, Semantics, Metamathematics*, tr. and ed. by J. H. Woodger (Oxford).

Tarski, A., Mostowski, A. and Robinson, A. (1968) *Undecidable Theories* (Amsterdam).

Thomson, J. (1969) 'Truth-bearers and the trouble with propositions', *Journal of Philosophy* 66, 737-47.

Van Heijenoort, J. (ed.) (1967) *From Frege to Gödel: a source book in mathematical logic, 1879–1931* (Cambridge, Mass.).

Vaught, R. (1954) 'Applications of the Löwenheim-Skolem-Tarski theorem to problems of completeness and decidability', *Konink. Ned. Akad. Wetensch. Proc.* Ser. A 57 (=Indag. Math. 16) 467-72.

Von Wright, G. H. (1957) 'The concept of entailment', in *Logical Studies* (London).

Wallace, J. (1970) 'On the frame of reference', *Synthese* 22, 61-94.

Wang, H. (1975) *From Mathematics to Philosophy* (New York).

Wittgenstein, L. (1961) *Tractatus Logico-Philosophicus*, tr. by D. F. Pears and B. F. McGuiness (London).

EXERCISES

Chapters 1-4

1. 'The logical form of a sentence is best understood by considering the order in which it is built up from simpler expressions'. Illustrate this with respect to

(1) Only if it is the case that only if it rains only if it pours does it hail is it the case that it snows.
(2) Only boys loved only by girls love only girls.
(3) Only those boys loved only by girls love only girls.
(4) All boys loved by all girls love all girls.

2. Write down a sentence of first order logic with identity which is true of all and only queues (finite or infinite), using only the predicates Px (x is a person), Bxy (x is behind y) and Cxy (x is a companion of y). You may assume that only companions can occupy the same position in a queue.

3.

$$\frac{\text{No fat person is bald} \quad \text{John is no fat person}}{\text{John is bald}}$$

Is this argument a counterexample to the law of substitutivity of identicals? If not, what is its logical form? Is it valid?

4. Let us call a person *hitched* to anyone whom he loves and who loves him. Let us call a person *confused* if and only if he is hitched to more than one person. Let $Lxy =_{df} x$ loves y. Assume there are only people. Write down a sentence of first order logic, using only the predicate L and the identity predicate, which says that everyone is confused. If everyone is confused, does everyone love everyone? If everyone loves everyone, is everyone confused? Justify your answers.

5. In the following diagram dots represent individuals and arrows represent relations. Using Axy to mean 'there is a single-headed arrow from x to y' and Bxy to mean 'there is a double-headed arrow from x to y' write down a sentence of first order logic with identity that categorically describes the diagram:

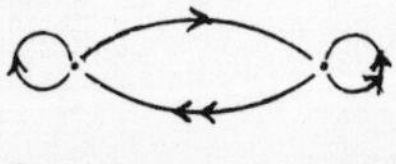

6. As for (5) with the diagram

7. Describe counterexamples to the following invalid arguments:

$$\frac{\forall x \exists y Rxy \quad \forall x(\exists y Rxy \supset \exists z Rzx)}{\forall x \forall y \exists z(Rxz \,\&\, Rzy)}$$

$$\frac{\forall x\exists y(Rxy\lor Ryx)\qquad \forall x\forall y(Rxy\supset\forall z(Ryz\supset Rxz))}{\exists x(\forall yRxy\lor\forall yRyx)}$$

8. Find both finite and infinite counterexamples to the following invalid argument:

$$\begin{array}{l}\forall x\forall y(Fxy\supset\sim Fyx)\\ \forall x\exists yFxy\\ \forall x\exists y\sim Fyx\\ \hline \forall x\exists y(Fyx\,\&\sim Fyy)\end{array}$$

9. Prove, or construct a counterexample to, each of the following arguments:

$$\frac{\forall x\exists yRxy\qquad \exists y\forall zRyz}{\forall x\forall zRxz}\qquad \frac{\forall x\sim Rxx\qquad \forall x\forall y(Rxy\supset\sim Ryx)}{\forall x\forall y\forall z((Rxy\,\&\,Ryz)\supset Rxz)}$$

$$\frac{\forall x\exists yRxy\qquad \forall x\exists ySxy}{\forall x\exists y(Rxy\,\&\,Sxy)}\qquad \frac{\forall x\forall y\forall z((Rxy\,\&\,Ryz)\supset Rxz)\qquad \forall x\sim Rxx}{\forall x\forall y(Rxy\supset\sim Ryx)}$$

10. Prove the following arguments, using only basic deductive rules:

$$\begin{array}{l}A\supset(B\lor C)\\ B\supset D\\ C\supset D\\ \sim D\\ \hline \sim A\end{array}\qquad \frac{(A\lor B)\supset C}{(A\supset C)\,\&\,(B\supset C)}\qquad \frac{\sim B\quad A\supset(B\lor C)}{\sim C\supset\sim A}\qquad \frac{A\supset(B\lor C)}{(A\supset B)\lor(A\supset C)}\qquad \frac{A\supset\sim A}{\sim A}$$

$$\frac{A\,\&\sim B}{\sim(A\supset B)}\qquad \frac{\sim(A\supset B)}{A\,\&\sim B}\qquad \frac{A\supset B}{\sim A\lor B}$$

$$\frac{\forall x(Ax\supset Cx)\,\&\,\forall x(Bx\supset Cx)}{\forall x((Ax\lor Bx)\supset Cx)}\qquad \frac{\forall x((Ax\lor Bx)\supset Cx)}{\forall x(Ax\supset Cx)\,\&\,\forall x(Bx\supset Cx)}\qquad \begin{array}{l}\forall x(Ax\lor Bx)\supset Cx\\ \exists x\sim Cx\\ \forall x\sim Ax\supset Dx\\ \hline \exists x(\sim Bx\,\&\,Dx)\end{array}$$

$$\frac{\forall x((Ax\,\&\,Bx)\supset Cx)}{\forall x(Ax\supset(Bx\supset Cx))}\qquad \frac{\forall x(Ax\supset(Bx\supset Cx))}{\forall x((Ax\,\&\,Bx)\supset Cx)}$$

$$\frac{\sim\forall x(Ax\supset Bx)}{\exists x(Ax\,\&\sim Bx)}\qquad \begin{array}{l}\forall x(Ax\supset Bx)\\ \forall x(Bx\supset(Cx\lor Dx))\\ \exists x(\sim Cx\,\&\sim Dx)\\ \hline \exists x\sim Ax\end{array}\qquad \begin{array}{l}\forall x(Ax\supset\exists yRxy)\\ \forall x(Bx\supset\forall y\sim Rxy)\\ \hline \forall x(\sim Ax\lor\sim Bx)\end{array}$$

$$\frac{\forall x\forall y(Rxy\supset\sim x=y)}{\forall x\sim Rxx}$$

11. Translate each of the following arguments into logical notation. In each case determine whether it is valid. If so, supply a proof using only basic deductive rules; otherwise, describe a counterexample.

Everything is red or blue
Nothing is red and blue
Not everything is red
___
Something is blue

John fools only Mary
Anyone fooled by anyone is loved by Fred
Only Mary loves Fred
___
Only Mary loves Fred and is loved by him

0 and 1 are the only objects
0 is not even
All perfect objects are even
There is at most one perfect object

Alfred is rich or Betty is poor
Betty is rich or Alfred is poor
No-one is rich and poor
Either Alfred and Betty are rich or Alfred and Betty are poor

Someone loves only himself
Anyone who loves himself is loved by no-one else
Someone is loved by no-one else

John loves only himself
No-one else loves only himself
Fred loves himself
John is not Fred
Fred loves someone else

Someone loves someone else
Only people who love only themselves love themselves
Someone does not love himself

Every point is to the left of some point
No point is to the left of itself
There are at least two points

Everyone's loved by someone
Everyone's loved ones once loved
Everyone once loved

Someone loves someone else
Anyone loved by anyone else loves himself
Someone loves himself

The cat is on the mat
The mat is round
Nothing is both round and square
The cat is not on anything square

12. If t and u are terms, let (tu) be a term. In the case of each of the following arguments, formalize the given informal proof by means of a proof in first order logic with identity:

(I) (1) $\forall x\; x+0=0$
(2) $\forall x \forall y \forall z\; (xy)+(xz)=x(y+z)$
(3) $\forall x \forall y \forall z\; x+y=x+z \supset y=z$
$\forall x\; x0=0$

Informal proof of (*I*): Consider arbitrary a. $a+0=a$ from (1). Also $(aa)+(a0)=a(a+0)$ from (2). So, upon substitution, we get $(aa)+(a0)=aa$.

But $aa=(aa)+0$ from (1). Therefore we have $(aa)+(a0)=(aa)+0$. But then we cancel by (3) to get $(a0)=0$. But since a was arbitrary this holds for all x.

$$\frac{\begin{array}{ll}\text{(II)} & (1)\ \forall x\forall y\forall z\,((xy)z)=(x(yz)) \\ & (2)\ \forall x\,(x0)=x \\ & (3)\ \forall x\exists y\,(xy)=0\end{array}}{\forall x\,(0x)=x}$$

Informal proof of (II): By (1) we needn't worry about order of bracketing. Take an arbitrary object a. By (3) there is some object, b say, such that $ab=0$. So $0ab=00$. But $00=0$ by (2). Thus $0ab=0$ whence $0ab=ab$. By (3) there is some object, say c, such that $bc=0$. Since $0abc=abc$ we therefore have $0a0=a0$. Cancelling 0 on both sides by (2), $0a=a$. But a was arbitrary. Thus $\forall x\ 0x=x$.

13. (1) I am in Edinburgh today
(2) If I am in Timbuktu tomorrow, I shall be in Peking the next day
(3) If I am in Russia the day after tomorrow, I cannot be in Britain today
(4) Edinburgh is in Britain and Peking is in Russia

Given (1)-(4), will I be in Timbuktu tomorrow? Justify your answer by arguing for the appropriate conclusion, citing the immediate premisses of each step of inference. Comment on the difficulties involved in providing a strict logical proof of your argument in logical notation. Could these difficulties be overcome?

14. Choose in turn one of the connectives &, $\vee$ and $\supset$. Show that the remaining two can be defined in terms of $\sim$ and your choice. Using your definitions, eliminate the defined connectives in the following proof:

$$\frac{\dfrac{\dfrac{A \,\&\, B}{A}}{A\vee B} \quad (A\vee B)\supset C}{C}$$

Which steps in the resulting 'proof' are not basic? Re-write it so that only basic rules are used.

15. Prove the following: $\overline{(A\supset B)\vee(B\supset A)}$. Is it true in general that $A \models B$ or $B \models A$?

16. Consider proofs built up using only the introduction and elimination rules for $\supset$, & and $\vee$, and the absurdity rule. Call them Proofs. Let $!A =_{df} A\supset$✱. A is *decidable* if and only if there is a Proof of $A\vee !A$. A is *stable* if and only if there is a Proof of $(!!A)\supset A$. Show that every decidable sentence is stable.

17. A two-place connective $\times$ is called idempotent if and only if A is logically equivalent to $A\times A$; and is called associative if and only if $(A\times B)\times C$ is logically equivalent to $A\times(B\times C)$. Investigate the idempotency and associativity, or otherwise, of &, $\vee$, $\supset$, $\equiv$, $|$.

18. The connective $\times$ is governed by the following introduction and elimination rules:

$$\dfrac{\begin{array}{cc} \overline{A}^{(i)} & \overline{B}^{(i)} \\ \vdots & \vdots \\ \divideontimes & \divideontimes \end{array}}{A \times B}{(i)} \qquad \dfrac{A \quad A \times B}{\divideontimes} \qquad \dfrac{B \quad A \times B}{\divideontimes}$$

What is the truth table for $\times$? Define $\sim$, &, $\vee$ and $\supset$ in terms of $\times$.

19. The one-place connective γ is governed by the following introduction and elimination rules:

$$\dfrac{A}{\gamma A} \quad \begin{array}{l}\text{(with the restriction that } A \text{ depend} \\ \text{only on premisses of the form } \gamma B)\end{array} \; ; \; \dfrac{\gamma A}{A}$$

How would you interpret γ? Using these rules and the usaul rules of propositional logic prove $\dfrac{\gamma(A \,\&\, B)}{\gamma A \,\&\, \gamma B}$ and $\dfrac{\gamma A \,\&\, \gamma B}{\gamma(A \,\&\, B)}$.

20. Consider the following definitions:

X and Y are contraries relative to $Z =_{df} Z, X \vDash \sim Y$
X and Y are subcontraries relative to $Z =_{df} Z, \sim X \vDash Y$
X and Y are contradictories $=_{df} X \vDash \sim Y$ and $\sim X \vDash Y$

Consider the following sentences:

All *A*'s are *B*'s
No *A*'s are *B*'s
Some *A*'s are *B*'s
Some *A*'s are not *B*'s

Which are contraries relative to 'There are *A*'s'?
Which are subcontraries relative to 'There are *A*'s'?
Which are contradictories?
Translate the sentences into logical notation and prove your answers to these questions, using only basic rules.

Chapters 5-7

21. The least number principle, expressed as a schema, is

$$\forall x(\sim\phi x \supset \exists y(\sim\phi y \,\&\, \forall z(z < y \supset \phi z)))$$

The principle of mathematical induction, expressed as a schema, is

$$\forall x(\forall y(y < x \supset \phi x) \supset \phi y) \supset \forall z \phi z$$

Prove each from the other, using only basic deductive rules of first order logic.

22. Show that any theorem of classical propositional logic of the form $\sim A$ is a theorem of intuitionistic propositional logic.

23. ϕ is highly falsifiable iff for every n there is some $m > n$ such that ϕ is false in some model of cardinality m. Show that if ϕ is highly falsifiable then

ψ is false in some infinite model. If ψ is highly falsifiable, does it follow that ψ has no infinite models?

24. Let Δ be a set of sentences of a first order language with identity and only finitely many extra-logical expressions. Suppose Δ has at least two non-isomorphic finite models. Show Δ is incomplete. Give an example of a theory which has infinite models, is categorical in some infinite power, but is incomplete.

25. Let ψ be a formula with two free variables built up from variables, the identity predicate and the logical operators. Suppose M is an infinite model. Show that one of the following holds:

(1) for all α,β in M $\quad M \models \psi[\alpha,\beta]$ iff $\alpha=\beta$
(2) for all α,β in M $\quad M \models \psi[\alpha,\beta]$ iff $\alpha\neq\beta$
(3) for all α,β in M $\quad M \models \psi[\alpha,\beta]$
(4) for no α,β in M $\quad M \models \psi[\alpha,\beta]$

26. A formula $\psi(x)$ of the language of successor arithmetic defines the set P of natural numbers if and only if

$$n \in P \quad \text{iff} \quad \psi(\underline{n}) \text{ is true in } \mathbf{N}.$$

Show that P is thus definable if and only if either P is finite or $\mathbf{N}\backslash P$ is finite.

27. Suppose φ and ψ have the same truth value in every model of Δ but are not interdeducible relative to Δ. Show Δ is incomplete. If $\mathfrak{M}$ is a class of models let Th($\mathfrak{M}$) be the set of sentences true in every model in $\mathfrak{M}$. Let Mod(Δ) be the set of models in which every sentence in Δ is true. Show that Δ is consistent and deductively closed if and only if $\text{Th}(\text{Mod}(\Delta))=\Delta$.

28. Show that any consistent decidable set of sentences is contained in a consistent decidable theory.

29. Let $'$ be a mapping on formulae defined as follows:

$$\begin{aligned}
A' &= \sim A \text{ for } A \text{ atomic}\\
(\sim\psi)' &= \psi\\
(\varphi\vee\psi)' &= \sim\varphi \,\&\, \sim\psi\\
(\varphi\,\&\,\psi)' &= \sim\varphi \vee \sim\psi\\
(\exists x\psi)' &= \forall x\sim\psi\\
(\forall x\psi)' &= \exists x\sim\psi
\end{aligned}$$

where we assume the language contains only the logical operators mentioned. Let Δ have the following closure properties:

for no atomic formula A are both A and $\sim A$ in Δ;
if $\sim\psi\in\Delta$ then $\psi'\in\Delta$;
if $(\varphi\,\&\,\psi)\in\Delta$ then $\varphi\in\Delta$ and $\psi\in\Delta$;
if $(\varphi\vee\psi)\in\Delta$ then $\varphi\in\Delta$ or $\psi\in\Delta$;
if $\exists x\psi\in\Delta$ then for some name a $\psi^x_a\in\Delta$; and
if $\forall x\psi\in\Delta$ then for every name a $\psi^x_a\in\Delta$.

Show that Δ has a model.

GLOSSARY

of frequently used notation

Set theoretical

$\varphi \in \Delta$	φ is a member of Δ
$\Delta \subseteq \Gamma$	Δ is a subset of Γ
$\Delta \cup \Gamma$	the union of Δ and Γ
Δ, φ	$\Delta \cup \{\varphi\}$
$\Delta \setminus \Gamma$	the result of removing the members of Γ from Δ
$\langle \alpha_1, \ldots, \alpha_n \rangle$	ordered n-tuple
$\emptyset$	empty set
$\{\ \}$	set
ω	set of finite ordinals
$\aleph_0$	first infinite cardinal

Logical

⋇	absurdity sign, *page* 40
$\sim$	negation, 16
&	conjunction, 16
$\vee$	disjunction, 16
$\supset$	material conditional, 16
$\equiv$	biconditional, 78
$\mid$	Sheffer stroke, 63
$\exists$	existential quantifier, 16
$\forall$	universal quantifier, 16
$=$	identity predicate, 32
ι	descriptive operator, 163
x, y, z	variables, 17

Syntactic notions

A, B, C	atoms
$\varphi, \psi, \theta, \eta, \zeta, \xi$	formulae/sentences
$\Delta, \Gamma, \Theta, \Psi, \Sigma$	sets of sentences
Π, Σ	proofs
Δ/φ	argument with set of premisses Δ and conclusion φ
$\begin{matrix}\Sigma \\ (\psi) \\ \Pi\end{matrix}$	(for definition see page 51)
$\dfrac{\Pi_1 \ldots \Pi_n}{\varphi}$, etc.	proof schemata

φ^x_t	52
φ^a_x	52
Π^a_t	66
$\Pi(a/b)$	66
Πt	67
$\forall\vec{x}\varphi^{\vec{a}}_{\vec{x}}$ $(\exists\vec{x}\varphi^{\vec{a}}_{\vec{x}})$	118
ψt	125

Metalogical predicates

$\mathscr{P}(\Pi, \varphi, \Delta)$	Π is a proof of φ depending on Δ, 50
$\Delta \vdash_I \varphi$	φ is intuitionistically deducible from Δ, 57
$\Delta \vdash_C \varphi$	φ is classically deducible from Δ, 58
$\Delta \vdash \varphi$	φ is deducible from Δ, 58
$\varphi \dashv\vdash \psi$	φ is interdeducible with ψ relative to Δ, 78

Semantic notions

T, F	truth values, 23
τ	truth value assignment, 89
$\underline{\tau}$	truth set of τ, 91
τ_φ	truth set of τ over the atoms of φ, 93
$\mathfrak{A}, \mathfrak{B}, \mathfrak{C}, M$	models, 29
$\mathbb{N}$	model of natural numbers, 30
$s(x/\alpha)$	modified assignment, 26
$s[t]$	denotation of t relative to s, 26
$s_{\mathfrak{A}}[t]$	denotation of t in $\mathfrak{A}$ relative to s, 29
$\mathfrak{A} \models \psi[s]$	s satisfies ψ in $\mathfrak{A}$, 29
$\Delta \models \varphi$	φ is a logical consequence of Δ, 72

Kripke semantics

$i \Vdash \varphi$	i forces φ, 109
$[i]$	set of sentences forced at i, 108
$i \leqslant j$	i precedes j, 108
$\underline{i}$	set of atomic sentences assigned to i, 108
$\natural_R$	natural Kripke model for R, 109
$\Delta \Vdash_i \varphi$	Δ forces φ by i, 110
$/i/$	set of terms in members of $\underline{i}$, 132

Special notation for Chapter 7

$\#, \natural$	codings, 136
c_P	characteristic function of P, 137
$\bar{\varphi}, \bar{\bar{\theta}}$	code-terms, 142
Q	finitely axiomatized subtheory of arithmetic, 152
$\underline{n}$	numeral for n, 138

INDEX

absurdity rule, 47
adequacy condition, 25
adequacy schema, 28-9
analogy, 43, 46, 57, 60, 69
Anderson, 46-7
arbitrary, 29
argument, 2: for theorems of metalogic, 125-9; semantical, 162
Aristotle, 10
arithmetic: successor, 145; second order, 146; successor and additive, 152
assignment: of individuals to variables, 26, 36; of truth values, 89
assumption, 43, 49
atom, 88
atomic closure, 109
atomic knowns, 107
atomic sentence, 16: truth conditions of, 22
axiom of choice, 175
axiomatizable, 141
axioms: Hilbert's for Euclidean geometry, 5; for orderings, 35, 132; for successor arithmetic, 145; for second order successor arithmetic, 146; of *Q*, 152; of Zermelo-Fraenkel set theory, 173-4

basic recursive functions, 154
Belnap, 46, 47
biconditional, 78
bound variable, 16
bracket plus infix notation, 19

cardinality of a language, 130
categorial analysis, 13
categorical, 32
categorically describable, 32
categoricity (in power), 141
categories of expressions, 12
census, 32
characteristic function, 137
choice, axiom of, 175
Church, 122
Church's Thesis, 136, 138
classical negation rules, 57-8
classification of Sheffer proofs in fully normal form, 117
closed terms, 19
closure: deductive, 104; atomic, 109; universal and existential, 118
coding, 136-7
co-extensive, 78
compact, 6, 89, 146
compactness corollaries, 131
compactness theorem, 35, 89
complete, 6
completeness, viii, 93, 94, 95, 100, 102-4, 129: constructive proofs of, 101-3; of theories, 141; of successor arithmetic, 146-52
composition, 154
computable function, 136-8
conclusion, 2
conditional proof, 42
connective, 16
consequence, logical, 2, 6, 28, 72, 89
conservatively extends, 120
consistent, 8, 104, 120
constellation, 96
contextual elimination, 165
continuum hypothesis, 175
contradiction, rule of, 40
conversion schema, 164
corollaries: to compactness, 131; to representability, 159
countable, 129, 131, 174
counterexample, 2, 30, 33-4, 113

decidability: of propositional logic, 103; of monadic logic, 122-5; of successor arithmetic, 146-52
decidable, 137, 141
deducibility, 59, 107: in propositional logic, 89; in a theory, 153
deduction: natural, viii, 7; justification of, 74
deductive power, 146
denotation, 22, 26
denotation rule, 168
descriptive terms, 163
diagonal (for a theory), 142
diagonal method, 136, 140, 143-4
diagonalization, viii; *see* diagonal method
dilemma, 48, 94
discharge, 42, 56, 95
discharge stroke, 51, 56
discourse, universe of, 4
disjunctive normal form, 98-9
disjunctive set, 109
disjunctive syllogism, 47
distinguished name, 29, 71

domain, 4, 29
dominant operator, 20, 22
double negation: rule of, 48; theorems, 106, 129-30
dualities, 59
Dummett, 74

effective method, 136
elimination of quantifiers, 147-52
elimination rules, 40-56, 57, 78, 169, 172
elimination of terms, 165-6
entailment, 46
equation, 138
equational system, 138
Euclidean geometry, 5
excluded middle, 47
existential: quantifier, 16: set, 133
explicit definability, 121
expressive completeness, 61
expressive limitation, 5
expressive power, 146
extending models, 72
extension, 78
extensionality: for logic, 77; for sets, 173

first order language, 4
forcing, 108, 133
form, 4, 10
formula, 18: well-formed, 12, 19
foundation, axiom of, 174
foundational questions, 7
Fraenkel, 165, 173
free occurrences of names in proofs, 66, 69
free occurrences of variables in formulae, 18-19
Frege, 5, 15, 76-7
fully normal form, 117
function, 16: computable, 136; recursive, 136; characteristic, 137

Gentzen, viii, 7
Gödel, 136
Gödel numbering, 136
grammar, 19

Haack, 74
harmony, 74
Henkin's method, viii, 103-4, 111, 125-9, 170, 172
Hilbert, 5

identity, 77
identity predicate, 32
implicit definition, 121
incompleteness, viii
individual, 3
induction, viii; mathematical, 31; first order schema of, 145; second order axiom of, 146, 163
inductive definition: of terms and formulae, 19; of denotations of terms, 26; of satisfaction, 27; of proof, 55; of sentence in propositional logic, 89; of disjunctive normal form, 99; of forcing, 108, 133; of recursive function, 138-54
inductive hypothesis, 31
inference: marker, 2; rules, 6, 40ff; infinitary inference, 31, 162; stroke, 47, 50
infinitary rule, 162
infinity, axiom of, 174
instance, 10, 36, 145
interdeducible, 78
interpolant, 117
interpretation, 3
introduction rules, 40-56, 57, 78, 169, 172
intuitionism, viii
intuitionistic: logic, 57, 106; set, 109, 133
iota, 163
isomorphism, 32, 144

Kripke
semantics, viii, 106-10, 132-3
model, 108, 113

language: first order, 4; of first order functional logic, 138; of arithmetic, 140; *see also* object language, metalanguage
law: Leibniz's, 11; of substitutivity of identicals, 11; of excluded middle, 47, 113
Leibniz, 11
lemma: on substitution in proofs, 67; on dilemma, 93; DNF lemmata 1-3, 99-100; complexity, 102; eternity, 110, 133; lemmata for undecidability of first order functional logic, 140; lemmata for completeness of successor arithmetic, 147-52; simplification, 171
limitative theorems for logic and arithmetic, 160-3
linkage, 17
logic: intuitionistic vs. classical, 57; propositional vs. first order, 88; monadic, 122; first order functional, 138; second order, 146; universally free, 163ff

logical: consequence, 2, 6, 28, 72, 89; word, 3; form 4, 10; operator, 16; truth, 47, 89, 163
Löwenheim-Skolem Theorem, 35, 130, 131, 141

major premiss, 57
maxim of shallow analysis, 12, 82
maximal: constellation, 96; set, 104
maximal consistent set, 103
maximalization, 104, 125-7, 133-4, 170
membership predicate, 164
metalanguage, 26-7, 74, 154, 162
metalogic, 8
metamathematics, 8
method: Henkin's, 103-4, 111, 125-9, 170, 172; effective, 136; of quantifier elimination, 147-52; diagonal, 136, 140, 143-4
minimization of regular functions, 154
model, 5: standard definition of, 29; natural, viii, 109, 127-8, 171; Kripke, 108-9, 132-3; **N** of natural numbers, 140; for universally free logic, 167
model theory, 7
modus ponens, 40
monadic, 122
Mostowski, 175
multiple quantification, 11, 15, 17, 25

name, 3, 16: distinguished, 29, 71
natural: deduction, viii, 7; model, viii, 109, 127-8, 171; numbers, 30, 140, 145
normal form, 76, 84, 85, 98
normalization, 6, 76, 84, 94, 96, 98
numbers, 4, 30, 35, 140, 145
numeral, 138

object language, 28, 91, 154, 162
ontology, 4, 174
operator: logical, 16; meaning of, 71
ordering, 35, 132
ordinal, 174

paradox: Russell's, 164; Skolem's, 174
parameter, 65
perfecting arguments, 6
Polish notation, 20
powers, axiom of, 173
Prawitz, viii, 7, 84-5
predicate, 3, 16: primitive, 22; identity, 32; membership, 164
premiss, 2: major, 57
primitive, 16: predicate, 22
proof, 5, 49, 107: system of, 5; by cases, 45; transitivity of, 49; transformations of, 49, 94-6, 116; subordinate, 51; intuitionistic, 57; classical, 57; depth of, 85; in propositional logic, 88; normalization of, 94-6, 116-17; order of, 97; canonical, 107, 132; ω-proof, 162
provability, 2
Pythagoras's theorem, 5

quantification: multiple, 11, 15, 17, 25; second order, 146
quantifier, 16: prefix, 18; switch, 33; rules, 53-5, 167-8; stroke, 63; method of elimination, 147-52
Quine, 12, 165

Ramsey, 22
recursion, 138-9
recursive function, 136-9, 154
reduct, 70, 96
reductio ad absurdum, 44: classical, 48
reduction procedures, 69-70, 96-7, 169, 172
reflexivity of identity, 77
replacement, axiom schema of, 174
representability theorem, 136, 156, 159
representing, 141
restrictions on quantifier rules, 64
rules: of inference, 6; introduction and elimination, 40-6, 57, 78, 169, 172; general form of, 50; interderivability of, 57-8, 62; for identity, 77; for successor arithmetic, 147; for *Q*, 153; ω-rule, 162; modified quantifier rules for universally free logic, 167-8
Russell, 164-7
Russell's theory of descriptions, 165
Russell's paradox, 164

satisfaction, 27, 29
satisfiability, 104-6,123: intuitionistic, 111-12, 134
satisfy, 24, 89
scope, 20
second order: arithmetic and logic, 146; logical truth, 163
self-representing, 142
semantical argument, 162
semantics: game theoretic, 35; Kripke, viii, 106, 132; philosophical and algebraic sense of, 106
sentence, 2, 3, 16, 18, 27, 88-9: atomic, 16, 22; connected, 22; quantified, 24
Sheffer stroke, 63, 101
situation, 2

Skolem's paradox, 164
Socrates, 7, 22
sound, 6
soundness, 72, 107, 110
strongly representing, 142
substitution, 64, 79: of terms in proofs, 42, 46, 67, 69
substitutivity of identicals, 11, 77
successor arithmetic, 145-52
surface form, 10
syllogism, 10
symmetry of identity, 77
syntactical, 5
system of proof, 5-6: equational system, 138

Tarski, 25
Tarski's adequacy condition, 25
Tarski's schema, 28
term, 16: closed, 19; inductive definition of, 19; non-denoting, 22, 71; descriptive, 163; class, 163
theorem, 7, 57: compactness, 35, 89, 129; Löwenheim-Skolem, 35, 130, 131, 141; classical soundness, 72; normalization, 76, 98, 116; extensionality, 79; truth set, 91; completeness, weak version, 93; completeness, strong version, 94, 100; inconsistency, 94, 106; DNF, 100; theorem-completeness, 100; weak completeness, 102; maximalization, 104; satisfiability, 104-5; double negation, 106; intuitionistic soundness, 110, 133; intuitionistic maximalization, 111, 133; intuitionistic satisfiability, 111, 134; interpolation, 116, 118; joint consistency, 120; definability, 120-1; finite satisfiability in monadic languages, 123-5; model existence I-III, 129; strong completeness for classical first order logic with identity, 129; countable models, 129; double negation, 106, 129-30; Trakhtenbrot's, 131; undecidability of first order functional logic, 140; I-VI on first order theories, 142-3; non-categoricity of arithmetic, 145-6; completeness of successor arithmetic, 152; representability, 153, 156, 159; limitative theorems VII-XVI, 160-3
theory, 7, 8, 141: model theory, 7; proof theory, 7; theory of truth, 28; in *L*, 120; properties of theories, 141-2; of ordering, 144; of successor arithmetic, 145; of successor and additive arithmetic, 152; *Q*, 152; theory of descriptions, 165; of sets, 173-5
Trakhtenbrot, 131
transitivity: of proof, 49; of identity, 77
transformations of proofs, 49, 94-6, 116
translation, 4, 27, 34
truth: conditions, 4, 22, 24, 89; tables, 23, 59, 63, 78; theory, 28; logical, 47, 89; set, 91, 93

undecidability, 122, 130, 136, 140, 160
unions, axiom of, 173
universally free logic, 163ff
universals, 22
universe of discourse, 4

validity of arguments, 2
variable, bound, 16
variable binding term forming operators, 164
variants: notational, 66; *t-u*, 77; with respect to $\bar{t}$, 79

well-behaved interpolant, 118
well-formed formula, 12
well-founded relation, 101, 131
winning strategy, 36-7
witness, 126

Zermelo, 165, 173